CNCROi.co
VOLUME V: THINK IT, BUILD I...

MW00823766

Special Thanks

I have to give very special thanks to my parents, whose support and encouragement even through tough times have made me who I am today. They not only gave me life but, more importantly, challenged me to get the most out of it! Thanks Mom and Dad!

A big thanks also goes to the designers, inventors and entrepreneurs that took time to shared their knowledge to contribute to this book.

Author: Jonathan Cantin
Copy edited by: Albert Cantin

Library and Archives Canada Cataloguing in Publication

Cantin, Jonathan, 1976-, author
        CNCROi.com : think it, build it, sell it! / Jonathan Cantin.
Includes index.
ISBN 978-1-896369-52-5 (paperback)

1. Machine-tools--Numerical control. 2. Laser beam cutting. 3. Lasers--Industrial applications. 4. Laser printing. 5. Three-dimensional printing. 6. Entrepreneurship. I. Title.

TJ1189.C35 2015   621.9'023   C2015-904255-0

Table of Contents

CNCROi.com
Volume V: Think it, Build it, Sell it!

Table of Contents

My business as of June 2015. See page 84 to see how it began!

Since the Last Volume

My last volume was published in Australia where I was set to live out my life but I had the opportunity of a lifetime and returned to Canada. The decision to leave was tough (winter!) but I always wanted to be involved in manufacturing.

I threw all my money and time into CNCROi.com, starting a custom CNC shop from absolutely NOTHING, no customers, no leads and a brand new Trotec Speedy 400 flexx! My parents were kind enough to let me take over their garage, then I started "Networking for Dollar$!"

It's quite a departure from selling CNC plans around the world - managing a growing global digital business. Then all of a sudden, a local physial one. I learned and continue to learn a tremendous amount from this entire experience that I feel honored to be able to share now, with you.

I listened to readers of my previous volumes who wanted far more details about how I go about actually designing projects across various CNC machines.

If you want to follow projects from nothing to finished design, I think you'll enjoy reading through the decision process behind each line and curve. I've been doing this for so long it's second nature now, but as you'll see, thousands of decisions go into even the simplest of designs!

I also seeked out notable individuals across the design and production cycle spectrum, from founders of large multinational companies to students learning the ropes of the industry. When you look at a product, you are looking into the soul of the designer whose experience help mold what you see on your shelves.

Condensing and balancing an industry was quite a challenge, hence taking two years to put it together. Yet again, a resource I wished I had when I was first starting out.

Jonathan Cantin
Starting my own custom CNC shop!

Founder of CNCKing.com
& CNCROi.com

V1: Aug 2, 2008
V2: Nov 19, 2009
V3: Oct 10, 2011
V4: Sep 26, 2013
V5: July 14, 2015

CNC Laser Material Database

Just about any material can be affected by a CNC laser, it all depends on the power and type of tube you have. Since I've entered the industry with my own Trotec Speedy 400 flexx, finding non-technical resources that were in plain English regarding the effects of lasers across a variety of mediums has been hard to find.

You will notice that vinyl based products like PVC aren't in this material database. That's because it releases caustic Chlorine gas when it's hit with a laser which is bad for the machine and damages the health of the operator.

This is by no means an exhaustive list, just something generic to get you started. Power settings and speeds are not given as they vary greatly depending on the type of machine you have, how much power your tube(s) have and types of sources you have at your disposal. What I've found is that nothing replaces hands-on material testing! Have fun!

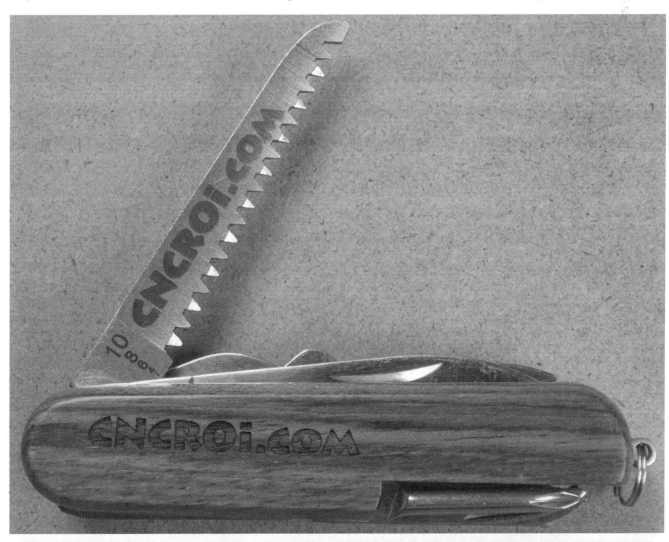

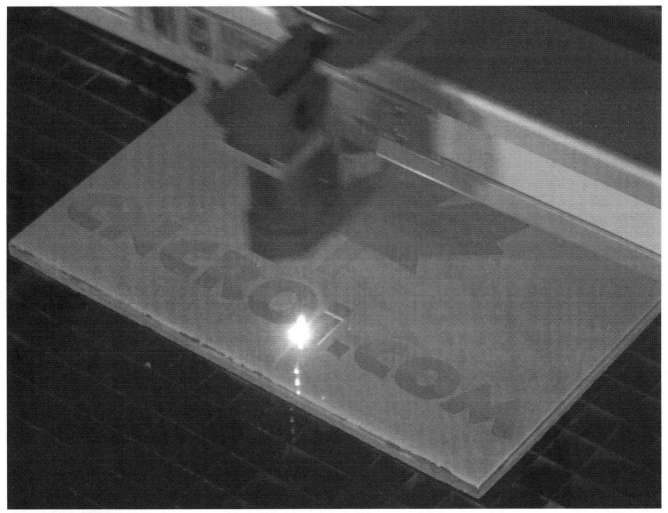

CERAMIC TILE

I really enjoy engraving tile! The results look great but you will want to infill paint it as raw laser engraved tile generally has lines or inconsistancies that aren't very pleasing to the eye.

What I've found works best is applying a mask over the tile, engraving it and then using enamel paint (sometimes with a primer) to colorize it. Sometimes you get very weird patterns in what seems like random areas of the tile substrate. If this poses a problem, ask the client to give you lots of extras so they can pick and choose.

Laser engraving tile is generally a slow process. I've found anything that has "rocks" in its composition all have the same basic laser settings and little can be done to speed-up the laser engraving process. Especially if you are planning on applying some secondary processes on the finished piece.

In the above picture, you'll notice that the surface (from the light refraction) is bumpy but the result in the substrate is completely flat in this case... I've had the opposite happen too.

I haven't noticed any differences between different tile styles, colors or shapes, they all tend to essentially engrave the same way using similar settings and depth.

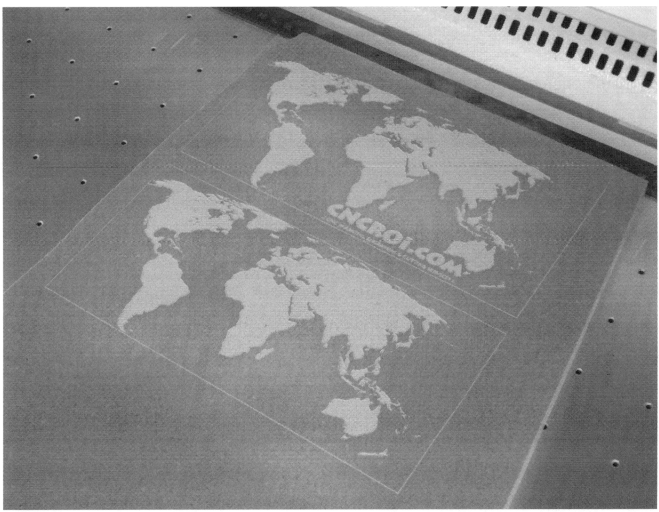

CORIAN

Corian was quite a surprisingly wonderful material to work with. The results are incredibly consistent, like engraving into hardboard or particle board and produces a wonderful contrast.

The advantage of Corian over wood is that there isn't any sticky resin or smoke damage which means you don't need to apply a mask over the piece. The powder is extremely fine and easily removed. It also works FANTASTIC with acrylic paint fill.

What I tend to do with Corian is add-in cut lines as I can't get all the way through with my laser and use a bandsaw to cut, then belt sander to polish. The resolution you get out of this material is impressive, far better than what you can get out of wood with a lot less post-production hassle. As for smell, I can't say it has one.

One of the drawbacks of Corian is its weight. Depending on thickness, it's as heavy if not heavier than MDF but unlike MDF, if it gets wet or humid, there is no effect, hence why it's a great material to have in a kitchen counter top. It makes for great cutting boards!

I have a massive bed with my Trotec Speedy 400 flexx. So doing larger pieces is definitely where the money is with clients as just about anybody can do the small stuff.

CORK

Cork is a wonderful material to use with CNC lasers! The results are nice and dark and incredibly sharp but be sure to use masking tape if you are doing more than just lightly marking it. Cleaning-up cork is incredibly difficult due to its surface properties.

The advantage over hot metal stamping is that you get very sharp results but it comes at the cost of time. CNC laser engraving is far slower than pushing down on an arm and burning in a pattern or logo.

The advantage over vinyl or screen printing is that whatever you do with the laser, it's completely permanent and will not fade over time. The disadvantage is the same as hot metal stamping, the process is slow with a laser and you are stuck using any color as long as it's brown/black.

Something that isn't apparent though is that with a powerful enough CNC laser, like our Austrian Trotec Speedy 400 flexx, we can custom cut cork sheets to any size to fit any application you have in mind. Again, the costs are more than using traditional woodworking tool but you gain an incredible amount of creative potential. Cork blanks are easy to find at the dollar store in a variety of pre-cut shapes, thicknesses and textures.

DELRIN

A brand name under DuPont, Delrin is a polymer that I've used extensively for seal production, though it can also be used in applications where metal would generally be used.

It's very lightweight and our CNC laser produces incredibly consistent and precise engravings into it with little effort. The added benefit of Delrin is that it can work at high temperatures and is very resistant to wear compared to rubber.

What I really enjoy about making seals with this material is that it's highly profitable and most of the seal production process is automatically controlled in my JobControlX after the design is sent over for CNC laser production.

This material does take a bit of testing to get right for use in seals. I've found that you need to actually engrave them OUT of focus by a few mm in order to achieve the best results. When the details in your seal are too precise and tight, the seal tends to wear out faster and even go out of alignment.

I use this extensively in my promotional packages as this isn't a service that comes to mind when you approach a company with CNC laser services.

FOAM

Foam is a hit/miss material that you have to be very careful about putting high energy beams into. It cuts like butter which is fantastic but it also catches fire like gas! Don't even consider cutting foam unless you have a powerful extraction system in your laser.

I've found out that, for thicker foam, you want to make a cut in several passes, each one "deeper" than the other if you are getting not-so-great results from a higher powered one-time pass.

As for types of foam, there are tons of them out there, each with their + and - when it comes to laser cutting but generally, I've found that the thinner stuff is easiest to work with and to build it up on layers to hold a piece down in a box instead of trying to grab and cut the thicker stuff with associated flames and smoke.

I have found that foam made-up with smaller "particles" produces better results when laser cutting, just like stones but this cuts dramatically faster.

Do not let the laser cut through sheets of foam overnight while you head to bed, you will wake-up to a shop in cinders. Be careful and attentive when cutting foam!

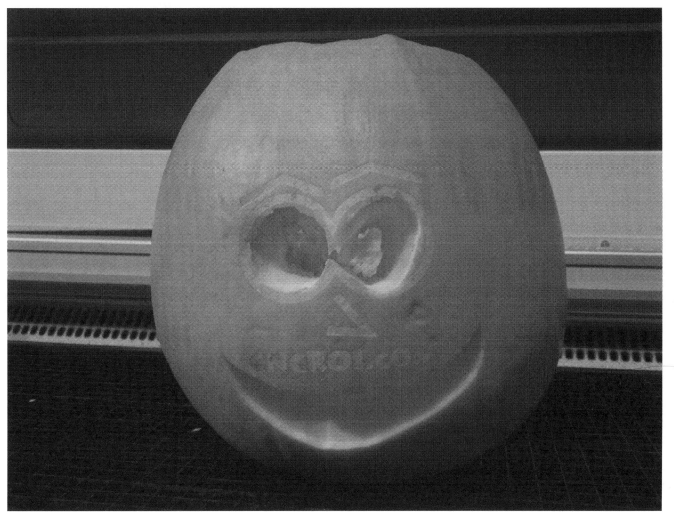

FOOD

Yep, you can engrave and cut food using a CNC laser! I've tried lots of stuff from bananas to pumpkins and even making overly expensive toast. It's fun to try different things under the laser and see the results on materials you wouldn't necessarily think of using in an industrial machine.

The most challenging aspect of engraving or cutting food items is figuring-out how to do it while producing the least amount of soot. Pumpkin for instance is a wonderful material to work with because it has a very thin outer shell followed by watery one. This means, you can really boost the power to engrave into it, which gives you much more tolerance within your working area even if it is rounded by more than a few centimeters (inch).

For best results, you want to focus on the mid-point, not too high or low.

The drawbacks of laser engraving food is that it does tend to muck-up your machine with sticky soot so you learn quickly to produce the optimal settings with very little testing which comes in very handy when a customer drops of "I don't know what it is either" type of material for you to work with. By the way, I used a knife to cut into the above picture, use the right tools for the job!

FORMICA

I've grown to really enjoy cutting out shapes and paterns out of Formica but the edges are like razor blades; expect to be cut up quite a bit while working with this material! The challenge with formica is that it doesn't hold it's shape, so you need to support it and it also tends to bow depending on the size of sheet.

The results achieved with a laser though are awesome, you can get incredibly fine detail out of Formica and, due to the durability and strength of the material, you have a lot more leaway than if you made the same project out of, say, paper.

It has the thickness and cutting speed of thick paper but the strength of plywood. It also bends... so be sure to have your hold down set-up!

One of my very first projects that I got when I opened-up CNCROi.com was a massive Formica project. Nobody else in the region could do the job as their CNC laser beds were too small and didn't have passthrough.

I had a massive bed and the ability to feed sheets of Formica through which allowed me to get this project done properly as the client requested. If you are going to buy a laser, buy more than you need!

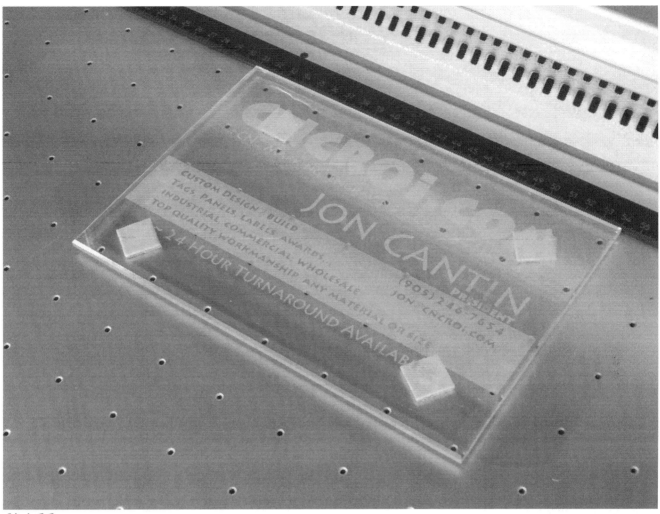

GLASS

Glass is one of the most challenging materials I've had on my laser bed. The material is surprisingly inconsistent and the results are very much hit and miss.

There are a lot of tricks of the trade like using a wet newspaper as a mask which you then laser etching through or using the cheapest glass you can find (surprisingly, it's generally better than more expensive varieties).

If I have a laser engraving where there is a large solid section to be engraved or thick text, I generally tell the client to use a sandblaster to do the job. Lasers are fantastic for fine detailed etching not possible using sand due to overspray.

Glass is one of those materials that I have yet to master and settings are different between different plates. You can have awesome results on one and then produce scrap on the next one you stick on your platform.

Surprisingly though, lasers are fantastic for scoring glass. So if you have a client that is a glass cutter, let them know you can help them out!

LAMINATES

Ask most independent CNC laser shop owners what material produces the highest ROI for them and the answer eight times out of ten will be laminates. Whereas for me, steel has been my niche, laminates is an area that I do partake in on a regular basis though.

What's great about laminates is that they come in endless varieties, textures and thicknesses that suit a host of different applications. Need a metal tag with 3M adhesive on the back to stick on a widget? Make it out of metal looking laminate and you'll get a far higher return than if you annealed a stainless steel tag. Need to make some quick key holders for a client with their contact information? Laminates. Need to create a wall display or welcome sign? Laminates.

The one drawback from laminates is that sometimes they are used in applications where other materials are best suited, but the client doesn't want to pay for the real thing.

For instance, I had a client who wanted a "cheap tag" to put next to his furnace. I told him to go with steel due to heat but they decided to go for a steel looking laminate instead... really not the best choice even after I told them it won't last long. Sadly, some clients tend to look at their nickles and dimes at the cost of their long term reputation.

LEATHER

Leather is an interesting material. It's very resistant to tearing, very strong and produces a fantastic contrast when laser cut or engraved on most types, even synthetics.

Genuine leather seems to consistently produce the best results with a CNC laser even if, by its natural nature, it's anything but. You can get so fantastic resolution on some of the denser leathers and the results are just as permanent. I've never had a need to mask leather as part of my post-production prep as the vaporization is just some dust that's easily removed either with a damp cloth or air compressor. After engraving a job though, applying a leather treatment may be a good idea, but I've found this isn't needed for most applications.

When engraving or cutting leather, expect the shop to smell like burned dead ants - you know, that smell when you were a kid playing on the pavement with a magnifying glass playing God. One thing I have found challenging with this material is that most of the time, a client will give it to you already formed, like a wallet or purse.

Make sure you average your leveling to account for this as I've yet to get a piece that's been parallel to the laser cutting bed. Luckily, you have lots of sway with leather that you don't have with steel due to the long surface focal range.

Metal (Anodized, Powder Coated & Cast)

I really enjoy working with anodized and powder coated aluminium. It's available in endless colors, can be easily cut to any shape and works great with either a fiber or CO_2 laser source. The material itself is extremely light to carry around. I always have one in my pocket and, due to their low price point, give them away to clients on a regular basis.

Laser engraving coated aluminium in general produces a fine powder around the work area. This is easily removed with a damp cloth but I have found that it's best to use slightly lower power settings than too much, as it tends to remove too much material.

The undercoating of the aluminium will remain by the way, so if it's coated or anodized blue, when you remove the coating, you will have a blue tinge and not pure white. I have tried using a fiber laser source and the results take longer than a CO_2 but are "whitter" which, to me, is worth it for most client applications.

Laser engraving cast aluminium is best done in several stepped passes, the CO_2 laser does a great job of digging into it but you want to be careful not to use too much power as it tends to blur the resuts you are trying to achieve.

Metal (Stainless Steel)

I've worked with a lot of stainless steel, my favorite is 304, but it is a tricky material to anneal. With my Trotec Speedy 400 flexx, the default lens has a very tight tolerance and when mixed with a fiber laser source, the results are sometimes inconsistent if I'm using a thin gage as the metal tends to warp off the table, taking it out of focus. I since got a fiber lens since and, wow, it's night and day especially for metal that isn't flat to begin with!

If you are going to be doing a lot of metal annealing, get a fiber specific long lens for this job with a far higher tolerance. It pays for itself in your reject count.

Regarding fiber marking, you have far more tolerances. So the results are consistent across the board but if you are trying to give your client a positive impression, annealing a solid chunk of 304 or 316 is tough to beat.

With either marking or annealing, you may end-up with a good buildup of soot on the surface depending on the grade used. Don't worry, all that stuff wipes right off using BBQ cleaning fluid. I've tried many other cleaning solutions and that one just works great on the first wipe with minimal effort.

Don't forget to do this BEFORE you work with it as well to remove any production film.

POLYCARB (Lexan etc.)

Polycarbonates are a very good material to use with CNC lasers but what you win on pure blackness of results using a fiber laser tube you lose on edge quality. This stuff burns yellow which is just about impossible to remove from the cut piece even with methyl hydrate!

What I suggest is you cut the blanks out using a CNC router. We have an awesome ShopBot Desktop, then make a jig to fiber mark them.

Depending on the application, you may wish to reverse fiber engrave the polycarb so you have an ink-black and smooth result. If you just do normal fiber engraving, the consistency isn't as black and rough like sand paper.

The benefit of polycarbonate is you have a lot of tolerance so even if there is some warping of the material, you are generally fine. It's also easy to cut and heat bend. I actually use my metal sheers to cut this stuff with very clean results for speed.

PAPER

Paper is surprisingly easy to work with laser wise. The challenge is getting your settings dialled in so you are using just enough power to vaporize the paper but not so much as to leave burn marks on the underside of your project. Having a vacuum table and gas kit make a massive difference in this regard... that's why I got both on my machine!

What continues to surprise me about paper is how much of a markup the industry has. You can literally turn a 4 cents of paper into a $10 wedding invitation and it doesn't have to be all that detailed either! This is really the area where having an awesome CNC laser makes a massive difference because you need the repeatability and precision to even the most detailed of patterns, your table must be square, your jigs dead-on and laser producing consistent power throughout the cutting (and engraving) process. If you do things right, there is very little waste and it can be easily recycled.

The tough part about paper is that you can't use any masking tape and you have to make sure you leave enough space around your cuts to support what's left.

Paper has no real strength and if you get into details that are too fine, you end-up just having a card that breaks too easily. Do some good testing on the results before production runs.

PLASTIC (random)

Fiber or CO_2? Only material testing will reveal which comes out best for random plastics companies drop off to us here at CNCROi.com. Generally, fiber produces a better result as CO_2 tends to melt the plastic. However, it depends on its density, composition and material properties. I've found no way to predict which works best so play around with settings until you have a result that looks great!

What you want to do, like wood, is engrave towards the extraction source. This makes cleanup a bit easier and there is no need to apply any masking tape, the vapors are generally just a fine powder that's easily wiped off using a damp cloth.

The challenge with some plastics is the smell. Some have none while others just reek and it doesn't seem to matter if you are using a fiber or CO_2 laser source either. As for color changing, that's just as unpredictable.

I've had some black plastics turn white while others gray or actually have no effect at all. I've also had some white plastics turn green, gray and black depending on their composition. If you are quoting a color changing job, be sure the client sends you the SAME PLASTIC that you used to generate your settings.

PLASTIC (acrylic)

I have a love - hate relationship with acrylic. The laser does an awesome job flame polishing this material when you are cutting shapes out and the engraving comes out consistent but I just don't like the flames that sometimes come out of this stuff.

Acrylic is a form of plastic which comes from petroleum... not something to be taken lightly when hit with lots of highly concentrated energy. There is also color change acrylic that you can use a fiber laser source on that works too.

With wood, you can have your extraction and gas kit going full power but with acrylic, this isn't possible as you'll end-up with rounded edges. So there is some material testing required and these issues just increase, the thicker the material you have to contend with.

Whatever you do, do not set-up a job cutting out sheets of acrylic and leaving your shop. This stuff does flare-up and I have had to open the case a few times to throw it onto the ground to put out the fire. Produces awesome results and cuts incredibly well but be careful with it and give it the respect it requires.

Cast or extruded acrylic? I haven't found a difference yet other than the sheet cost.

RUBBER

I've grown to enjoy making custom stamps of all sizes and shapes using my Austrian CNC laser. The results are consistent (if you have good rubber material!) and it's a very profitable stream of revenue if you can break into companies providing this type of custom service.

The advantage that my shop has is that most of our projects are 24 hour turnaround. So even if we charge a little more than the going rate, once a design is approved, they get it the next day! The only thing I don't like about rubber is the smell.

There is rubber that doesn't smell as bad but I've just gotten use to it. Engraving a wood project after doing a rubber stamp run is a great way to improve the smell in the shop!

I tend to go with the thicker rubber so I can engrave deeper into it and use double-sided tape to hold it in place with a custom piece of board. To remove the soot from this, just a little dishwashing soap and a toothbrush does a great job.

I've also recently gotten into the hot stamping mold business too, the rubber is far denser and comes with an aluminum backing already set on it.

STONE (beach)

If you want to make some easy money, go to the beach and pickup a bunch of stones and engrave personalized messages and logos on them using your CO_2 laser source. You'll see in the right side of the photograph a piece of glass I found... the results are by far the best I've ever gotten on glass!

What I really like about beach stones is their endless variety. They are generally very polished with a smooth surface and easily sealed for paint filling. If you are lucky, you can also find some fantastic chunks of wood that are also nicely sand sanded which work great in a CNC laser.

I've found that stones made-up of larger particulates tend to not engrave particularly well due to the lack of a solid consistent surface.

Things like composites and asphalt is probably the worse due to color and toughness of what's left over after the ocean has worn it down for a while. Worn down brick has consistently given me awesome results.

Since I got my Trotec Speedy 400 flexx, I have a tough time leaving a beach without my hands and pockets full of stones, can never have too much!

STONE (brick)

Brick tends to be a hit and miss when it comes to laser engraving as the results very much depend on the particles that make it up. Brick is also a tough material to paint fill as the surface to begin with is uneven. So clean-up isn't the easiest.

What I have found works best is to coat the brick first and then use the CO_2 laser to vaporise off that coating instead of doing things the other way around. The results are a lot cleaner and it's a dramatically faster process overall.

I have laser engraved cinder blocks, paving stones and random man made concrete forms and the power you need to use on these material is on the high end. Production is slow and when it's happening, a blinding light is produced so you only really see the results AFTER everything is done.

STONE (field)

Unlike beach stones, field stones tend to have some vegetation on them and rarely have an even surface. Don't take the moss off... leave it there as after you've laser engraved the rock, it will pop back to life! This also provides an awesome contrast and all you have to do is leave the rock in the garden.

What I really like about field stones is that surface qualities follow into the engraving as you can see in the above picture. I never clean rocks before laser engraving them unless they are particularily dirty because this just adds to the contrast you achieve.

You do not need to apply any masking tape. The process is slow but the fine powder that ends up all over your bed is easily removed by just running the stone under running water.

Do keep in mind that you want to have a strong extraction system set-up when engraving stone because the particulates (dust) gets everywhere and that isn't good for your lungs or the machine components... yet another reason to get a high quality machine with all it's sensitive electronics protected and cleaning your machine spotless!

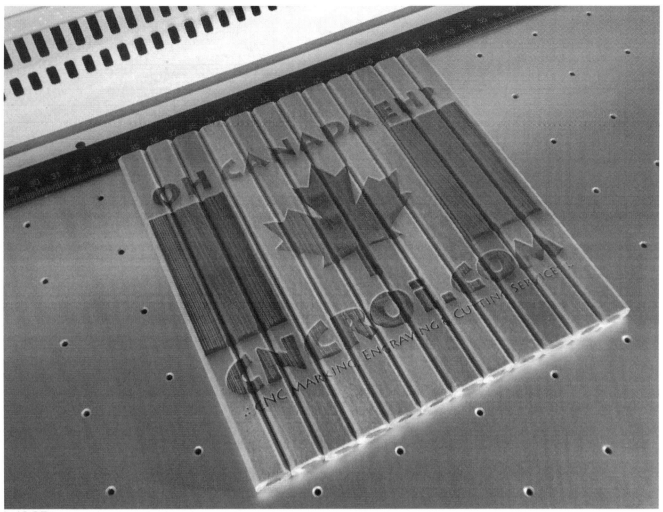

WOOD

By far one of my favorite material to work with! It comes in endless varieties, densities, colors and is incredibly easy to work with which comes in handy when I build some of the projects I've designed over the past years over at CNCKing.com. It's also easy to find just about anywhere and you can get free scraps from most lumber yards too!

What I enjoy most about cutting wood with a CNC laser over just about any other tool is that there aren't any splinters and the laser produces an awesome burned edge whose contrast works great! It really adds a lot to a model giving it extra depth and visual appeal. The fact that my shop smells like a camp fire for a few hours is a bonus!

I've easily cut through more than my fair share of wood using a variety of tools but for CNC lasers, you want to make sure you apply masking tape on the material as smoke stains can be very difficult to remove efficiently. Some woods have resins that vaporize and stick to the base material, rendering your sand paper useless.

I've also screwed-up lots of pieces thinking I could use a belt or orbital sander. The results aren't very good unless you are engraving especially deep.

Bamboo

Bamboo is a beautiful material to work with, it engraves very well with a laser, like maple, pine and oak but is harder to find here in Canada. As such, it's a premium product that's great for clients who are willing to pay a premium for something that really stands out.

Like other woods, it takes paint very well but if you are going to pay extra (in my case) for this material, just seal it with mineral oil as the grain is worth keeping natural.

Hardboard, MDF & Particle Board

On price alone, MDF, hardboard and particle board is tough to beat. It's great for jig making but in my opinion, awful for model making. Many pros in the field will not agree with me on this point. I consider these materials glorified carboard with more glue in them than wood. They have their use but tend to wear out pretty quickly due to their lack of strength.

If I had a jig that needed to be used for more than a few "production cycles", then I'd use acrylic and not these materials; they just don't stand-up well. I tend to stick to 3 mm hardboard and laminated MDF.

Plywood

I use a lot of wood in my shop and the one I can never have enough of is plywood. It's strong even when cut full of holes and is easily cut and available in a variety of thicknesses. Plywood is also available just about anywhere and is very cheap. I've yet to splurge for the laminated and expensive varieties. I just head for the bargain bin, even grabbing plywood intended as a subsurface for tiled floors. Great for bond fires after the fact!

I tend to have 3 and 6 mm in stock (same as acrylic) as that's what I use for my model making where using solid soft or hardwood isn't in the budget.

Veneer

Great for making CNC laser business cards, veneer take a bit of time to get use to and generally requires to be held down. There are different quality as well, sometimes I get veneer that's just too brittle and just won't lay flat and other times, it's smooth and plyable, very easy to work with. Generally, I use veneer for laser cutting small details or cards and the like as it's a rather fragile material to work with.

Oh yeah, with wood, you want to engrave towards, not away from the extraction point(s) so the dust doesn't fill your engraved areas with sticky soot. Don't even consider sanding off the soot from laser engraving wood, it just makes more of a mess of everything.

CNC Laser: 10 Fire Prevention Tips

I have four friends thus far who have joined the "laser fire club", it's similar to the woodworkers "lost thumbs club" of which I have two. You don't want to be a member of either club!

Laser fires aren't cheap and the range of damage has been from the tens of thousands to the millions, don't expect insurance to cover all your loses either!

What they all seem to have in common is getting too comfortable with their lasers. The laser works, years and years under constant supervision, totally fine without any hint of flames. So, you give it another job and go about your business and you start to smell something you can't believe is happening in the room next door.

Although every industrial machine is capable of catching fire - which is why you see (or should) fire extinguishers all over the shop, lasers are in a class of their own due to their very nature. High energy generally hitting a combustiable material with plenty of oxygen.

Here is what I've done at CNCROi.com to reduce the possibility of fires.

1) I always watch the machine when it's working on something that may catch on fire... sure, it's boring and a waste of time but one fire can mean my business is shut down for at least a week if not more and throw in having to repair or buy new machines; it's a good use of time. Of course, if I'm annealing stainless steel or fiber marking anodized aluminum, no problem, I'll still be AROUND but I don't need to be next to the machine.

2) I have a fire extinguisher less than a meter away from the control panel. Remember that if a fire happens, do not lift the lid as it will cause the flames to shoot out as oxygen rushes in but at least dose with the lid slightly opened before opening it further. The machine will be a writeoff either way but at least nothing else in the shop will catch fire! A fire extinguisher will cause damage to your machine, using it is a last resort in my book best avoided and used as minimally as possible in an emergency.

3) My floor is concrete - sure, it's not comfortable and I do have a rubber mat on top of it where the machine is but if there is a small fire on material that I can't extinguish using compressed air, I can open the lid and throw it on the ground to put it out. Fires happen fast, you got to be quick! If this isn't an option, have a sand bucket next to your machine to do the same. You shouldn't have carpet around a fire pit so why would you have it around a CNC laser that produces energy hotter than the Sun?

4) I have a gas kit in my Trotec Speedy 400 flexx laser machine. It throws PLENTY of air down onto the project beyond what an internal air compressor can do on most machines. This puts out any flames before they have a chance of happening and with a powerful extraction system, any fumes just don't have time to build-up.

5) DO NOT LEAVE YOUR MACHINE RUNNING OVERNIGHT! If it's working, be there AWAKE and AWARE! Although there is little to no possibility of a fire happening when marking metal, I still don't have anything run while I'm not there. If something happens, it will do so when you least suspect it, when it's the most inconvinient time.

6) Clean your machine regularly, soot and other crap develops all over the internals of your machine overtime and like a chimney, makes it more prone to catching fire. Keep it as spotless as possible especially after a big job. Don't forget to inspect the hoses out back and the extraction unit itself too... stuff builds-up in those too!

7) Check and clean your lens and mirrors often, if you have any doubt, check it. It's one thing to have a concentrated beam of energy, quite another to have it dispursed, which requires you to move slower with more power to achieve the same results. You'll crack a lens, become inneficient and that's when bad things happen.

8) Buy a quality machine! I have a few friends who built their own machine. One of them is an engineer and genius in all respects but to me, it just isn't worth it regardless of the savings. Deal only with reputable manufacturers who build their own machines using high quality parts. The machines will cost more but at least there will be a reduced chance of something not on the menu happening. If you are buying a CNC laser, you shouldn't need a degree in engineering to troubleshoot if it was well built to begin with.

9) Keep the area around your laser clear of inventory or stock. If something happens, the last thing you want to have to become is Bob the UnBuilder to try to clear things out around your machine. Ideally, you can go around your machine with little effort. Sometimes the vacuum hoses get loose, you get an electrical short or just for easy cleaning it's nice to have full access.

10) Fires happen fast with wood but acrylic and foams are an especially flamable beast that you really want to be fully attentive about when cutting - I've rarely if ever seen even a flare when engraving acrylic but cutting, it's incredibly common. Be ready to stop the machine the moment you see a flame that seems out of control. It's always better to scrap a job and redo it later than to take a chance on your bread winner to save a bit of time. When working with a flamable material, be especially cautious.

The investment into a CNC laser is among the biggest I've made in my life thus far. My CNC laser cost as much as a house but you know what, unlike a house, it will MAKE MONEY and the depreciation on a CNC machine is a fraction of what it is for a car.

The serviceable lifespans of a good quality CNC equipment including lasers, plasmas, waterjets and routers are more than a decade.

Let me repeat, you have 10 years to make back your investment! What a deal!

Made in China: CNC Machine Game Changer

It started "innocently" when I was running my industrial 3D animation studio back before the .com boom of 2000. I was in the middle of contacting every manufacturing company in the world in order to offer my companies 3D animation service ("What's that?" Was the typical response) and telling them to go see Toy Story to get a sense of what's possible.

This was BEFORE the days of YouTube, when servers cost a fortune, bandwidth, phone systems etc... it was nowhere near as bargain basement as things are now. My industrial dual core workstation cost over 10K and your iPad is most likely more powerful!

Offshoring Trends

I started noticing a trend over time talking to manufacturers. At first, they'd start to send their molds over to China (and India to a lesser degree) to save a fortune from doing it themselves in their home country (generally Europe or the USA). Once they found a confident and reliable partner, the molds became parts... why not, it's far cheaper... than to machine components... why not, it's far cheaper... than machine assemblies... why not, it's far cheaper... and eventually, entire machines. During this time, the owners of these manufacturers were saving a fortune, able to cut staff and demand concessions from their workers.

Back then, manufacturers were ironically slowly killing themselves, buying Japanese, American and European machinery for their factories - having no trust in those produced by the Chinese. Yet their own machines were increasingly being manufactured in China. The economics were there, companies were paying full price for a machine mostly manufactured (parts and components) in China and they were making a killing!

They'd come back, rewire and fix the issues before sending it to customers but even so, they were saving a lot of money offshoring.

3D animation business dies...

Well, it wasn't long before Chinese manufacturers got a hold of 3D software and began undercutting my services big time - their sale to existing clients was a no brainer - pirated software was cheap, highly talented and educated employees were a plenty and I couldn't afford to even keep the lights on for the price they were charging manufacturers for industrial 3D animations.

I'm not resentful, I knew it was happening but the speed took me by surprise. I noticed the same trend with programmers, increasingly, companies where sending jobs to Pakistan, India and Hungary for jobs to get done at a fraction of the price. This was my other big bread winner that went to the wayside rather quickly at the same time.

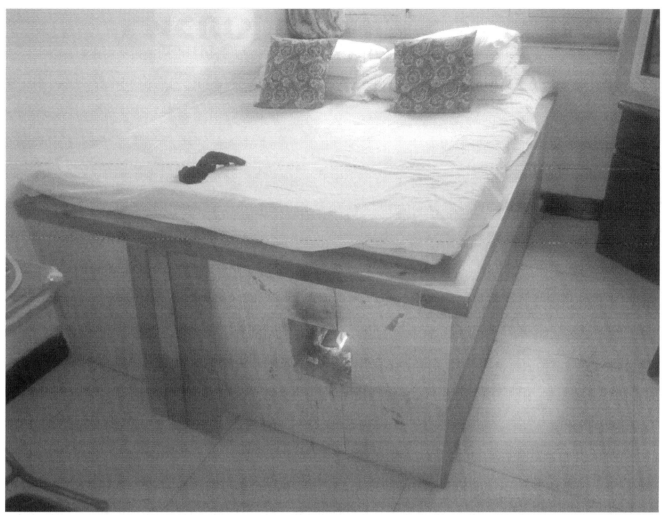

Want a warm bed? Put a fire under it! Worked great and no fire extinguisher in sight!

I had to do this as well to keep margins healthy before everybody got wind of off-shoring and then the boom began. Companies got smart and began sending jobs directly offshore too!

For all the glamor you may think there is in the 3D marketplace, it's mostly gone now, replaced by mega-studios that increasingly fight for smaller and smaller bread crumbs and are always one or two projects away from bankruptcy... not a business model I wished to invest in so I just let it die.

Chinese Mindset

Now, I'm going to make sweeping generalities here. I lived in China for two years and talked with many manufacturers there as well as married a mainland native while I was there. I also have been dealing with manufacturers for more than 15 years (wow time goes fast!).

While I was in China, I taught ESL from primary to high school and a few things struck me at first and have stayed with me since.

Temples and the countryside are incredibly beautiful... quite a contrast to city living!

They are DRIVEN and AMBITIOUS

These kids would wake-up at 6 am and be in school until 10 pm at the high school level... this was TYPICAL! The classes were boring and mind numbing - I don't know how they managed to stay awake, but they were given endless paperwork to complete and give back to the teacher.

They were robots, here's a task, get it done in x minutes, give it to the teacher then receive another task. It seemed to work for everybody involved. As soon as there was no longer "anything to do", the entire classroom would transform into a zoo! A teacher learned rather quickly that keeping the class busy was the best method of control.

I also taught at the elementary level and did some university prep for students studying to go abroad. These kids were more driven than I ever was at their age. They wanted to make their country proud, make a lot of money and were keen to "work within the system" in order to make their dreams come true when they return to the mainland.

Coming from a one child family put a lot of pressure on them as they were their parent's only hope at a better life.

The Chinese are HUNGRY!

I'm a Canadian, so if you've done international business, an American is YES or NO generally. They make decisions quick and stand by them but the Chinese are at a whole other level. They'd easily cream the typical American if it wasn't for just one "flaw", their language and cultural barriers which are falling by the wayside with the upcoming generation who spoke better English than me as well as other languages!

Canadians have a more layed back approach to business. We are polite and aren't generally boastful or ego driven. The Chinese are hungry for the deal... HUNGRY! Think of Americans but without the regulations getting in their way.

You'd be too if you were in constant competition your whole life from primary school to business where only the best and the brightest get a chance at making a name for themselves. China is crowded!

Creativity

The Chinese educational system is fantastic for creating robots who do A to get B. Creativity counts for very little and as a result, most students I taught had trouble with anything that was off the cuff or required thinking for oneself. Square pegs learn early-on that they need to become round to fit in the holes set before them.

The Chinese have such a rich culture and inventive past, from gun powder to the printing press (yes, they were the first), but due to the environment they find themselves in with hyper competition and their communal way of thinking, individuality has taken a back seat.

For instance, I'd be teaching a class - using lots of video and images which they LOVED - and if I asked them to imagine what their reaction to a certain hypothetical situation would be, they'd generally say "I have no idea" or, with a bit more questioning, say exactly the same answer as the other student. The teachers? Well, they were exhausted. Imagine having a class of 70 students to teach day in and day out for very little pay or reward.

Businesses are for the owners, not the employees

When I visited a factory making porcelain pots and other items, I noticed how proud the owner was, with his brand new Mercedes on the lot next to what seemed like an abandoned building boasting at how much his workers wanted to work for him.

It struck me as odd as nobody really wants to work 16 hours a day, and nobody really wants, after working 16 hours a day, to do overtime but guess what, they'd ask him all the time if they can work an extra hour or two. I was teaching a business class and the owner knew no English so I asked the students I was with to translate for me.

Major building developments in the middle of NOWHERE!

What became evident was that the employees didn't want to work there 16 hours a day much less ask for overtime. They had no choice! Their wages were so low and they had no other opportunity to make money. To them, taking a break or sleeping was a lost opportunity to make some extra money!

They were working themselves to the bone for very little money while the owner of the company was boasting about his new car, going to restaurants with local officials etc. The employees knew what was going on but were powerless to do anything about it.

China doesn't allow unions, protests or anything resembling dissidence or collective bargaining. Ironically they are allowing this to happen for foreign companies. Business is set-up to enrich the owners, not empower or lift-up the employees. This exists in the West as well but it's far more extreme in developing countries.

This isn't the case everywhere, it's just what I saw and experienced first hand living there.

With the long work hours and commitments after work, there is little time for hobbies. The students only knew school, and they were all taught in the same manner. So developing things to do out of interest beyond listening to music was stiffled.

Environmentally, China was awful

Factories don't have environmental standards. They dump stuff everywhere or burn it away just like the local citizenry. If you hear me cough, more often than not, it's because I've just come back from China. If that wasn't enough, they also smoke everywhere., I think its because the cigarette filters act as a mechanism to clean the air around them.

The rivers were dead. I think I once saw one fish in a river, it was asking me to take it out of the water. You hear stories of the smog issues in Beijing. Don't forget, it's just as bad if not worse in most other cities across China where little press is made to solve the situation.

The "beautiful" countryside was generally desolate. There are pockets of stunning beauty in China but you need to travel to find them. Like the Philippines where I lived for a few months, beauty for me was found outside of cities or towns.

Manufacturing Context

I'm not saying everything about China is bad, but overpopulation and the lack of standards (manufacturing, employment, environmental...) have created a great opportunity for heavy industry where cheap and highly skilled labor is plentiful and profits generated selling to other countries without these issues are massive.

Manufacturers outside of China know that the playing field is really stacked against them. They have standards they must follow, higher electricity costs, unions fighting for better worker and compensation standards and the list goes on.

You really can't blame them for being severely attracted to the incredible advantages China has to offer them. It's very hard to turn down how big the opportunity is within China and using them as part, if not all, to fulfill your manufacturing needs. The government is also overtaxed trying to keep 1.3 billion people content with their rule.

European and North American governments, for some odd reason, don't seem to care about what's going on. There is a reason why manufacturing is having trouble around the world.

This isn't China's fault but when a friend of mine recently bought a CNC router for a third the price of a locally produced one that comes at the cost of high end manufacturing jobs. He was boasting that he was now able to compete against and undercut profitably, his competitors that did support companies with local manufacturing.

It's a deviously cyclical pattern that almost "forces" others to do the same just to compete and only getting worse with increased globalization.

CNC Importers

The number of CNC importers is exploding! There is severe pressure being put on non-Chinese manufacturers: the more they get done locally, the more their machines cost but they beat-out their Chinese counterparts in quality. You absolutely get what you pay for! For now anyways.

Talking with an importer, what astounded me about our conversation was that he pointed me to a Chinese manufacturer he was working with. He knows Chinese machines have issues, so he inspects every machine before importing and hired a full time tech to fix machine issues at the factory itself - I was blown away.

This was the first Chinese company that was going full-tilt, head to head, against major brand names in the CNC world. How? Well, they ADVERTISED that their stepper motors were from Japan (best in the business), they translated their CNC control software into more than a dozen languages and had a roadmap of software and hardware updates.

What blew me away the most was their website. It was written as if an American manufacturer wrote it. I told the importer that this isn't a Chinese company and he told me I was right. It was a partnership between a Chinese factory, an European and an American enterprise. Basically, these guys ARE CNC and knew what causes most CNC purchases to second-guess going Chinese and dealt with it right away.

Now, for the American boasting, they had logos of all the companies they were competing head-to-head against and not only was their software compatible with these manufacturers but the models looked very similar as well.

They offered a host of custom options and just going to their listing, you knew they were serious about the international market. Each pain point was addressed head-on... that's the American way!

I saw this company and I saw the future of Chinese manufacturing. The other guys will eventually catch-up and that will put incredible downward (price wise) pressure on European and American CNC manufacturers. Why? Well, they can't drop their prices in half without pissing-off their own customer base so they are "trapped" in their high-priced tier and their staff, equipment etc... are far more expensive to maintain than their Chinese counterparts. Like I wrote, it isn't anywhere near an even playing field.

CNC Manufacturers Solutions

I have a few solutions to this issue but I fear that it's most likely too late to do much about it. The ball has already started to roll and gained enough momentum that stopping it would be ill advised for the global marketplace.

Raw coal is bought by the kilo and used for everything from cooking to heating.

<u>IP and copyright protection</u>

China has made great strides in this area but it still has a long way to go (as do most governments in the world by the way). Manufacturers spend billions every year developing novel and innovative technologies that help them stay in business that much longer and get patents and design copyrights to allow them to pay back that initial investment.

Why would a company invest this money if it can just copy from the other guy without repercussion? The Chinese are incredibly good at copying a machine and turning around and selling it without having to be concerned about the amount of research and development required to build the machine in the first place. The result? They have no ROI required for that innovation, so they can sell the machine for a lot cheaper! This hurts innovation across the marketplace.

You wonder why the machine you bought from China is SO cheap? Very little to no R&D investment and just built it "good enough" without any need for external inspections.

That's why it didn't last and why you have so many lemons out there.

I hope this guy doesn't meet any bridges along the way!

Protectionism and tariffs

I hate protectionism like the next guy but seriously, the governments of the world have to wake-up and realize what's going on before their manufacturing base is completely decimated. Just look a the massive drop seen in North America over the past decade.

Either let American and European manufacturers dump their garbage everywhere, let their employees fight among themselves for who will work the hardest for the least wages and severely weaken regulations in general or raise import tariffs to account for these massive discrepancy.

I have yet to meet a big CNCROi.com client who hasn't already or is in the process of offshoring their production there to compete.

More partnerships

This may sound counter-intuitive, but manufacturers, if they hope to survive, must partner-up with their Chinese counterparts. I really don't see things working any other way. You either let them eat all your fish or fish together for bigger opportunities.

Incredibly ironic to see Chairman Mao soluting the Walmart across the street in Guiyang.

VISIT CHINA!

If you've never been to China, you really need to go there for a few weeks. I lived in many countries over the past decade and China, if you put aside the smoker's caugh, you'll develop and the constant noise, is one of the most interesting places I've had the pleasure to live in. I've never felt unsafe and I've been in some very rough neighborhoods.

The people are fantastic, the food is great and the cost of living is incredibly low.

If you are in manufacturing and you haven't developed contacts in China yet, you are severely behind the 8-ball in this regard. For all the "bad" things I can write about China, there are even more "good" things.

Unlike most of North America, you'll get to experience a culture that's thousands of years old (get off the beaten tourist traps) and you'll make some new friends rather easily even if you don't speak a word of Chinese.

Your perspectives will forever be changed.

Ryan Patterson, Getting the Most out of your Bits

Ryan is the head of Production Support and Custom Applications at ShopBot Tools Inc.

Avoiding the cutters from building up heat is the goal to achieve a good quality cut and to maintain bit life. To help reduce heat, this is done by selecting the correct geometry cutter for the material, and selecting the optimal feeds and speeds.

The heat is pulled away from the cutter in the chips produced by cutting. The bigger the chip the more heat is being pulled away. Every material has a natural shape to its chip. The geometry of the cutter should match the shape of the produced chip. The feed rate and RMP are determined by the chipload for the material. Chipload is the size chip that is made by the cutter.

Every material has an optimal size chip. The size of this chip is controlled by the number of cutting edges (flutes), RMP and feed rate. The higher the RMP and the more flutes, the smaller the chip. A higher feed rate equals a bigger chip. Here is a link that will explain about the tooling http://www.onsrud.com/xdoc/Resources .

The basic rule is to cut as fast as you can at the lowest RPM without sacrificing edge quality. When cutting, you want to produce a chip not dust. By producing a chip, you will get longer life from the tooling and a better cut.

There are basic chip load charts that you can use as a guide but don't assume that the calculations are correct: (Chipload = Feedrate / [RPM x number of flutes]). Use the chip load chart as a starting point for the first cut. Then start lowering the RPM until the edge quality starts to decline. Once the quality declines, add 10% to 20%. Then do the same with the feed rate start cutting faster until the edge quality declines, back the speed off by 10% to 20%. Cutting direction also plays a big part in cut quality. The rule of thumb is composites plywood and plastics use conventional and lumber uses climb.

One of the last things to help in getting a good cut is hold down. If what you are cutting is not held in place you will not get a good cut. You also have to think about holding the scrap as well, if the scrap is not being held in place, the scrap will vibrate and bounce into the tooling.

What are some simple preventative things I could do with my bits to make sure they last as long as possible? I've seen some systems that actively cool and I even have a buddy who puts his bits in the freezer when not in use!

Do not let them get hot. Putting the cutters in a freezer would not do any good. Some material needs to use a cooling system if it be air or misters. Aluminum is the biggest that would need cooling.

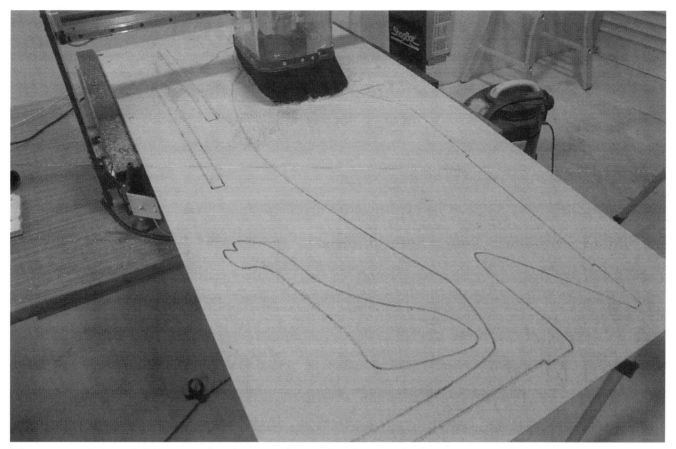

There are lots of bit manufacturers, how do I know if the bit I'm getting is of good quality and why do some bits cost exponentially more than others that have similar geometries?

It is the make up of the cutter. You will hear a bit is solid carbide but there is no such thing. Binders are used to hold the carbide together. These binders are cobalt and vanadium. Each manufacture has their own recipe for the cutters.

It is also important to have at least 80% of the collet filled with the shank of the cutter. Some manufactures will shorten the shank to save money. Heat is a bad thing because the binder cobalt will break down with heat and carbide is lost and the bit is weakened.

Shopbot offers a nice range of "starter bits" with their CNC routers. To be honest, before starting CNCROi.com, my ShopBot Desktop had only ever used two bits, a straight double flute bit and a wide bit for resurfacing down the sacrificial board. How many bits do you actively use and which ones are your favorite and why?

It all depends on the material I am cutting. If all I cut is 1/4" plywood. I would use a bit that is designed for that material. You should not use the same 1/4" cutter for plywood as you would for plastic. It will work but the edge quality will suffer.

Using a desktop to cut plywood, a single flute cutter should be used because with a double, the chipload would be too small. Most woodworkers think to get a better cut would be to slow the feed rate and increase the RMP. This is the wrong way.

Alain Albert, CNC Routers: Justifying Ownership Costs

Alain Albert has great enthusiasm for CNC technology and the woodworking industry. He most recently founded WISNet.ca which is a local woodworking club that I really enjoy attending. He ran several companies in the wood manufacturing industry and joined FPInnovations in 2006 as an Industry Advisor to help companies across Canada get the most out of their technology investments and improve the skills of their woodworking staff.

FPInnovations is one of the largest non-profit forest research groups in the world dedicated to the Canadian forest industry.

You can find out more about Alain Albert and FPInnovations by visiting http://wisnet.ca, and http://fpinnovations.ca.

Levels of Ownership

The cost of a CNC machine might make most manufacturers nervous but the benefits of owning a CNC router will most likely justify the cost in very little time. The first cost to take into consideration is the price of the machine. Some vendors offer bundled deals that include installation, software training and shipping charges. But in most cases, everything is sold separately to allow for customization of the CNC router.

Light duty

Low-end machines cost from $10,000 to $30,000. They are usually bolt it yourself kits made of bent sheet metal and use stepper motors. They come with a training video and an instruction manual. These machines are meant for do-it-yourself use, for the signage industry and other very light duty operations.

They will usually come with an adapter for a conventional plunge router. Accessories such as a spindle and vacuum work holding are options. An example of a CNC router manufacturer at this level is the ShopBot Tools (http://shopbottools.com). These machines can be very successfully integrated into a high production environment as a dedicated process or as part of a manufacturing cell.

For instance, one of these CNC's can be programmed to drill hardware holes on drawer fronts before assembly.

Medium duty

Midrange CNC machines will cost between $30,000 and $120,000. These machines are built of heavier gauge steel or aluminium. They might use stepper motors and sometimes servos; and use rack and pinion drives or belt drives. They will have a separate controller and offer a good range of options such as automatic tool changers and vacuum plenum tables.

These machines are meant for heavier duty use in the signage industry and for light panel processing applications. These are a good option for start-ups with limited resources or manpower.

They can perform most operations needed in cabinet making although not with the same degree of sophistication or with the same efficiency.

Industrial strength

High-end routers cost upward of $120,000. This includes a whole range of machines with 3 to 5 axes suited for a broad range of applications.

These machines will be built out of heavy gauge welded steel and come fully loaded with automatic tool changer, vacuum table and other accessories depending on the application. An example of a CNC router manufacturer at this level is Thermwood.

These machines are usually installed by the manufacturer and training is often included in the price.

NOTE from Jon

I interviewed Ken, the founder of Thermwood in this book, be sure to read it!

Shipping

Transporting a CNC router carries a considerable cost. With routers weighing anywhere from a few hundred pounds to several tons, freight costs can range from $350 to $3,000 or more, depending on location.

Remember that unless the machine was built nearby, the hidden cost of moving it from Europe or Asia to the dealer's showroom is likely included in the ticket price.

Additional costs may also be incurred just to get the machine inside your building once it is delivered and it is always a good idea to use professional riggers to deal with this kind of operation.

Installation and training

CNC vendors typically charge from $500 to $1,000 per day for installation costs. It can take anywhere from a half day to a full week to install and test the router; this cost can sometimes be included in the price of buying the machine. Some vendors will provide free training on how to use the hardware and software, usually onsite, while others will charge $500 to $1,000 per day for this service.

The Formula

In the book "Furniture Manufacturing in the New Millennium" by K.J. Susnjara (founder of Thermwood), the author describes how he would justify the cost of buying a CNC machine for a woodworking operation. The formula that he puts forward can be used to compare present processing costs with future costs using a CNC machine.

Processing Cost = Machine Cost + Labour & Overhead + Tooling Cost + Handling Cost

Using this formula and also referring to many websites and magazine articles, it can be concluded that any company of 2 or more workers cutting 15 to 80 sheets a week and selling around $300,000 per year or more should seriously consider purchasing a CNC router.

While it is always hard to justify this kind of capital cost using proven arguments and quantifiable facts, consider the following: a machine that is fully loaded with a vacuum table, pump, attached computer terminal, automatic tool changer, and additional accessories can cost upwards of $200,000.

A lease over 60 months on a $200,000 machine with 10% down and a buy back option of 10% will cost approximately $3,500 per month. All told, that is roughly the same amount of money as a $20 per hour worker.

The New Factory

Wood products' manufacturing, like any other discipline, is in a state of constant evolution. While there is certainly a great deal of turmoil in the industry in North America today, it would be foolish to predict its demise. Those companies that make good use of available technologies such as CNC will have a better chance of survival.

For the last fifty years and maybe more, the industry has remained the same. The methods and the tools in use today have been refined and modernized over time but the industry is essentially the same as it was after the Second World War.

The wood manufacturing industry is steeped in tradition and the old formulas simply don't compute anymore. Competition is no longer in a local marketplace with just one or two shops that make similar products.

The economy and markets are now worldwide. Factories halfway around the world can ship their wares to our customers with ease. They benefit from very cheap labour and heavily subsidised raw materials. Even when one factors in shipping costs, their product is less expensive than anything similar that can be made in North America.

Another factor to consider is that the consumer's tastes and habits are evolving very rapidly. They have access to a world of choice through the internet and they can research anything from wood species to styles in an instant.

Consumers today are configuring and customizing their purchases online and they expect to receive their orders in very short order.

Can the same stale products of yesteryear continue to be delivered with a long turnaround time of 6 to 8 weeks or more?

The North American secondary wood manufacturing company of the future may look somewhat like this:

> It will be a modern manufacturing plant with the latest automated equipment.

> This company will be lean. No inventories and the production flow will be fine-tuned so that once an order is started, it doesn't stop until it's in the customer's hands, along with the invoice. The production cycle will be measured in days, not weeks. The product offering will be fully customizable.

> New product introductions will utilize the principles of mass customization. The manufacturer will stay away from commodity products and his offering will be much differentiated and most likely cater to a niche high-end market. The manufacturer will sell directly to the end customer and will take advantage of a complete online presence.

New Techniques

As CNC technology becomes more sophisticated, so do the techniques. Three-dimensional machining is becoming commonplace. Combined with portable laser scanning technology and powerful CAM software, intricately detailed carvings and turnings are not only possible but easy to do.

Other simpler procedures are making the life of the modern manufacturer much easier than that of his ancestors. Blind dado joinery, nested dovetail drawer boxes and countless other techniques are making the integration of mass customization into today's factories possible.

All these innovations are blurring the line between specializations as well. Indeed, a kitchen cabinet manufacturer today can make children's furniture and office furniture as well as kitchen cabinets and closet organizers.

New Materials

There is an amazing array of new materials available to manufacturers today. The days of knotty pine and red oak as the only two choices are long gone.

Lightweight panels, reconstituted veneers, sustainable and low VOC particleboard are only a few of the items that are readily available today.

One can buy metal laminates and reconstituted stone that can be cut with a CNC router. The combinations are limitless and are bound only by the limits of the imagination.

To quote a well-respected CNC manufacturer:

"CNC machine engineering is a highly complex science. It involves physics, electronics, pneumatics, mathematics and a bunch of other disciplines. There is no scientifically proven best way to design a CNC machine. Every decision, every component is a compromise. In no area of machine design can you gain something without giving up something else."

Remember this when looking to purchase a machine. The only really accurate way to judge a machine is to judge the results.

· How well does the machine actually perform its tasks?
· How good is the quality of the machining it produces?
· How easy is it to use?
· How well does it hold up in production?
· How reliable is it?
· How long will it last?

· How easy is it to upgrade or change?
· What does it cost?
· How much can you rely on the vendor for after sales service?

While it is true that much of the North American wood products manufacturing capacity has now moved to developing countries, the new market opportunities that are now open have never been more plentiful.

Find a niche and make it happen. CNC technology should help a business become more successful and improve the bottom line.

The one common fact that has been experienced by countless manufacturers of wood products around the world is that a taste of CNC technology will change a business forever.

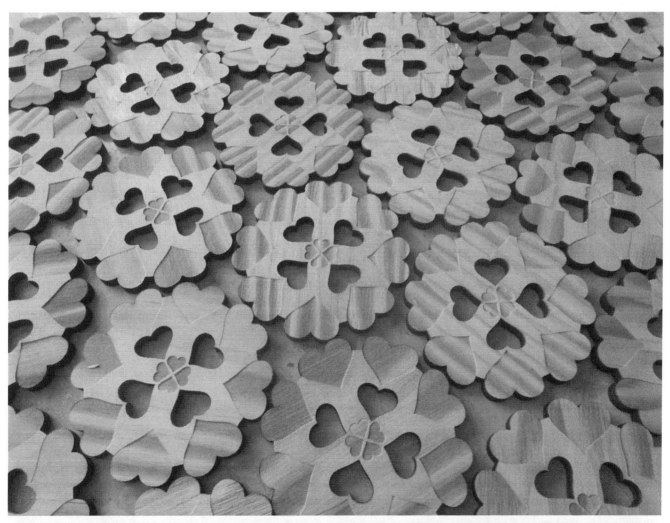

Jig Tips

Jigs are a fantastic way to get a lot of work done in one sitting, it's an efficient use of time and it allows you to do some incredible volumes ACCURATELY. Generally, when I build jigs, I try to use even spacing x and y spacing with key numbers such as "250" if a jig holds over a thousand pieces for easy counting. Also, you want to use cheap and thin material, 1/8" (3 mm) acrylic or MDF in two layers (one backing, one with holes) so that you can empty or load a try jig while the other is in production.

You also want to add four markers or registration points to confirm your jig is straight on bed, there is nothing worse to have a loaded jig only to find out that it isn't straight and everthing is off!

For jigs that involve larger pieces, I tend to stick with 1/4 inch (6 mm) plywood due to strength concerns especially if it involves having the front and/or back of my bed open. Stuff moves on you and if you use a material that isn't strong enough, it will shift.

One last tip, hold down your jig using duct tape so it doesn't move!

I have found that jigs, by their very nature, tend to warp overtime especially if you have wide temperature and humidity swings. I've yet to find a solution to this other than adding physical weights to keep the jig down on the bed when you do see it curl up on the sides.

I had a client ask me once why I didn't add tabs for easier removal of products from the jig once they are completed. The simple answer is that it's more efficient to simply turn the jig over than to peel them off one by one and you can get a lot more product per jig.

What I have started to do though was add small diameter circles on the backside of the jig. Sometimes you have pieces that just don't want to come out (usually due to warping of the jig over time). So having a way to push it out with your finger from behind saves a lot of time instead of having to try to dig for it to pull it out.

With my laser, I have a vacuum table with both an aluminium grid and a solid flat table. I've used both with my jigs and found no real difference in "flatness" but, for larger and heavier pieces, I've steered towards using a flat solid table.

My Austrian CNC Trotec Laser has rulers along the X and Y axis for the flat table which helps me better position things.

Something I learned at Evright.com while I was working there in Australia was that Legos can be used to make a quick and dirty jig. Most of the time, it works great but other times, it's best to invest your time in building your own solid jig.

In the picture below, I cut out some sample rulers from 3 mm thick acrylic... it may look messy but the results were fine. If you look closely, you'll noticed I laser cut round holes into the Lego plate. I had a problem with smoke build-up underneath and having a vacuum table meant it was useless as the plastic was solid.

After I made the holes with the laser, the jig worked great with no smoke issues (which causes fires) under the acrylic.

Depending on your production run and material being engraved, you can use either MDF or acrylic. If you are annealing stainless steel plates, DO NOT USE ACRYLIC as the heat from the laser will melt your tag right into the jig! Alternatively, you don't want to use MDF if you have thousands of samples to make using your jig.

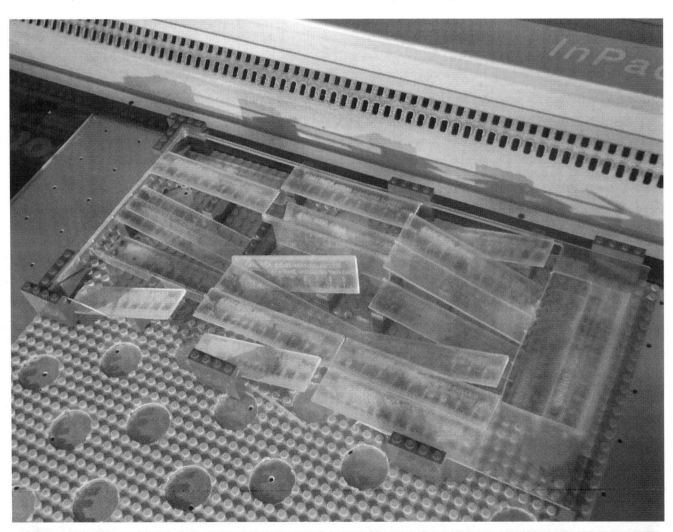

There is no right or wrong way to make a jig. You can make very clean ones for clients using two layers of white 3 mm acrylic or very strong ones using 10 mm plywood. We've made both and every variation in between. Sometimes it's a good idea to put "push out" holes underneath, such as what you see in the above picture and other times just using one layer you put flat on the CNC laser bed is more than adequate.

Regardless of what material you use, don't get complacent with your jigs. Only because your jig is straight and your bed is also, doesn't mean the engraving will be! Some jigs, especially MDF, warp with changes in humidity and temperature; another great reason to use acrylic though it does get brittle over time. Use multiple reference points as well. They can be a corner, a small mark you built into your jig (registration marks) or even a letter you engraved or marked into your jig.

When putting your material into a jig, leave about 1 mm of play, so if your material is 100 mm long, make the hole 101 mm so it's easy to move things in and out of it.

There is nothing worse than having to cram in a small piece of material and then not being able to take it out! Being able to push through of just flip the jig upside down will save you a lot of time and ultimately, make your shop have a higher ROI.

Mike Dean, Founder of Epilog Laser

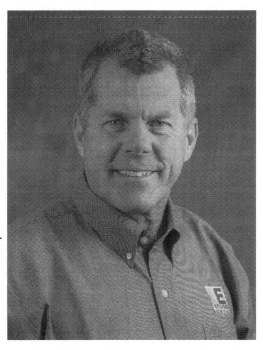

I'm in a slightly unique position with CNCKing.com where I have been talking with CNC laser owners around the world with just about every brand of CNC laser in the market for the past 7 years.

Although there is a lot of play when it comes towards purchasing a CNC laser, from the market segment you hope to serve, where you are based, applications and budget you are contending with, Epilog Laser is a name that keeps coming up over and over again.

I've been following Epilog Laser for almost a decade and have had the pleasure to talk to a number of their customers, sales reps and staff through the years.

Mike has played a pivotal role in the CNC laser industry to turn niche machinery into mainstream throught his enthusiasm, drive and desire to get innovative new technologies to market.

You can visit Epilog Laser at their website http://EpilogLaser.com.

You co-founded Epilog Laser almost 23 years ago. Did you think back then that Epilog Laser would become one of the world's largest manufacturer of small and medium sized CO_2 and fiber laser systems? What encouraged you to want to jump into the industry back then and how has the ride been thus far?

When we got started we had a business plan that showed if we could sell five machines a month we would be on top of the world! We knew there was a market, but we really underestimated its size and scope so, no, we had no idea what was to come.

The reason we started the business was that we were young, entrepreneurial, and thought it would be fun to start our own business.

I had worked with one of my partners - Steve - at a different manufacturing company and we had similar business philosophies that were at odds with the people we were working with at the time. We thought it would be great if we could be in charge and run a company the way we wanted to run it. The ride so far has been great!

We work with so many good people and it's been so interesting that it's sometimes surreal to look back at Epilog's progress. I tell people that I'm so lucky, that I knock on wood so often that my knuckles are raw!

There are many CNC manufacturers that have branched out into other CNC technologies as they've grown through the years such as Plasma, Router etc. but Epilog has always been a CNC laser company. There is a certain amount of synergy across CNC machines and their related customer bases where this can be seen as a very profitable progression. Have you ever considered expanding your offerings into other CNC machine types though the years?

We see the synergy with other types of CNC machines, but we've never wanted to manufacture anything other than lasers. There are so many opportunities in the laser market that we don't feel the need to branch out.

Every different type of machine requires its own level of expertise and while there are similarities between CNC machines, they all have their own secrets that you need to know to make them great.

We feel like we would be diluting our laser efforts if we had to learn the secrets of how to make a really good CNC router or plasma machine.

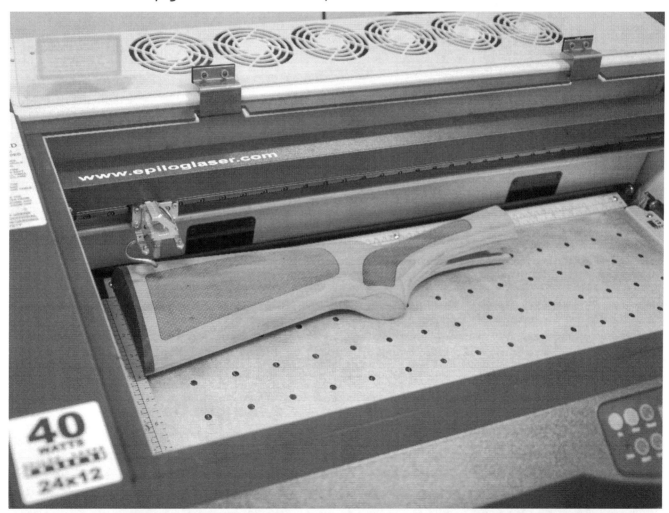

We all know that software is as important, if not more important, to a CNC machine's overall functionality and ROI than the hardware. What are some aspects of Epilog's job control software that allow an operator to both get up to speed FAST on an Epilog and turn a good profit?

The Job Manager saves every aspect of every laser job you print to the laser. This allows users to go back to previous jobs and repeat them without having to think about what they did or how they did it. We have lasers in our production area that run the same jobs over and over. When we gave the Job Manager to the operators, one of them said "It's the best thing since the invention of the laser!"

It made their daily lives so much easier. We have a great group of software engineers that really understand the user experience and they developed the Job Manager for our customers, not for themselves.

The 3D printing space is a rapidly evolving ecosystem where the prices of the machines keep dropping while their functionality keeps rising. Why haven't we seen that in the CNC laser industry? If anything, it seems like quality CNC lasers keep going up in price as their functionality increases!

Relative to the laser industry, 3D printing is a well understood and simple technology that many, many people understand. I always tell people that producing a laser requires a certain amount of black magic and you can sense that it's difficult just by looking at the very small number of companies that manufacture laser tubes. If it were easy everyone would do it.

What are some of the programs and methodologies that Epilog Laser employs to improve the ROI of customers buying your CNC lasers? What technologies have you built into your lasers that help improve the bottom line of your customers over the long term?

In your earlier question, you asked about rising prices. Many of our customers see a greatly improved ROI because prices have actually come down dramatically.

When we started, we sold a 25 watt laser system for $18,000. We sell a more powerful system today for less than $8,000.

Additionally, speed increases have allowed for much higher throughput and ease of use improvements have reduced the training it takes to operate a laser.

They are now so easy to operate that Epilog manufactures the only laser system that is operated by the consumer at your local PetSmart store.

Every laser operator has their favorite materials and applications for their laser - what are yours? I love working with wood, are you an acrylic, wood or metal guy? Why?

I love working with wood and cutting acrylic. My family thinks I'm nuts, but when we're out together, I'm always able to find laser engraved wood products and I point them out.

I usually take photos of what I find and I have probably hundreds of photos of laser engraved wood products that I've discovered over the years. I don't know why, but I'm just intrigued by what people have done with wood and their lasers.

I love acrylic because it's easy to incorporate color into the laser process. There are dozens of acrylic colors available, and making signs and acrylic structures with different colors is a great creative outlet for me.

I made a backdrop out of colored acrylic pieces for a wedding that people loved! Nobody knew what it was, how it was made, or who made it, but I heard many very positive comments about it.

You recently came out with your Fusion line of CNC lasers. It seems like a natural progression from your Zings to Legend series. How long had the Fusion been in development and how did you pick and choose what you wanted in this new platform to both make it standout in the marketplace yet affordable for people to purchase?

I really like the direction Epilog Laser took with this new platform btw. The Fusion was in development for several years and we choose the Fusion path by listening to our customers.

Epilog has a lot of loyal customers and they really liked their earlier machines like the Legend series, but they wanted bigger, better, faster, so we tried to accommodate what they requested.

The Fusion 40 is our biggest machine. At 40" x 28", it has a lot of user features like the Job Manager, and it produces a better product. I would like to say that we were responsible for the Fusion design, but mostly we listened to our customers and tried to give them what they asked for.

The CNC industry has changed tremendously over the past few decades. They are easier to work with, more mechanically sound and their software... well, I don't even need to know G-Code to design things! How do you see the industry evolving over the next few decades and what role does Epilog see itself playing in growing the CNC laser industry?

I wish we had unlimited resources. We have so many ideas that we want to develop. It will keep us busy for decades. You're going to see more power at lower prices, much higher speeds, and especially the ability to easily process many more materials.

Some of this is happening now, but it takes time to properly develop difficult technologies. I've been asked many times over the years whether I think the laser market is getting saturated. I say: "Not even close!"

It's a great business to be in and we continue to grow every year for many years. To give you an example, earlier this year we tripled the size of our cleanroom production area and it's already maxed it out.

We're excited!

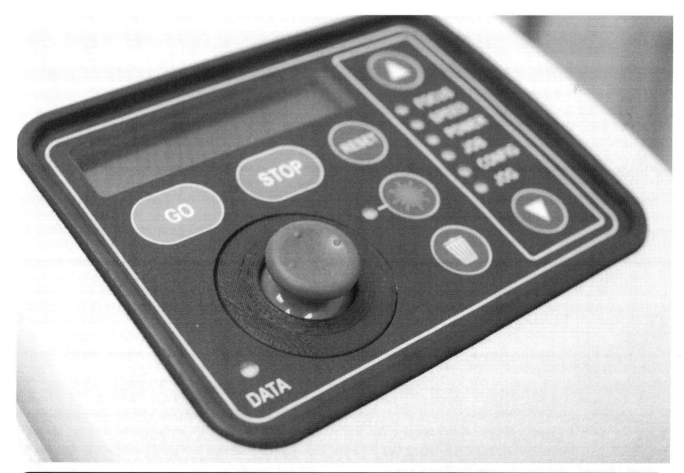

Paul Mason, Owner of Millennium Laser Systems

I've been designing things for CNC lasers (and routers) for many years now but a lot of the fundamentals about the technology behind them, the source, the tube... I knew next to nothing about. I approached Paul, who has a PhD in Laser Physics and is the founder of Millennium Laser Systems, to see if he could answer my questions in plain English and he thankfully agreed!

You can visit Millennium Laser Systems at http://millenniumlasers.co.uk

Can you explain to me what the difference is between a CO_2 and a YAG laser is and why they have such vastly different effects on the material they are engraving/cutting? You'd think energy is energy regardless of source.

All lasers emit different wavelengths (colour) of light. All materials absorb different colours of light at different rates, so it's "simply" a matter of which wavelengths are absorbed by the material best. Energy is only really a factor with the laser if the material can absorb that colour.

Basically high energy and high absorption gets more work done in a material processing sense. There are other key factors too, such as thermal conductivity and non-linear index of the material which plays vital roles application.

A laser tube holds gas that reacts with electricity to generate power. How much of the power output (watts) is defined by the density of the gas relative to the type of gas found in the tube? Are these gases difficult to source and can you mix and match to affect output quality?

The CO_2 laser is a molecular gas laser; a yag is a crystal laser. The gasses inside are numerous, often proprietary, and each playing key roles. There is scope for varying gas parameters but it is not a "Carte Blanche" for success. Often and from experience, many thousands of hours are invested in perfecting these systems.

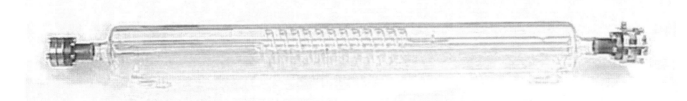

One thing that's been bugging me for a while is why do some laser tubes cost hundreds of dollars while other cost thousands for the same output? How much of the cost is based off the gas relative to the casing holding it? Are there any other factors that have a bearing on gas tube costs?

See the previous point. Today and often the main difference in price is down to Western vs Asian manufacture.

The West obviously has higher cost base but also every part is more expensive, with a genuine higher specification. It all adds-up.

The cost of some of the reprocessing systems can be expensive if you are doing it right but generally, a Western tube may be 5x more expensive than a Chinese tube, but will last 10-30x longer. You get what you pay for.

What are your views on ceramic tubes compared to metal and glass ones? Trotec Laser came out with Ceramicore recently that promises increased efficiency and more stable power output. They have no weld joints as well, so gas leakage is no longer an issue.

Gas leakage is always an issue. Companies have been using ceramic cavities for a long time, way before metal cavities. In fact, some big brands still do it! It comes down to more to the resonator design and power level desired to determine the best way forward.

There is no golden rule. All sealed CO_2 lasers must have seals somewhere and there is a lot of variation in sealing methods such as metal, rubber, glue. Synrad uses rubber and can achieve 20 years sealed life.

So, any conclusion could be drawn. Millennium uses its own proprietary methods for sealing from metal, glue and others.

Millennium Lasers Ltd. is now offering 400W and 600W tubes. What are some of the challenges present with tubes as you go higher-up the wattage charts? What is the major limiting factor that you must face when designing laser tubes and how are they overcome?

Increasing power from a sealed system is not easy. There are many challenges and these differ whether you use RF or DC power technology and also depending on the material used for the resonator structure.

The Millennium design is under development and is our 3rd manifestation and offers the potential for the lowest cost and highest reliability system you can think of. It's a little "left field".

Your company does extensive consulting for some of the biggest CNC laser manufacturers in the world. What are some of the developments that will be coming out in the next few years in the industry that you can share with us?

That's a tough one. I tend to advise and steer on that topic rather than trying to innovate. The users know their game far better than I, so I simply follow their lead and help to make it better. They know what they want and I simply facilitate that for them.

The biggest in-house innovation I can think of for the ever growing CNC market is the higher power Millennium CO_2 systems which should be idea for metal marking and cutting of thin steels, economically pitched prices starting at around £25,000.

Why do tubes eventually wear-out? If the gas doesn't leak from the tube, then nothing is lost or gained inside the tube so it should be able to run indefinitely, no?

Everything leaks, it's all about the rate of leak gases "leak" out of the laser environment and gases leak into the laser. This all kills the ionisation process inside the laser cavity.

There are many other factors which are proprietary knowledge too. The gas degrades with life and the break-up of CO_2 in a non-recoverable way if not managed properly. It's all about management and what you know is happening.

Anything else you'd like to add?

Only that I am regularly contacted by people who have purchased a low cost cutter or laser tube from China or a Western "badged" item that breaks down all too quickly.

They cannot afford the price to repair or buy a new one, so at the end of the day, they lose everything invested in that project. Don't buy too cheap expecting BMW quality!

Ask where does the M/C come from and also, the laser tube and power supply. A reputable US M/C supplier with a good CNC system may be using a low cost Chinese laser tube with a 2 000 hours lifespan and poor beam quality and so on.

Interview Andreas Penz, CEO Trotec Laser

Trotec Lasers, manufactured in Austria, are the Mercedes-Benz of the CNC laser world. I've known the company for many years previous to buying my very own Trotec Speedy 400 flexx as the name kept coming-up from customers buying my digital plans at CNCKing.com.

Since getting my laser, I've gotten to know quite a few people from Trotec and got to use their full range of equipment while working in Australia at Evright.com.

If you want to learn more about Trotec Laser, I've made lots of videos showcasing their capabilities on my websites.

Visit them online at http://TrotecLaser.com.

Can you give me a bit of history about why Trodat decided to build its own laser systems? And what about the origin of Trodat's self-inking stamp engraving making Trotec Lasers unique in the marketplace?

By working with rubber stamp makers worldwide, Trodat discovered that its customers were dissatisfied with the existing products on the market and their quality. Rubber stamp makers have particularly high requirements in regards to reliability and precision of a laser system - the text plates need to show perfect engraving quality for a satisfying stamp impression.

Due to this, Trodat decided to begin producing laser systems. High demands for consistent quality still characterize the company today.

What was the decision-making process that let to the creation of Trotec Laser? What does it offer to companies around the world? Was this always the intention, or did things align themselves where it made sense to enter the highly competitive CNC field?

The endless number of laser applications and the wide range of materials that can be processed with the laser led to enormous growth. This made the company's laser technology a very important pillar for the Trodat Trotec group. Because of this, Trotec was able to develop and evolve into a global company with growth in many different market segments worldwide, and a presence in more than 90 countries.

You've been the CEO of Trotec Laser since 2001, how much has the CNC laser marketplace evolved since then, and how do you manage to keep things growing smooth and steady with such explosive worldwide growth?

As a company, Trotec is always focused on the best laser system solutions for our customers. The laser market is a continually growing market with new applications and challenges. Thanks to our innovative products, we are setting the standards in the industry. Just to give one example, in 2015, we are celebrating 10 years flexx technology.

This is the innovative technology that enabled us to introduce the first laser machine with both a CO_2 and fiber laser technology. This innovative spirit permeates our daily business, and inspires our exceptional team.

Working with such talented engineering, technical support, marketing and sales teams allows me the freedom to focus on all aspects of the Trotec group, and move Trotec forward as an industry leader.

Trotec Laser recently built new factories and a headquarters. Can you talk a bit about what makes it unique, and share some of the accolades that Trotec Laser has received as a result?

In my point of view, innovative companies have to be committed to fulfilling social responsibility in addition to expanding their own interests. Trotec absolutely acknowledges its social responsibility.

This is demonstrated with the ISO14001 certificate or our new headquarters which was awarded with the Green Building award.

The award recognizes the building as a major solar installation that is energy self-sufficient in terms of heating and cooling, and generates no CO_2 emissions for heating and cooling. The building's core activation provides surface heating and cooling systems.

This technology, in conjunction with optimum thermal insulation, ensures low heating and cooling demands and low temperature fluctuations due to the building's high storage capacity.

With the new headquarters, Trotec is setting new standards, not only in regards to sustainability, but also as a comfort factor for the Trotec team.

I'm the proud owner of a Trotec Speedy 400 flexx. It's such an awesome machine on both the hardware and software side. Can you give me a glimpse into what kind of effort was required to research and bring it to market? How has this machine been received in the CNC laser marketplace?

Thank you for the great feedback.

First of all, it is one of our principles to listen carefully to our customer's needs. With this feedback from the market, we set ourselves ambitious goals as the technology leader.

We have a genius R&D team and we also work with universities and research institutions, for example, when it comes to ergonomics for the laser user. The great customer feedback we receive proves that we are on the right track.

Trotec Laser has had a very distinctive method of growth through acquisition of key markets from its competitors. What are some of the challenges present with merging different cultures together and how do you try to make the process as smooth and painless as possible for both clients and employees?

Our team is at home around the globe. We speak 15 languages. One of our corporate mottos to be successful is: "think global, act local." The laser market is a global market. To be successful, we need to listen to all our customers and anticipate their needs.

What are some of the more unique Trotec applications you've seen? How do you manage to share your vision for the company when it has several hundred employees around the world?

For one, Trotec Lasers are used for cutting stents - lifesaving products with highest demands. Trotec developed a special product with a femtosecond laser source for this special application.

Another unique application is the laser processing of the solar panels for mars rovers. Every vision has a radiant power. We want to make our customers successful. Trotec can look back on an enormous growth and we have even more ambitious plans for the future.

This is only possible with a great team spirit.

Interview with Ken Susnjara, Founder of Thermwood Corp

Thermwood Corporation has an impressive range of industrial CNC routers but more importantly, Ken started the company back when NC was transitioning into CNC nearly half a century ago!

This makes Thermwood the oldest CNC router company in the world. His machines are industry leaders and I have several CNCROi.com customers who love their Thermwoods so much that they have more than one in their shop!

Visit them online at http://Thermwood.com.

Back in 1969 CNC machines were very much in their infancy in the United States. What drove you to start a company instead of working for somebody else in the industry? Did you achieve amazing entrepreneurial success right out of the gate or did it take a while for people to warm to CNC routers back then?

There were no CNC routers in 1969. In fact, there were no microprocessors. Thermwood started when I was in college, a small engineering school in central Indiana now called Rose Hulman Institute of Technology. I was in school and needed money. I got a job in the school cafeteria, worked a week, was paid $14 and quit.

There had to be an easier way!

I decided to start a company because people who owned companies seemed to have a lot of money. At the time I didn't have a car but was taking flying lessons whenever I could scrape together enough money.

It was a four mile walk each way to the airport. From that experience I decided to make airplane parts because they were expensive. So I wouldn't have to make a lot of them because I didn't have a lot of extra time.

Working with a friend, we built a thermoforming machine using army surplus parts in the school shop and we started thermoforming wheel pants for fixed gear aircraft. The only other wheel pants were made from fiberglass and cost $54 a pair.

We sold ours as a kit for $22. They cost us $3 to make. $19 profit on a $22 sale.... Sounds about right! This seriously warped my judgment.

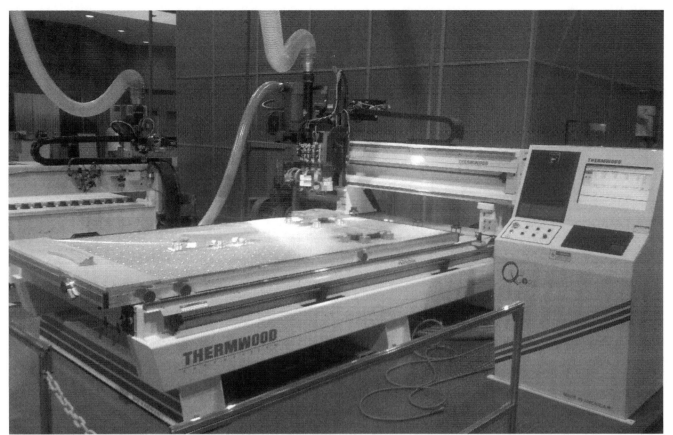

I left school, got a really good job at Alcoa and my standard of living took a nosedive. I began working in the evenings and discovered a way of making thermoformed wood grain parts which were perfect for the furniture industry at the time.

They were making plastic parts using an injection molding machine running $10,000 molds on a minute and a half cycle. My process used half the amount of plastic, on a $500 mold and a 5 second cycle, and the parts looked the same. I quit my job and was in the plastic business. That's where the name "Thermwood" came from, thermoformed wood grain parts.

Things went great for a few years until the Arabs decided to place an embargo on oil. The price of our plastic quadrupled and the furniture industry quit using plastic parts. We had to turn to other products and these new products needed to be trimmed. After hand trimming for awhile, we decided we needed to automate.

There were some machines called NC routers that used punched tape to move around but they were a quarter of a million dollars each. Good idea but way too expensive.

At the time I bought a new product called a "calculator". This was an amazing device it could add, subtract, multiply and divide and only cost $960.

It had nine memory positions which gave me an idea. If we could make each position represent a point on the machine table, we could cut things that had up to nine moves. So how did this thing works?

I was told it used a new device called a microprocessor. I didn't know anything about that but did find a book. It was loose-leaf paper in a three ring binder. I read the book and understood virtually nothing but I did have the name of the author.

I called him and asked if we could do what I wanted. He said no problem. It would cost about $6,000 - $8,000 and take about six weeks. It actually took eighteen months and cost a million and a half dollars but we had the first commercially available CNC control.

There were minicomputer based CNC controls used by the military at the time but this was the first CNC control you could actually buy on the open market.

To understand how crude we were, all programming was done in hex using a small keypad as there were no assemblers at the time. There were a lot of all-night sessions, however.

As things advanced, we began using CPM and operating system developed by Osborne Computer. It didn't work very well so we wrote our own operating system, which was a complete, multi-tasking system able to run four independent threads, all before there was MS-DOS. When MS-DOS came out we switched to it and somehow used it as a multi-tasking system.

Eventually we switched to OS-2, which was pretty nice and finally, when that got killed off by Microsoft, we switched to Windows and turned it into a real-time system.

In this type of fast moving business, there is no instant success and even less stability. Things can go great today and be absolutely awful tomorrow. You just have to keep moving.

In the early eighties we got into the industrial robot business which was touted as the next huge growth area. We found you could make a small fortune in industrial robots, you just had to start with a large fortune. After losing more money that you can count, we turned back to CNC routers.

It's a fast moving market with a lot of competition. We have tried to compete by offering new, fresh and innovative technology to separate us from the others. We are all pretty technical here and this does let us play with all the new toys.

This thing keeps moving and today we are working on an all new approach that could very well replace CNC routers or at least the way CNC routers work today.

We hope to have it out the early part of next year.

Thermwood has an incredible array of CNC routers - it's quite impressive how there is something to suit just about every industrial market segment. Did this range evolve over time or was a large diversity of CNC routers part of the plan from the beginning?

First, there was no plan in the beginning. You do what seems right at the time. You must really get to know your customers on a personal basis and try to understand what they really need. Then, you use all your creativity, experience and skill to try to offer a solution to their needs.

Make money by helping them make money. We don't sell machines, we sell what the machines do. We sell solutions that make more profit for our customers. That's our focus.

As we get into more and more markets, the solutions for each may be a little different, so you end up with a large range of products.

Over time, all of those products will continue to change as our customers change.

Other than your divestiture of Digital Sky, Thermwood didn't follow the traditional route of acquiring to generate marketshare, instead, it seems you've just been slow and steady wins the race. Do you think this approach is what has allowed Thermwood to survive and prosper for almost half a century? Did you ever consider launching Thermwood into the public markets?

We have an innovative, can-do, swashbuckling culture at Thermwood. We can turn on a dime and abandon practices that are ingrained almost instantly. I'll give you an example. Years ago, a salesman came here to demonstrate a three-dimensional laser. We already had a huge investment in straight line lasers and had developed technology, at great expense, that allowed us to align and compensate our machines to a high level of accuracy.

We had everyone involved in this process in the demonstration, from the hourly workers to top management. We were impressed, held a twenty minute discussion and ordered two systems at $150,000 plus each before the salesman left. We had to completely abandon existing technology and develop all new systems. We made that decision in twenty minutes. It worked great, vastly improved our products and saved a ton of money.

The problem with this is that there are not a lot of companies comfortable operating this way. Most find it totally unpredictable and unstable, and some even call it reckless.

We have looked at other companies but the cultural clash would not have worked. In the markets we focus on, we tend to be the technical leaders so it is unlikely we will gain valuable technology or market share by buying into it.

We could potentially gain some market share by moving into aligned products but, most likely, these will be markets and areas we don't really know.

Just because you do well in one market doesn't mean you will be successful in others. I've seen a lot of successful companies fail because they thought that their success in one area meant they would be successful in anything else they tried.

As for being public, we tried that. We went public in the early eighties in the midst of the robot hysteria. We were listed on the American and Pacific stock exchanges. That didn't work all that well.

I often feel that as we came to New York, the investment bankers looked out their penthouse windows and said, 'Lookie here, here comes some country folks". It was very expensive, took an inordinate amount of management time and we got very little for it.

Once they started passing new rules for public companies in the late nineties, we bought back enough stock that we were able to de-list and become private again. As you might imagine, it doesn't hold much appeal for me.

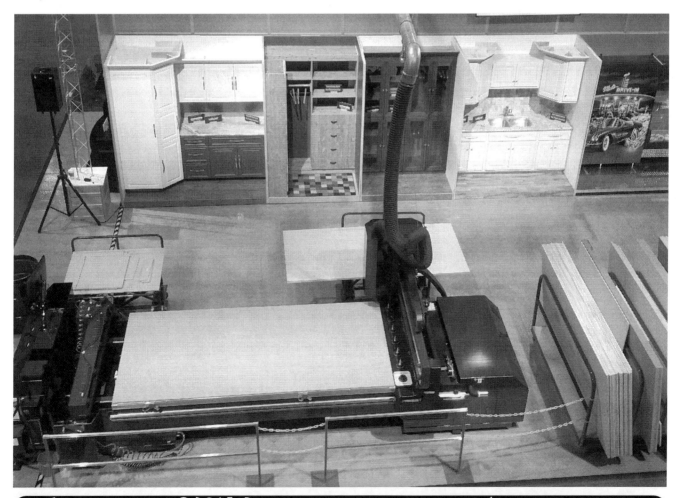

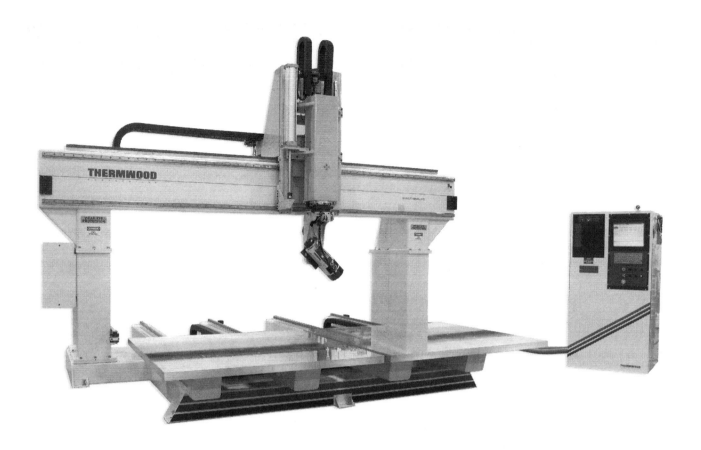

From virtual service and control nesting to dynamic CAD drawings and 3D laser compensated cutting tables, you have quite a bit of technology that goes into each Thermwood that most people would never even think was needed, much less realize the benefit of prior to machine acquisition. How much of your sales cycle is focused on educating customers on these features that differentiate it from the competition?

We do try. As we compete, all others try to focus the discussion away from the control toward the machine mechanics or low price, or anything else trying to convince the customer that all controls are the same and they shouldn't bother with that. There are two things that really help us in our efforts.

First, if we can get the customer to come and visit us, we can demonstrate all the features that help you make more money with our machines. Also, we have customers in every part of the country and I would not hesitate to have a prospect talk with any of them. They know how well these things work. Most new prospects know of one or more of them which helps a lot. Repeat sales are also a large part of our business.

Recently we started a program of separating ordinary routers from "Smart" routers in the marketplace, a smart router being one that has the advanced features you mention. When you tell a customer he has a choice between an ordinary router and a smart router, he naturally wants to know the difference and you enter a serious conversation about advanced features and how they save material and labor, and reduce errors and scrap. That effort is starting to have an impact but it is still fairly new.

Thermwood is very active in social media including YouTube and I was wondering how important you've found this method of outreach towards acquiring more customers vs more traditional means like tradeshows and mass mailings.

As we entered the financial downturn a few years ago, the guy that was heading up our very traditional marketing effort decided to retire. We put my tech savvy son in charge of marketing and gave him some other young guns to help. We told him we would meet a couple times a week to teach them all the techniques and practices.

Don't make waves until we work our way through this.

Within two weeks he had cancelled 85% of our print ads, cut trade show expense in half and switched focus to the internet and social media. They began giving management training sessions on push and pull marketing and electronic media to teach us how things are done today.

They went from focusing on three markets to focusing on over a dozen. The three markets shrank to the point we would have gone out of business. The new markets supplied enough business to keep us going. At this point, I think this "social media" thing is rather good, although I'm still not sure I totally understand it.

Thermwood offers "Smart Router" with features such as internet servicing and tooling error avoidance to machining a profile edge without a profile tool and even noticing if parts are moving while being cut! How much of a difference can going "smart" make in a typical shop?

Actually, "smart routers" were only the first step toward a new type of machine that we feel will appeal to an even larger user group. We announced this new machine, called a "cut center", at the 2014 IWF show in Atlanta.

We have found that the single biggest impediment to embracing a CNC router and the single biggest ongoing cost in operating a CNC router is programming. These machines require a skilled, trained programmer and someone technically competent to set up and run those programs. Programming also requires a huge amount of time, even with the best software. Operating with these programs is time consuming and can be confusing.

Our "Cut Ready" cut center does not require software or programming. You don't even need a computer. Simply tell the machine what you want to make and how you want it made and it makes it.

The first impression when you hear about this is that everything must be pre-programmed, but that's not how it works. Our initial machine can make over twenty million different products and there is no practical way to create and save twenty million different programs.

It can make those products out of different thickness materials and every time you change thickness, the programs change. There is no way to pre-program it. Instead, the machine actually knows how to make things.

The cut center works with product definitions. For example, a base cabinet with two doors and a drawer. This product can be made a lot of different ways, frame or frameless, one or two sided material, different material thickness and different construction joinery.

Tell the machine how you want to make the product and the material you want to use and it automatically creates the necessary code to cut it.

With the approach the fundamental way, you interact with CNC changes. For example, once you make cabinets, you can make the doors and drawer fronts by simply selecting the design and telling the machine how you want them mounted (full overlay, partial overlay or inset) and it makes them. You don't worry about quantity, size or anything else.

Just tell it to make doors and drawer fronts for those cabinets and it makes them. It also makes the drawer boxes, and moldings, the same way.

This type of machine is also incredibly simple and easy to use. You can install it and be in full production in less than a day. It guides you step by step and takes care of all complex areas such as tooling, operating settings and maintenance tracking automatically.

As an example, during the IWF show, we had several people walk up to the machine, having never seen it before, and make a cabinet with no outside instruction or help. It's really that easy.

This new type of machine is as different from a CNC router as an iPad is different from a PC. We believe it will bring new capability, perhaps a different kind of capability to a new group of cabinet and furniture shops who otherwise would not try to tackle the technical requirements of a CNC router.

Today, people with computer skills still buy PCs. Others buy an iPad or tablet. Today those with programming and technical skills still buy a CNC router. Others now have the cut center. By the way, more iPads and tablets are sold than PCs. Think about it.

I absolutely love CNC routing... coming up with projects and seeing a CNC machine cut my virtual ideas into physical prototypes is mesmerizing even after two years - does this feeling ever go away?

No. It's always fascinating. I have been running machines for almost forty years and I am still fascinated when they cut something new. In our business, we work with hundreds of companies from around the world making almost anything you can imagine.

It's actually fun because you never know what's going to come through the door next.

Thermwood has an extensive dealer list and aggressively expanding to more countries around the world. What has been the leading fuel for this growth abroad?

We want to sell more and, a few years back, we said "why don't we try to sell overseas", and it's been working pretty well. We have found the key to entering a new country is finding some folks that you can work with, who are excited and enthusiastic.

So we expand into areas where we find the right folks to partner up with.

What are your thoughts on 3D printing? Do you see one day additive and molecular production methods ever replacing subtractive ones?

3D printing is really fascinating but probably for a different reason that what you think. The process itself is not particularly efficient and, although there are some exceptions, virtually anything you make can be made faster and cheaper using mass production techniques.

The real appeal for 3D printing is that you can make anything you have an electronic file for and you can make it locally.

There is no packing, no shipping, no handling, no hassle. We call it "distributed manufacturing". The product is not made in a factory and sent to the customer but is made at or near the customer from an electronic file.

There are huge benefits and appeal to this. We have been developing technology to make furniture using distributed manufacturing cells that can operate inside a retail store. Imaging going to a furniture store, selecting the furniture and size you want and having it made right there so you can take it home. This is not all that far off.

Each time I think everything is about done, a whole new wave of ideas and technology breaks. We are going through just such a period right now. After almost fifty years in business it's still fun.

Jumping into Entrepreneurship

I'm probably one of the worse people to give advice to others regarding entrepreneurship as a lifestyle choice. If you haven't already, you can read my bio in the previous volume - suffice it to say, I've lost everything and gained it back and then some a few times in my life thus far.

It's a horrible experience losing everything but equally as satisfying to get it all back due to sheer work, determination and passion.

The way I've always seen things is that the difference between an employer and an employee is that an employer can see the pink slip coming and change course.

I have many friends who have taken the same leap, some succeeded wonderfully while others failed so much they ended up having to get a JOB. I believe that's the moral of the story though, the worse thing that can happen is you end up working for somebody else... not a bad plan B and you can still be entrepreneurial after hours!

As for me, I just really love the responsability of runing my own ship, plotting my course going full steam ahead through the fog. It's the adventure that I enjoy, the "not knowing" part that really excites me.

I can go to a dozen networking events or tradeshows and find NOTHING then hit that one lead who gives me a nice project full of fat... I love that! Entrepreneurship is like a drug, probably the best you can ever have! When things are going great, everything clicks, you are making money, everybody loves what you do and you are written about in articles around the world. When they go to shit, well, everybody wants their money back, everybody hates you and you are written about in articles around the world.

Building a business is easy, anybody can do it. The trick is staying in business long enough to develop positive cashflow so that you can STAY in business. Just because you have incredible passion, industry leading machinery and a wide range of experience, doesn't mean people and businesses will flock to your door throwing money at you. Infact, expect to struggle, even after you have achieved a certain level of success, for every contract you successfuly bid on.

Don't think these cashflow issues magically dissapear as you succeed either! Just about every company owner, from small sole proprietors to large multinationals, have a keen eye on their weekly payroll. You get to a point where your overhead quickly exceeds your personal capability to cover it if should things go South on you. The stress builds-up quickly if things don't go the way you intended regardless of the customer base you think you have to pay the bills on a regular basis.

A company founder may seem lucky but each gray hair has been fully earned!

Where WoodMarvels.com (now CNCKing.com) all began... my South Korean apartment!

Building a sustainable and profitable business is not a one-time thing you focus on when you start but a constant that must be in the back of your mind with every decision you make. Having a lean operation is a great way to reduce wasted time and resources but that's only the beginning!

A sustainable business can be as easy or as hard as you want to make it. The biggest obstacle you may have is simply opening your eyes to the opporutnites present all around you. Since I started CNCROi.com, I have yet to find a business that can't benefit from the services I provide. The trick then isn't trying to find applications, it's trying to find customers with money to pay MY company for those services.

It's a very fine niche. Companies that are too small don't have the disposable income required to invest in us and large ones will just buy the machine I have and do it inhouse.

Sooner or later, while playing around with your CNC machine, you'll come-up with something that's unique and marketable... it has happened to all of us! As such, I've created a new section in this book focused on actionable and focused interviews from people who have been successful in the invention business and can also help you!

Entrepreneurship is not an easy road to travel on, but it offers the most freedom.

Pilot training facilities in Iloilo, Philippines... across the street from my ESL "job".

The stress that comes from entrepreneurship is high during the valleys but gone in the peaks, realizing that you are driving to the beach while other people are working their 9-5 on really nice days is tough to beat.

I fell into entrepreneurship after university because after I graduated, I had no job prospects at all. Starting my business was the only way forward - though I was lucky to have realized this a few years before graduating so I already developed a plan B that I was pretty much doing full time anyways in my latter years.

I've done some crazy things in my life, most recently, leaving a well paying job in Australia to return home with a brand new high-end CNC laser without any customers waiting for me. Oh yeah, we are in the middle of a worldwide depression and the manufacturing base in my hometown is almost nill. Yes, I've also been gone for 7 years too! Great way to invest your life savings and then some isn't it?

Although I miss Australian life greatly, there isn't a day that I don't wish I was swimming at the local beach after work. I realized that I needed to make far more money than a job could ever give me to live well and fulfill my dreams.

I enjoyed my job, I found it rewarding, but the aspect I enjoyed the most was meeting other businesses and each time I did, I wanted to "be them" again.

I've been an entrepreneur most of my life and that desire just never left me and it got to the point where I had to take the leap again. I wanted to settle down a bit more permanently and start a family. It just felt weird getting a regular paycheck, knowing ahead of time what it would be and the deductions for rent and living expenses following... it was just mind numbing to me. I'd never see a check for 25K again!

I've run several companies since I was a kid, from growing a paper route to founding an industrial 3D animation studio back in 1996. The paper route was in the prime time for paperboys, every house got a paper back then. So it was quick and easy money while the 3D animation studio, I was ahead of the curve, a full decade and a half BEFORE the current boom in "3D" everybody seems to be talking about nowadays.

The number one question I ask myself is not where but HOW do I start. You see, WHERE always has an obvious answer, it's your present location using your present resources and contact list but HOW you start is a far deeper one.

That's what most people get stuck on and is the hardest to get through.

My bedroom view during an entire year in Sooncheon, South Korea.

Something I picked-up while living in China.

Before starting a business, you need to decide what you will and will not do from the start - find your niche and stick to it! This is where the HOW fits in.

How do you differentiate yourself in your local marketplace enough to get your first customer? How do you market yourself and your business? How do you deal with problems? How do you gain the confidence and energy required to make it all work? How will you pay your bills and lines of credit on time... and the list goes on.

Finding solutions to all these questions and a lot more are what I enjoy most about business. It isn't for the faint of heart and there are no shortcuts. It feels like juggling, sometimes you have a perfect order and all the balls are exactly where they should be; othertimes, the balls are all in the air and at other times, they are all falling to the ground.

The general public has an odd fascination with entrepreneurs. People expect you to be flush with cash and worth a few billion after a quick IPO! I think you have a better chance of winning the lottery than having this happen regardless of planning.

They'll ask you why this and why that, without realizing that the vast majority of entrepreneurs actually end-up just creating their own job. The lucky ones end-up moving onto a career and the extremely small minority of entrepreneurs actually strike it rich after a lifetime of work until they get a lucky break that turns them into overnight successes.

You will screw-up, you will have angry clients and YOU WILL STRUGGLE to get your first customer and it will be very tough during this time to turn projects away that you could do to stay focused.

Notice I didn't write your first PAYING customer. Expect to be stiffed along the way by those you most trusted. It has happened to me many times and it always seem to happen when I REALLY needed the money! Customer's payroll goes ahead of your invoices and thereafter, never seem to show-up in the mail after multiple promises that it was sent before you get a note that the company was either acquired or bankrupt.

Expect things to take longer than you are promised and expect to have many long sleepless nights and deadlines that you miss regardless of how much planning you put into things. Entrepreneurship is very much a lifestyle rather than something you can do "on the side".

Entrepreneurship is an adventure where the only way to start is to put caution to the wind, close your eyes and jump straight into it. If you are still wondering HOW to start, then you either haven't done enough research or this lifestyle just isn't something you are ready for at the moment.

You'll know when you are ready!

The very first Trotec Speedy 400 I ever saw... it was love at first sight! Perth, Australia.

Avoiding CNC Shop Loses

Everybody seems to know how to make money with their CNC but few people realize that some of their habits are actually costing them more money than they are generating when you add the fourth dimension - TIME.

These are the top 10 mistakes or issues that you'll come across operating a CNC machine that are eating away at your potential profit margins.

Buying the WRONG machine

There are a lot of CNC manufacturers out there - from small garage start-ups to large multinationals, but regardless of the route you go, getting the wrong machine for the application you have in mind is by far the best way to lose lots of money.

For instance, you can technically cut through thin gage steel using a 30 watt fiber laser but in all seriousness, why not save yourself the time and money and just buy a plasma cutter to do the job or even subcontract that out to a company with a kw range laser?

My parents' 2 car garage where CNCROi.com began, first day of business! August 2014

I've seen people who know very little about CNC machines (they didn't invest in buying my last volume) and they come-out with all these wonderful ideas and I don't know if they are just too wealthy or just too stuborn but they end-up so driven to buying a specific CNC machine type over the recomendations of the sales people they are talking to that they are blinded by the huge mistake they are about to make.

If you are cutting out 30 mm thick doors day in and out and want to engrave some cool details on it, the most efficient way to accomplish this is to use a CNC router to cut the door out, then a laser to engrave the detail.

Sure, you could do this all with a laser but the production time would be exponentially longer. Same with engraving the door using a CNC router, you lose resolution though it may not matter depending on the application! LISTEN to people who know CNC machines and get a second opinion before buying.

I've found that most sales people in the CNC industry are incredibly honest and more than willing to share their thoughts as to how to proceed with the most efficient production pipeling for your application.

The more expensive the machine, the better the knowledge and expertise by the way as they want repeat business, referrals and have a reputation to maintain. The CNC world is actually a very small community considering how large an industry it really is.

Not investing in a QUALITY machine

The second biggest mistake I see, and this one is repeated over and over again, is seeing the price tag for a QUALITY CNC machine and instead going for an offshore machine for a third to a quarter the price and expecting the same results.

There is a reason why some machines cost more than others. Sometimes this difference can be pure perception in the marketplace - which is why it's important to talk to many people in the industry before buying - but generaly, you get what you pay for.

Yes, that machine costs MORE but you know what, you won't have to rewire it once it arrives in a container. The frame will be SOLID and never go out of alignment, the software it comes with is maintained with regular updates and the guy who sold it to you isn't going to disappear in a few months after dumping your crate from the back of their pickup truck! These aren't headaches you want to ever live through.

If you are a highly technical person with a degree in mechanical engineering - offshore machines can be an amazing value as you can fix problems yourself but if you aren't - stick with reputable brands that have a long track record of customer service and CNC expertise. I know in my case, if something breaks - I'm screwed... knowing this severely limits who I'd buy a CNC machine from. Knowing your limits in this case is a good thing!

Not investing in training

You got a brand-new machine and you are ready to convert it into a cash cow but there's one problem, the person operating it has no experience! What do you do? You throw them onto it to learn as they go, hey, they used a plasma cutter before so a laser or router can't be all that different right? BIG MISTAKE!

If the manufacturer you are about to buy a machine from doesn't offer comprehensive training either on-site or at their plant, the first thing I'd do is drop them out of consideration.

It's one thing for an employer to learn "on the job" but quite another for an employee who could be generating revenue right out of the gate.

Each machine is different: they have their own quirks, software and optimization routines. For instance, an Epilog laser has a different software set-up than a Trotec but they are both CNC lasers at the end of the day.

An entry level Trotec Rayjet is a very different animal than a Trotec Speedy 400 flexx, just like an Epilog Zing is a very different machine from a Fusion M2 or a ShopBot Desktop is to a Thermwood Model 77.

The time you invest in training your employee (or yourself) with a new machine is probably the best immediate ROI kick you can achieve with your new CNC machine. You need to be making $$$ from the first project onward!

Being blinded by hardware at the expense of software

CNC machines are awesome, especially when they are shiny and new right out of the crate, but after a few weeks, they get digged, dirty and start to lose their physical luster. If it doesn't, you aren't using it enough!

Just like a beautiful woman, don't be seduced by her looks at the expense of her brain... the most important part! The software that's behind your CNC machine is the real gold. I'd take a half-working machine with awesome software over a perfecly working machine with awful software any day because when it does work, it will work perfectly. The nice thing is, if a machine has awesome software, the hardware will be equally as awesome.

How do you know if the machine you are about to buy has good software? It has had both a long update timeline and a roadmap going well into the future. Ask the manufacturer to provide you with these details and don't be scared to ask them DIRECTLY how their software is better than that of the competition.

Yes, you are buying a machine but in reality, without software, the machine is worthless.

First surprise expense, 8K to upgrade the electricity in the garage! (before upgrade pic)

Not using jigs

A CNC machine has 99.9999% repeatability on parts if you bought a good one... the problem is you don't. You can position something on/in your bed and no matter how hard you try or how many times you measure, it will always be a few fractions of a mm off. Who cares? The customer might and this will be noticeable especially if you are engraving long parts or if it has some angles to it where a quick comparison with a ruler going across will show your stuff being croked.

A simple way around this is to engrave rather than cut a piece, then you don't need a jig and everything will be 100% perfect. But if you say engraving 100 corporate awards or name badges, a jig is an aboslute must as you can just place the objects in it, then put this on the bed.

This saves you time measuring things out and also makes things more efficient as you can use multiple jigs. If you are laser engraving a pen, why not have another jig that you can empty and fill while the process is occuring on your CNC machine?

Jigs take a bit of time to build but a good one will more than make-up for this in the long run with time saved.

It's an incredibly efficient method to get a lot of work done with as few errors as possible. Be careful though, a screwed-up jig will not produce good product.

First attempt at annealing 304 stainless steel using a flexx lens... not bad!

Focusing on small jobs over large ones

Which of these two alternatives seems the most profitable to you? Running after a thousand customers to engrave 25$ worth of pens or running after one customer with a thousand pens for 10$ each? The pens cost the same, one "job" gives you 25K while the other gives you 10K.

I'd go with the 10K... running after people for small amounts of money is an insane way to run a CNC business. Imagine the paperwork, overhead, phone calls and returns you'll have with a thousand individuals! You couldn't even use a jig as the quantities are too low. You just created yourself a job where your ultimate ROI is below minimum wage!

There are several ways around this situation: one is having a minimum order with set-up/design fees, another is offering volume pricing as I have shown in my example.

The focus of your CNC business must be to make as much money in the shortest possible amount of time to pay your machine and expenses off ASAP.

Each hour your machine is sitting there doing nothing is costing you money but it's far better than having it running full-time barely breaking even with all the associated wear and tear that's involved on both me and the machine. I love my machine but rest assured, when it's working, it's making me money as working at a loss makes no sense to me.

I know it's tough. A guy has one or two widgets they need engraved or cut - don't do it unless you charge through the nose for it. Reason being, by the time you've set-up the job, booted up your machine and did the work, you will have very little left at the end of the job in the way of profits.

If they ONLY have extremely small volume, set them up on a "paid in advance" tab at a bare minimum, a promise of future work if you do "this work" rarely actually pans out.

Leaving your machine alone

I have four friends who have burned their machine (and some their entire shop) due to letting their CNC machine run overnight or while off doing other chores. I can't think of a better way to lose not only your CNC but also your livelyhood!

A broken CNC machine is bad but having it and everything you worked for over the course of years burn down is a far bigger hit to your CNC ROI.

Never leave your CNC machine running alone, even for a few minutes, the one time you do this will most likely be the time everything goes to hell and you are out of business for an extended period of time. Totally avoidable!

Not using nesting

The easiest way to save a fortune in materials, time and machine wear and tear is to nest EVERYTHIG you cut - for lasers, you have the added avantage of using shared lines. So one laser pass cuts the outline of two parts but for routers and plasma, you are better off cutting each part separately for hold down purposes as well as grain lift.

That being said, if you aren't nesting your pieces, meaning either manually or automatically positioning and rotating pieces for optimal material use, you are throwing lots of money away? How much?

With my ShopBot Desktop, I've been able to save as much as 50% of my material - that's 50% of material I don't have to throw-out, 50% of my material budget I don't have to touch and 50% of my material my machine doesn't need go over doing nothing.

Sure, the bond fires aren't as big in the backyard but that's a small price to pay for real savings across CNCROi.com's operations as well as my growing physical kit and shapes business over at CNCKing.com.

Your cutting times do go up dramatically with a very efficient nest but hey, that's when you make money, during the cutting and engraving, not the overhead gantry traveling between far flung parts! You get more done per sheet so longer production times in this case is a positive development.

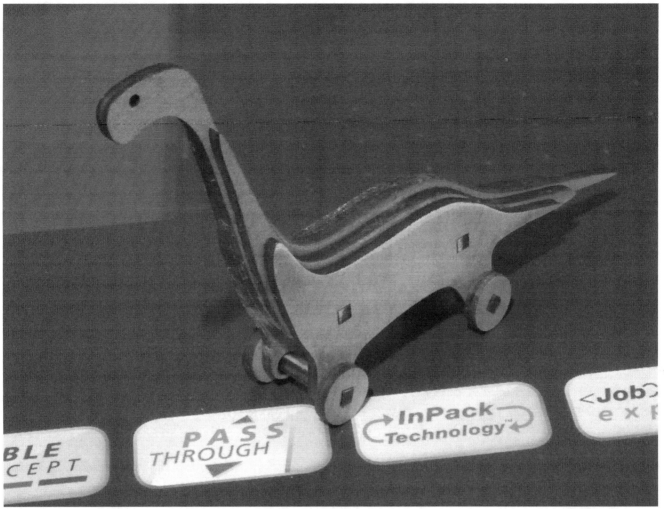

My Trotec Speedy 400 flexx is guarded at all times by a dinosaur I designed! Don't touch!

Not keeping your machine clean and in tip top shape

This is somewhat related to the type of machine you buy, but a good high quality CNC will have built-in mechanisms to protect key parts. For instance, my Trotec Speedy 400 flexx has belts along the sides and on the gantry to protect sensitive parts from corrosive vapors and debris.

I also augmented this "automatic cleaning reduction" by buying a powerful extraction system (optional but makes a huge difference) so that vapors are quickly sucked right out before they have time to coaless onto the machine's bed and a gas kit that throws lots of compressed air from the head of the machine which further protects the optics.

All these things and more help make sure that all the crap that normally builds up within a CNC machine is kept to an absolute minimum during production with greatly reduces the amout of cleaning I'd have to do during and after a job.

This saves me a lot of time and by extension money from unnecessary wear and tear.

Buying a CNC machine is one thing, keeping it clean and by extension, operational, is quite another. Wipe it down regularly, check optics or bits, update software after it's been fully fleshed out and be sure to get regular maintenance on it even if there aren't any problems.

The less down time you have during produciton when you need the machine working at 100%, the higher ROI you'll be able to generate in your shop.

When not in use, the machine should be covered-up, as dust and mirrors don't mix.

Tracking inventory

One sheet of plywood is easy to keep track of when you are a one man shop, but when you start growing in inventory, remembering quantities and types of materials gets increasingly taxing. Throw-in a growing pile of scrap that's "still good" for something down the road and it's easy to forget what you have of in what quantity.

Start sorting your material and keeping track visually of what you have, writing notes down as soon as you see a need of what you need to buy next time you are at the lumber or plastics store.

I've also bought lots of cases to store my metal tags of various sizes and coatings. So I can quickly visually see if I need to re-order some more in addition to buying an industrial metal drill press.

Sometimes, the client wants holes in their plates and it's more efficient for me to make the holes inhouse (to their specs) than to order a bunch of plates with different "hole options".

*Bonus! 11- Excluding auxiliary production costs in quotes

Some machines have few consumables beyond materials such as CNC lasers while others have ongoing consumables beyond electricity such as CNC router bits. These little costs add-up quickly especially as your volumes increase.

Material costs are relatively easy to factor in but if you are required to use a rather challenging material, throw-in some extra margins so your profits aren't eaten up by consumables. To make my life easier and that of my clients, I give quotes that are all inclusive, meaning I don't nickle and dime them for each little upgrade they may want to their project.

It makes keeping track of job expenses far easier (the fewer the numbers the better!) and the client knows what the tier pricing I offer them will give them once everything is finished to their satisfaction.

Don't Build on Rented Land

Youtube is having a few bumps recently. To sum it up, they have too many partners (creators) trying to make money from a limited pool of advertisers which is causing the CPM (cost per thousand impressions) to drop. The result: you need MORE videos in an increasingly crowded market to make money, and by extension, a living. This is a loss for creators and advertisers alike.

Facebook, to me, is a broken model for companies and people. As they get increasingly targeted ads and more people on it, they also have a problem with advertisers, too much availability to fill which drops down CPM and by extension, they need to display more of them which, in turn, makes people not see the ads anymore as they are so easy to tune out.

What do these two situations - you have the same problem with Twitter etc.. btw, have in common? Businesses who build their model based on a platform they do not own and worse, have no other outlet!

For me, YouTube is wonderful. They host more than 700 videos for me at no charge and better yet, pay me and cover the bandwidth which would be atrocious with almost 3 million views in my channel alone! My business model isn't built on YouTube, they just compliment it. Facebook is a different animal because they want to charge me so my followers can see my postings. Why would I do that? Send them to MY WEBSITE where it's "free" so that business model no longer works for me either. Twitter and their kin, well, borderline useless but there is no cost to be there so why not. LinkedIn is also quickly approaching the point of saturation.

When I have almost 4K connections and views per post now hovering at under a hundred, you have to question the increasingly dismal return for my time on these "social" sites that are increasingly commercial, charging me to keep in contact with my fans. I've completely given-up on FaceBook where I have almost 2K "fans" and generally less than 20 "views" per posting. Of course, they also want to charge me to increase my "reach".

Even while I was the largest shop on Ponoko years back, I got more traction from my YouTube videos and notice little to no uptake after they got a big advertising win. I was making exponentially more sales on MY land than theirs and they have wickedly more traffic and exposure than me! I want to engage my customers and visitors on my land! Same goes with my books, I sell more on my site than on Amazon.com and also keep more of the sale!

Advertising is dead?

I think this opens-up an interesting fact that social media sites such as Youtube have created. Where the old advertising use to be "bug them till they buy", that no longer works as it's just too easy to skip over ads.

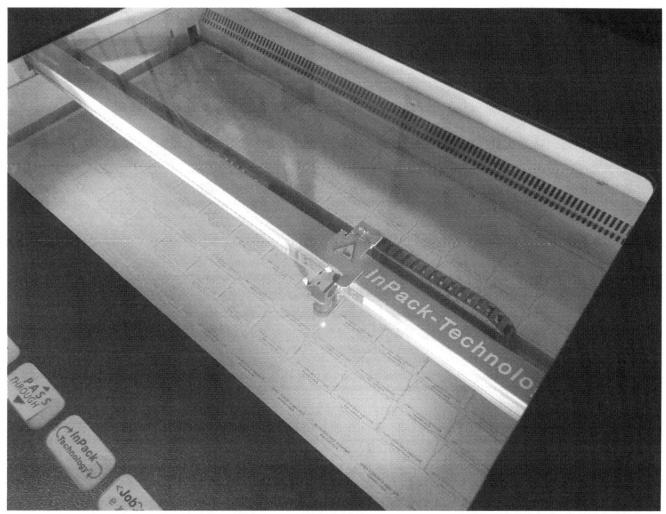

CNC laser engraving and cutting promotional mirrored acrylic pieces for a mailout.

I honestly don't remember the last ad I saw on any of these sites because I've become so efficient at tuning it out. I'd prefer having one customer visiting my site and buying something than a thousand who are just browsing around. The internet is great, but it has created a massive stomping ground of browsers who expect you to bend over backwards even if they have no intention of paying.

Each time I login to my online chat platform on CNCKing.com, guess what I get asked... "can you give this to me for free?" or some deviation of this.

With the advent of 3D printing sites like Thingiverse, the market for "designs" have become a comodity, like the music industry, where people feel entitled to free stuff. Thankfully, search engine robots don't know how to chat yet... more on that later.

I did give free stuff away a while back. The results? Nothing... I've come to the conclusion that if you don't have 10$ to buy a file NOW to cut with your 10-350K machine, you won't have it later.

Put more bluntly, if you don't want to spend money with me, then you don't have a machine or business model that's sustainable for me to enter into a relationship with you.

Sales through education! 304SS fiber annealing on the left, marking on the right.

What I do find interesting though is how adamant "free" has become on the internet. People promise me lots of future sales if I give my first for free. I tell them nicely that if they are willing to pay my rent or buy a machine for me, I'd be more than happy enough to give them a "free" model. They go away quickly as is the intention. This isn't being insulting, it's being efficient.

Advertising in the internet age can be summed-up with one phrase - too much supply, not enough demand. Regardless of money spent on production, people just do not want to see advertising. They live with it to get what they really want - maybe the Super Bowl is an exception but that's just because watching football is so damn boring that you need something creative to keep your attention span going and even to me, neither has yet been of high enough value for me to watch.

Video Advertising

Much like Tivo when I was growing-up, people bought it because it allowed them to skip the ads. Trueview is doing the same and YouTube is also offering this. The benefit? People watching the ad are doing so because they want to see the ad or in my view, are busy doing something else and not paying attention... but that doesn't sell video advertising.

Usually when I'm "watching" Youtube or another media show such as Frontline (fantastic documentaries), if an ad pop-up, I immediately tune out and do other things.

I think video advertising before a show you want to see will be dying. The CPM won't be high enough for creators to make a living and the ROI for advertisers just as dismal - hence the low CPM. Mid-stream and post-roll ads again are an annoyance and only use the "old" advertising method that we all tune out.

Curation is key

I don't see people running out to watch advertising and buying stuff unless they really need it. When you have too much choice in a market, you end-up with confusion which leads to a requirement of curation. That's what I see CNCKing.com becoming - a curation that distils the best out there so you find what you need when you want it.

In the rush for internet riches where bigger is better, I think we've found that it isn't necessarily the case. So what if Facebook has over a billion "customers", how many are paying or better yet, how long before they jump ship because you are broadcasting too much advertising?

They have a strong pull, friends and family. That's their strength but also a major weakness and the next generation coming onto the internet have little interest in sharing their lives with their mothers and fathers publically as we've been doing.

Crowdfunding

Although I like the concept behind the crowdfunding business model, it really isn't one I've found any success at thus far. The tough part about crowdfunding is the amount of time and money you need to spend to have it go viral. How well did that viral video go for your business on YouTube? That's what I thought, because so many people are jumping onto the platform, you can't separate the noise from the value and hence, you spend more time spinning your wheels for less results on an exponential scale.

Like anything in life, once one person discovers a way to make money, a legion of people follow doing the same thing or a variation of it. I tried it myself and failed miserably. I will be giving it another go shortly but have my doubts, not because I fear failure, but because I'm unsure if I want to devote a month of my life on ONE platform (which I don't own) when I have so many other things I want to do.

The days of uploading a "cause" and sitting back while the money fly in are long gone. Why do these crowdfunding systems work so well for some users? Well, they are promoting the hell out of their campaign and guess where all that traffic goes... the crowdfunding platform!

Why not skip the middleman and send them to your site instead? Hmmm... then you don't benefit from the crowdfunding platform "virality" coefficient (or potential). You can read experiences with crowdfunding in the "funding" section of this book.

If you look at Kickstarter, you'll notice something interesting: now many people with campaigns have videos, very NICE PROFESIONAL videos. It's like Youtube all over again. People upload crap and a few send good stuff. They get more "hits" and so it brings the bar up for everybody. This keeps going until everybody does the same thing in the hopes of getting views for being unique. I hope you are seeing a pattern here.

Buying views, fans and fake visitors

Another problem with all these third party platforms and increasingly your own land (but at least you see them there) are robot visitors - taking-up resources, watching videos etc, but that will never buy a thing. Looking at my cloudflare account for CNCKing.com, I notice something striking: half my visits to my website aren't people but web crawlers! Even worse, they made my site go down several times because there were so many of them!

I had to get an upgraded server account just for that one domain to handle traffic that will never convert and I have no choice on the matter! Like a mosquito, they just go there, don't care if they live or die and just don't follow robot.txt directions.

Facebook is great, they allow you to "buy" fans. Youtube lets you "buy" views and many other systems offer to do the same with accounts like Twitter etc... so, let me get this right. For social proof, you are actively promoting a third party site (rented land) to drive-up traffic by robots so that they may eventually visit your site (owned land) and maybe buy something. The business model just doesn't work.

Like I said, we need to use these services as a compliment, not a business model and usually that means skipping the middleman and paying little attention to them in the first place.

What does this all mean? Well, the metrics you are given to help you track your "online success" are bogus. What the heck does "audience reach" mean or even "views" - they are there for one reason, to make the platform money by giving you an incentive to make whatever number you currently have to go up.

People love seeing a number go up, whether it's in their bank account or video views or fan base but at the end of the day, the only one I care about is the first, my bank account. So far, I've gotten by far the biggest bang for my buck ON MY OWN LAND!

Solution?

If you run a business, do NOT rely on social media to bring in sales, do NOT rely on XYZ platform to bring in customers and although there are other business models like arbitrage (buy product A, advertise it for B and keep the difference), I think generally that the old way is still the best way.

Targeted direct educational physical mail has a higher ROI than any social media site!

For instance, my own blog post hit over 10K people immediately upon publishing, but how many people will actually see it?

Thanks to Google's promotions tab, that number of eyeballs drops by 25-40% if they are using gmail, and the list goes on as to why most of them won't see it.

Now, more then ever, you need to concentrate on your business on your land and not funnel customers through third party sites. I know there are exceptions, I know some people love to share on Facebook etc... just like people who retire thanks to a lottery win, but generally, find your customers, send them to your land which you own and service them there.

Third party sites have their niche but always funnel them back to your place and don't get them use to visiting or seeing you on another platform unless it goes right back to your site.

A note about competition...

I don't know why people tell me "competition is good" because, as a business owner, it isn't! It doens't keep me on my toes, it doesn't influence how I operate my business. But what it does do is cut into my margins.

From a customer standpoint, competition is great regarding getting projects done but at the other end of the stick, I highly doubt that they themselves would say "competition is good" for their own line of business.

If you look at how global things are now and only getting more so, I see competition really hurting companies in the long run. Why? Well, in Canada we have taxes, fees, environmental and worker's comp to content with along with a host of other services we must have as a business but in China, where you can get a highly trained and educated employee for half the price and environmental considerations etc. Thrown out the window, how is that fair?

Competition is no longer local, it's global and unless the standards are even, completely unfair. You wonder why manufacturing has moved overseas?

They can produce more, faster and cheaper than locally given enough volume to offset customs and shipping because the playing field is slanted in their favor.

This is not a good thing, it's a bad thing and "free trade" I think is a huge detriment to businesses when the playing fields aren't even on both sides of the goal post.

There is a reason why most shopping malls are filled with fashion retailers: they have massive margins even during their 50% off sales and for the same reason, why you'd be hard pressed to run a service type business such as a woodworking shop in those places.

For me, I decided early on that I wouldn't go the "trophies & awards" route with my laser. It's a tough existence and you are competing against anybody and everybody with a laser, be it high or low end. I knew I had to gun for manufacturers, designers and builders.

Their expectations are higher but so are the profit margins and volume.

Sure, I could engrave some awards and do some name plates, but that isn't work I'm actively going after. The way I think of it: I bought the best damn CNC laser machine on the planet, a Trotec Speedy 400 flexx, so I'm only going to chase customers who appreciate what this machine can produce and are willing to pay top dollar for it.

I consider Trotec Laser to be in a league of their own in the CNC laser industry for the segment they serve, and by extension, CNCROi.com in the same light.

Optimal Tradeshow ROI

Tradeshows are a great way to gain industry contacts as an entire industry can be found in a heavily concentrated room. To get the best ROI time and money wise, here are a few things I've learned by going to hundreds of them: do keep in mind that there is a certain aura at these shows, basically everything is generally positive, people want your services etc... This wears off after the show to get a hold of them ASAP to follow-up.

Be early and alert

Arrive early when the people are fresh at their booths and when the show is still relatively empty so you have time to talk without any distractions by other visitors.

I generally go to these shows for two reasons, meet-up with the owner/CEOs of the company (more often than not, they are there in the morning) and to introduce my company, its services, and to try to find a way we can help one another out. Yes, I go there to find/meet customers and generate invoices just as they do.

How can I help YOU?

Don't pitch to them first, ask them about their business and how they got started. THEN use that information to fit your business model into theirs.

For instance, a transformer manufacturer may tell you they make a thousand a year locally, you can ask for a business card while you give them yours and tell them you can do all the metal tags for them.

If they import, then you can suggest they can do business with you and get some "Canadian offset credits" (program here in Canada) by having you do something for them locally. There are many ways to approach a sale rather than a straight in-your-face high pressure method.

Don't be in a rush

Give yourself a lot of time. Sometimes the biggest ones are the ones you fly through the fastest and vice versa. There is no way to predict how long it will take you to go through the whole show, yet another reason to arrive early. Speeding through a tradeshow does nobody a favor.

The biggest I've done thus far was the Toronto 2014 IIDEX and wow, there were A LOT of booths there to visit. I got through only half of them over the course of an entire day! I got one sale out of that which more than paid for my time and entry fee. In hindsight, I should have attended the show another day but I assumed that the first "room" was the same as the first, the second was 2x bigger than the first!

Just about everything I have is branded... with my business card!

Seek other local opportunities

Once you are at one tradeshow, generally the building will host a few others at the same time venue depending, so once you are done with the one you wanted to attend, drop in to others.

Remember, I'm in the custom CNC business, there is not a business or vertical that can't use my services. The trick is finding companies that have enough of a need to pay my fees to help them do so.

Register in advance

Book early - you can often get free or heavily discounted attendance tickets if you register online a few weeks ahead of time. Exhibitors also are given free tickets to handout to customers too, so ask around, more often than not, you can skip the line-up and get right on selling at no real cost to yourself. Of course, be sure to reciprocate with those who have helped you, offering them free tickets when you are an exhibitor... it goes both ways.

Be a shotgun, not a sniper

Bring a ton of business cards. This is probably the most targeted networking you will be doing. Be sure not to run out of them, and don't bring brochures, just business cards are fine. Brochures and other media make it look like you planned on going to the tradeshow to network and sell, it gives the wrong impression. You can mail those out after the event.

Sure, I go to most shows to find customers for my business, but I've also spent thousands of dolllars on equipment and supplies from companies presenting at them as well. I'm also a exhibitor at many shows, so I feel fine playing on both sides of the fense.

Drop your phone

Turn your cell phone off. Actually, whenever you meet anybody, that phone should be OFF or better yet, not even with you! Nothing worse than talking to somebody and having your phone ring. It shows that they aren't important. If you forgot to do so, pick it up and turn it off and tell the potential lead your conversation is more important than a phone call. When you are meeting with somebody, no distractions is always best.

Visitor to exhibitor

If you've had fantastic success at a specific tradeshow, consider being an exhibitor the next time around. I tried this a few times, it's worth a try but hit and miss. TALK actively to visitors, find their needs and try to establish rappor so they remember you when you call them back after the show.

Bad breath stinks

Bring mints and plenty of water. You will be talking straight for hours on end, your breath will start smelling bad and your voice will crack by the halfway mark.

Take a break, drink plenty of fluids and if you are hungry, grab a protein bar. Unlike networking events, you can't walk around with wine and beer on your breath during these events.

Have fun

This shouldn't be seen as a "I sell you" but as a way to build your contacts and maybe find resellers or customers for your products and services. You'll meet some great people and it will lead to new business.

There is so much potential out there it's astounding. So many companies to meet, so many people to talk to and networks to establish both locally and internationally.

Networking for Dollar$

I started CNCROi.com from absolute scratch in my old hometown after being gone from North America and owning a physical business for 7 years! All I had was a half-built website, I 500 business cards and a brand new Trotec Speedy 400 flexx. My inventory was the local lumber yard and plastics distributor. I had no samples to handout and no pictures of the stuff I've done previously to show.

As I'm entirely self-taught in the CNC world, I had no industry contacts, old teachers or even potential customers and worse, began in August when "it's summer break" here in Canada. The world economy is stuck in what seems a perpetual recession and marketing budgets were held by mizers who would fight for every penny that left their pile. I couldn't think of a better time to invest my life's savings into a high-end CNC shop!

Networking

Despite the challenges, I knew from my previous business experience that advertising for the services I have to offer is a great way to dig a hole for myself. Advertising is very much hit and miss... and in the CNC field, the prices are as astronomical as their tolerances for finished pieces. So where do you begin? NETWORKING!

How do you meet a demographic (leaders of industry) that, on a good day, are tough to get a hold of in person much less by phone? Networking by joining trade associations with their (sometimes) sky-high fees. I tried a number of "free" networking events, I spent months going to more than my fill of them and got nothing.

I knew who would pay top dollar for my CNC services and that doesn't include individuals wanting to laser engrave a cutting board they got at Walmart!

No volume and the moment they found a place that offered those services for a few pennies cheaper, they were gone. The volumes are too low, collecting money is a hassle and generally future business is rather limited. I was building a custom CNC shop, not a trophy shop, which to me is a massive difference.

It's one thing to meet a prospective client, quite another to find one willing to spend money for your services. I joined a few industry specific ones and bang, started to gain some traction! The local industrial association got my name out with local aerospace, manufacturing and industrial services companies.

What's funny about networking is that you often get referrals to other businesses that you wouldn't have met otherwise. So you have to be selective as to who you give your information. Otherwise, you'll get never ending calls from clients that won't be able to get you to where you want to go with your own company.

Another sample I mail out and give to customers, anodized aluminium plates, fiber marked.

Tracing back how A lead to B and C, which gave you a project, seems to have as much serendipity as anything else in life. Meeting the right people at the right time and having them REMEMBER you when one of their friends need your services is an incredibly random process.

Networking is still very much based on relationships. The more you stand-out, the better.

Meetups

Most associations have networking events and tradeshows where a group of people join-up in a room or we all rent out a hotel or something together with the goal of finding new business opportunities. Some contacts you meet-up often enough that you end-up becoming pretty good friends, but never forget you are there to find business.

This might sound harsh but you spent money getting a membership, time driving to the event etc. You really need to triage people otherwise you can spend the entire event talking to somebody you'll never have any business prospects with, wasting your time and theirs in the process.

Want to make your samples stand out? Make them seasonally appropriate!

Your job is to introduce yourself to everybody in the room. So practice your pitch, don't sit in a corner and talk to one person or wait for people to approach you. This isn't a highschool dance, don't be shy! If there is no interest, thank the person for their time and move along. If there is a lot of interest, tell them you'll give them a call or email and move along as well! You have a whole room of people to field!

Once you've got a good handle of everybody you spoke to, either go back to the people of interest if they are still there or just leave. You don't want to be seen just standing around chatting on your cell phone with too much time on your hands.

Most of these networking events have a buffet, don't pig-out! Dirty hands and a full mouth aren't condusive to finding business, and being drunk because you had a few too many glasses of wine or bottles of beer isn't much better.

One of my employees in my 3D business went to one of these events, his first time! He was having such a great time and drank so much that he passed-out in the middle of the floor! You do not want to be that guy. I drove him back home and had no memory of the entire networking event!

Oh yeah, I find alcohol does get rid of bad breath better than a coffee which gives you dog's breath. So if anything, get a glass of wine, wosh it in your mouth a bit before swallowing and just repeat every 10-20 minutes, it will last you all night and won't give you a dry throat like mints tend to do.

I like to wear a shirt with two pockets up front and pants with lots more pockets. You want to carry a stack of business cards in one of them, the cards you receive put them in another, put samples in another pocket and cards meant for the recycle bin which you have no intention of following-up upon in the last.

People can't imagine laser engraving, marking, annealing or cutting so always have small samples to show. I also have my sample case in the car at all times!

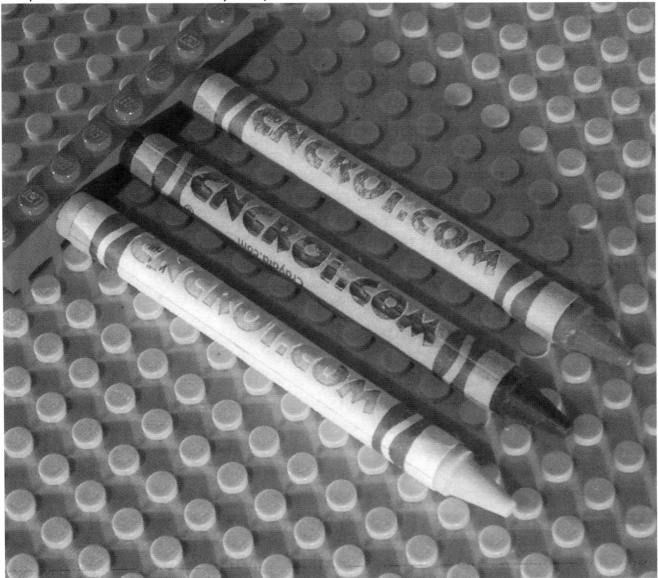

You can make samples out of ANYTHING!

Inserting yourself into supply chains

There is no way around hitting the pavement and meeting people that are in the same industry as yourself. Yes, some are competitors, but generally shops, specialize in specific services and use other firms to augment their capabilities.

For instance, you might have one CNC shop with only a top of the line Thermwood CNC router but sometimes, in need of sharp inner corners on laminate, a Trotec Speedy CNC laser my be required, instead of buying one, customers send me their projects that they couldn't do alone otherwise.

CNCROi.com has itself worked with a number other CNC shops to produce some of our stuff for our own clients! It's not an industry that gives and takes, it's more like inserting processes into a supply chain to provide the end client with exactly what they need regardless of who does what. Each cog gets their cut by the way, to be competitive and leave some margins for the next level up so they use you again in the future.

What I discovered is that high quality machinery "word of mouth" leaks out and other companies tend to gravitate to that. I've lost track of how many GMs and executives I've met who ask me, in on way or another, where my CNC laser comes from.

Each time, they were RELIEVED that I had an European machine. Say what you will but the premium you pay on certain machines is well worth it and many told me that if I told them I had a Chinese machine, they would have nothing to do with me.

Sure, I could have saved myself a fortune buying an Epilog Zing or going Chinese like a few "competitors" have around here but I'm now getting projects BECAUSE I invested into a large format dual source laser, the FIRST Trotec Speedy 400 flexx in Canada! Zings are good little machines but don't have passthrough or dual fiber and CO_2 capabilities in one machine. My clearances are so big that I can fit a Zing in it for direct engraving!

I hate to say it but, in manufacturing, price is really the LAST THING you should be looking at though there are some numbers out there that will make your head pop.

I'm probably an outlier as I gave two deposits on my machine within an hour of closing the deal to purchase my Trotec to make absolutely sure I secured a slot in their manufacturing plant! It took me about a minute to decide to go Trotec once the opportunity present itself and I've never regretted it. Sales is generally a long slog, having a customer who's passionate and going out his way to give you money really gets your attention and works its way up the food chain!

In fact, in quotes, I specify that I have an Austrian CNC laser, that I have a fiber tube (for metal projects) and even send the spec sheet upon request. I play-up my investment, experience and designing skills, even throwing-in a copy of my latest book!

Ah, the nice smell of laser engraved and cut card stock!

My goal with CNCROi.com isn't to be the cheapest custom CNC shop, but the BEST! I have no problem walking away or declining a project that doesn't fit into the direction my company needs to go, not because I'm rich or a stuckup jerk, but because I can't afford to take-on clients who will be a headache or need to send the bill collectors after for pennies on the dollar. I only work with the best clients and my clients KNOW this!

Nobody is calling!

So, you joined a bunch of related associations and are networking like crazy. Guess what, the phone still won't ring off the hook! Like most companies, real profits come from a small subset of the entire client base and, in manufacturing, that subset can be rather small.

The more capabilities a shop has, the more niche they need to drive their investments in order to help their clients to the upmost of their requirements.

If I ran a pizza shop, I'd be frightened but this is manufacturing where the specs are best sent by email with a phone call to confirm details and timelines. There isn't much "dropping in and chit chatting" going on especially with my larger clients.

The more specialized you become in the manufacturing world, the more you attract specific verticals and build-up a name for yourself to find other like clients. The phone might not ring as often but the cheques tend to get exponentially higher over time if you don't screw anything up.

It's quite astonishing some of the opportunities I have in the air at present. It's very easy to sit back and wait for them to come in but, as a friend told me a long time ago, the worse thing you can have is machinery that isn't moving in the shop. That's a constant loss that takes away from future potential! (I'd add that even worse is doing a job at a loss, which means paying for a project with a negative ROI).

It's a very fine balance as you don't want to be known as a CNC sweatshop either.

Cementing yourself with clients

It's really not unheard of my clients getting delivery of projects and getting some extras thrown-in. Depending on the client, it may be a sample to stick in their showroom, some extras of a project they trusted CNCROi.com to do for them.

Other times, it's something that's useful and personalized like a whiteboard with their logo engraved into it and paint filled with their corporate colors. This costs money and time but keeping a client happy is far cheaper than trying to find new ones!

It's an incredible amount of work finding these guys and building up a relationship where money is exchanged for a project. So I try to put a lot of effort of being sticky with them. I want to always be in the back of their minds when they are quoting a project.

That whiteboard, for instance, in their office that they use, will remind them of me and do a better job promoting my presence than a stack of business cards with empty promises and missed deadlines. I always remind myself that I'm only as good as my last job.

This holds doubly for project screw-ups! Be upfront about it and let the customer know right away, excuse yourself and give them a plan on how you plan on fixing the problem. The customer decided to go with you so they have no headaches, don't make them regret that decision and go to a competitor. Everybody screws-up, it's how you handle it that's the differentiator.

I've sent photos and videos of the problems so that the customer knows exactly what the issue is. Don't beat around the bush, these customers are busy and the last thing they want is to have to take control of yet another situation that's out of their hands.

Be professional, admit mistakes and give rewards when things go good. Clients like free stuff just like you do, and don't forget to leave the secretaries something neat!

Marketing Despite NDAs

If you aren't familiar with NDA, they are a document you generally sign with customers saying essentially any work you do with them cannot be told to anybody else, including the customers they are subcontracting your work with or customers and suppliers.

For instance, a manufacturer may be making oven panels with specialized branding which they cannot do inhouse. So they contract your company to laser engrave for select markets. They want their customers to "think" they are doing it but in reality, they aren't.

The biggest challenge I've had with CNCROi.com has been to showcase our capabilities without revealing any of the work we do. Sometimes this is because of NDAs and other times it is to keep competitors out of my pockets. I want my clients to STAY my clients.

I'd love to boast about some of the projects we've done but then I'd give away some of our secret sauce! A customer might say "can you laser cut or engrave XYZ" and you have to be able to give them confidence that you CAN do that without actually showing or telling them of previous applications you've done, sometimes with their competitors!

With CNCKing.com, I built everything myself from scratch, I owned the entire supply chain from start to finish while with CNCROi.com, I'm a cog in a larger wheel the vast majority of the time. So, how did I do it?

Show the building, not the rooms!

Much like new residential or condo units, they sell the sizzle before any meat is put into the frying pan. Visitng the CNCROi.com blog, you'll see videos, pictures and detailed explanations of completely unrelated projects. This builds confidence in potential customers that we really can do anything while keeping out mouth shut regarding what we are actually doing.

Some stuff is off the wall, what kind of custom CNC laser shop engraves pumpkins and stones? Well, that's a marketing gimmick. It gets visitors as it's so unique but then they see we do other things like solid stainless steel annealing.

The broker will tell you how awesome the view will be, and the services you get, and show you a few rendered rooms with a sample room to walk through but the focus is always on building confidence that you can trust them and the unit will be perfect for you while, in reality, a few meters away, there is a big hole in the ground and your unit is nowhere near built yet!

If I can confidently cut, etch, market or engrave anything under the Sun. Whatever application you may have a need for, you can rest assured it will be done professionally with a huge amount of experience behind the RFQ (request for quote).

Ken Cooley, President of ShapeMaster Inc.

Ken is the owner of a thermoforming and manufacturing company in Illinois, USA. His company has been offering custom solutions across North America and the world.

You can visit them at http://Shape-Master.com.

Can you tell me a bit about your background and how you eventually fell into providing custom forming services?

I have been designing and building things for sale since I was 12 years old. Learning methods of manufacture, marketing, direct sales and promoting our product in retail stores.

For over 34 years, I have been working in wood and metal to create displays for retail. Since right out of high school and through college in machine tool technology, I was taking projects in to pay for new tools and equipment I was purchasing.

Always "bootstrapping" my way into a business and shop. The best way to pay is with cash.

What was the spark that ignited enough passion in you to start your own company almost 25 years ago?

This business ShapeMaster began as a need to "mold" plastic into three dimensional shapes.

I had been interested in plastics since high school in 1975 and dabbled with them in R/C airplane and boat building but it never met the need or desire I had to learn how to mold a part 3D.

My pattern making abilities learned in my first wood working business that launched in 1981 and ran through the end of the 80's gave me a start. I began asking questions, read a lot about machine building and launched into building my first vacuum forming machine.

Actually, I took in a job that required advanced vacuum forming methods and I needed to build a machine to do that work on. Nothing like a deadline and pressure to get you moving.

After my first machine was built and making me money, I continued on the design of a new "proto" machine that would let me free up my first forming machine that was now being run in production runs which consumed it and kept me from having time available on it for my quick "one-off" prototype projects which we built our business around in the early days.

Next came growth. A new building, full and part-time employees were added and with each passing year, we attempted to build a new building, add equipment and improve what we had. At the same time working very hard to promote our company nationally and do it on a shoestring.

Advertising in The Thomas Register of American Manufacturers, locally and word of mouth, we found that always without fail those who referred us via "word of mouth" did the best for us.

We have a nice network of friends, business owners and customers who think highly of our goods and services and this is the best form of advertisement you can ever have. It begins with trust and ends with fulfillment of that trust.

From 1994 when we moved into our current Main Street location, weathering the 1996 tornado that destroyed much of this town, growing through Katrina which brought us a huge deluge of work from one of our largest customers, a dehumidifier manufacturer, to plowing profits and labor back into the company we have grown to over 6 times the square footage and have all new facilities with many new pieces of equipment.

It hasn't been easy but it has been rewarding. We've weathered many storms quite literally and a fire or two along with too many economic downfalls in the state and nation. Still, our company has such a wide range of diversity and appeal that we continue on riding high as we look at 2015. We are coming up on 20 years in this location in Ogden, IL.

You contacted me telling me how pleased you were about Thermwood's routers and that you just bought another one (giving you 3 CNC routers now). What is it about their machines that stand-out especially when you consider there are far cheaper alternatives from abroad?

We currently have two Thermwood Routers. A 3 axis I bought used in the winter of 2006 from a professor of metallurgy in Madison Wisconsin. He was machining aluminum panels on this for Melges racing boats, http://www.melges.com and we nearly took over that work for Melges.

What I've learned many times is that people who work in a business in a hobby they enjoy many times have no idea what that project is actually costing them vs. the profits they need to receive to stay in business.

Much was the case here and after just a few larger than the table size .5" thick panels were machined in my shop, I declined the contract and sent Melges back to their own area to find a company who could make these for them. This router was doing a bang up job making rudders and boards for the best racing boats in the world but I couldn't make money on them so we decided machining aluminum on the Thermwood in production was not for us.

We had this router rebuilt from the ground up in February 2011. This crew from Thermwood does such a professional job and we were very, very impressed with them. They came in and tore this machine down to the steel. All new controls, table, vacuum system, spindle, the whole 9 yards and done right here in our shop.

Prior to purchasing this machine used, we purchased a new 2005 HAAS 3 axis mill that would allow us to cut aluminum tooling and build plastic and aluminum molds for our vacuum forming and plastic casting departments.

The Thermwood added large sheet plastic and wood routing along with the added Z height of 11" we could do surfacing of new tooling and even trim plastic parts in production.

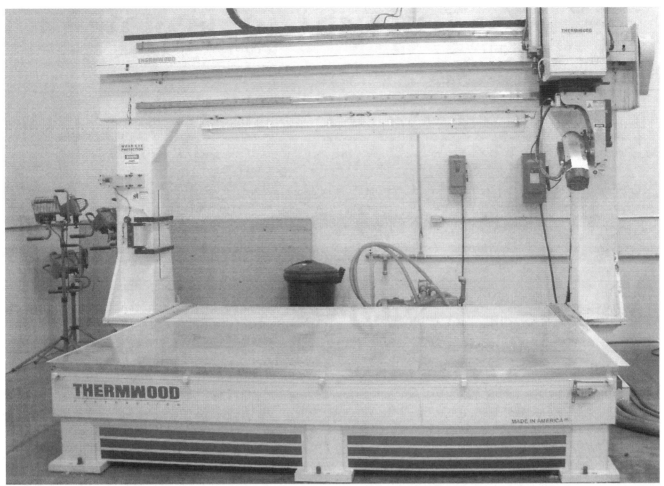

I cannot stress the importance of good software though. Solidworks and Mastercam kept to most recent level and full maintenance from a qualified sales company is important. Also, we hired a good friend who is outside independent trainer of software for CAD modeling and programming and he comes in to train initially our new recruits.

This combination has given us an edge in the industry because we know how to save and store files, proper methods of design in CAD so we are not designing like "CAD" guys but machinists and knowledge of our materials for both tooling and production materials. All of these things are key.

We have a man who is leading our CNC department who is very accomplished. He is a veteran Marine and over 5 years at the University of Illinois graduating with an electrical engineering degree has given him or enhanced many of his personal discipline and thought processes to make him a great in house trainer but also department head.

In the Winter of 2012 we added a new 5 axis router for trimming and tool and fixture building purposes. Those parts that best benefit from the 5 axis trimming are run across this machine. Tooling can be built on it and we use both mechanical clamping and vacuum hold down to complete this process. This machine can handle up to 5 foot X 10 foot by 36" height on the table. With a 6 tool changer, we can use it for multi-tool trim-drill-saw and also machining soft vacuum form tooling. Very handy.

Once again we found Thermwood's technicians to be of the upmost help in setting up this machine and training our staff. I can't say enough good about Thermwood.

Our newest purchase will be a brand new built for our 3 axis 5×10 foot table with new vacuum hold down system for routing flat panels of plastic which has grown to become a major part of our fabrication work.

Are there some very common design problems you see repeatedly when customers send you their files for a quote? What is the solution to these issues?

With our business being custom, we see everything from a scribble on a napkin to an attempt by an engineer to use CAD software to create a vacuum formed part.

We must be able to import every file known to man. If we were solely in house design/manufacture we could get by just fine but we are not and most of the files sent to us are from those with various forms of software from "educational" to Pro-E advanced.

The primary issue is that most of the folks submitting have very little design for vacuum forming background and invariably want us to make a part that cannot be made with nearly any process on earth. So, the education begins and if they allow us to, we teach them about vacuum forming of plastics so they can design parts in the future with limited or zero undercuts and create shapes that are economical to mold. This is the key.

Make a design that CAN be made and for a reasonable sum.

As for solutions, I propose that anyone wanting to submit an idea for manufacturing quote should first of all contact the vendor and determine if they will help them with design. Why do it twice, or even ten times before a shape is achieved that is manufacturable?

After basic sketches and hazards of design are discussed, then a preliminary design may be created in CAD and submitted. This begins the dialogue. Don't be shy, just ask.

What are some of the more unique projects that ShapeMasters has had a role in?

Wow! From giant golf balls, to giant moose heads, to urine collection stations that rapidly cool the liquid to feces collection trays for research, a giant pig maze to determine how pigs learn cues, to giant crows for fund raising projects and giant tomato stems for a local pizza delivery truck fleet, hundreds of new projects are launched here at ShapeMaster each year, many are under disclosure and cannot be shared on line or in print.

Come to think of it, we do a lot of "giant" larger than life items but also a great deal of precision vacuum thermoforming along with machine work. Much of this is run across our 3 and 5 axis Thermwood routers.

With the advent of 3D printing, do you still see a strong demand for your services in 10-15 years time as they are now or are you investigating jumping onto the additive bandwagon to augment your current services?

I see 3D printing as a toy, a fun thing and, for the most part, a novelty for now. The cheap desk top machines you can buy for under 5K are tempting for many but are not realistic for more than quick protos that go nowhere.

However, for those in manufacturing who are making real hard parts to put in an airplane like Cessna has done, or others similar they can justify both the expense of the machine and the time it takes to make one off parts. However, for more than that, it is dicey but still something to think about.

For the future, I see ShapeMaster jumping right into the middle of the 3D printing world and offering it from our base here in Ogden which we can very easily do. We are looking for the right machine and then will begin the investment.

For now, we do all the CAD design in SolidWorks and send the files to our friends who offer us competitive rates on printing so we can offer this service to our customers who have either no CAD software or the knowledge of making the plastic parts.

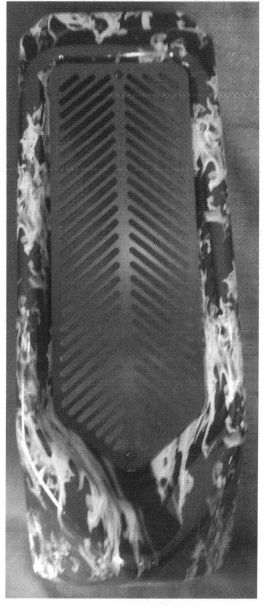

We have created 3D printed models for prototypes, mold making for casting plastic parts and in fact, over the years, had some of our industrial accounts invest tens of thousands in parts made for production that began with 3D then into silicone rubber and rigid part casting while waiting for our injection molding group to get tooling done for mass production runs of 10,000 parts or greater.

The 3D printing has its place for sure and if used in those areas, it is a wonderful addition and has in fact created a lot of new businesses and services which is fun.

You offer a lot of very specialized services. Can you share your insight as to how you find dedicated and ambitious employees to fulfill them? Do you offer internships or have relationships with local educational institutions?

We have tried the educational institutions and find them to be of very little help. The honest truth is that I've had high school teachers and even local community college educators tell me "you don't want any of these guys coming out of my classes". Very sad.

The work ethic of many "Americans" is so poor and the "entitlement mentality" has literally sunk the ship we may need to, one day, sail on with regard to a resurgence of manufacturing in the States.

I think the goose is cooked but perhaps a remnant exists out there of young men and women who will work hard to get ahead and strive to learn. I think they are out there because I know I've raised two of them myself. With the help of a very hard working woman, their mother, of course.

ShapeMasters offers a host of services from vacuum forming to CNC machining to custom fabrication and drafting services. Did you envision being able to offer so many services to customers from the start or did you just grow where demand seemed to lead you?

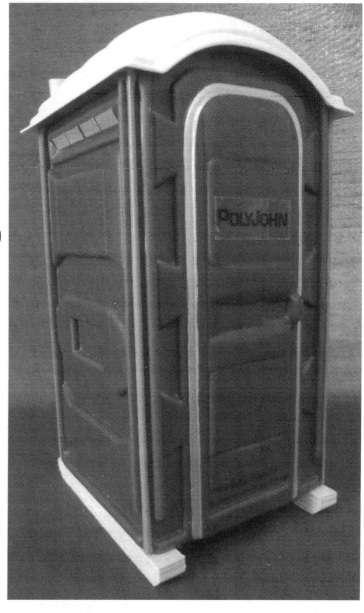

To be quite honest with you, this company and the level it has achieved has been a dream come true for me. I hoped to one day have manual machining equipment like a Bridgeport mill in my personal shop as I attended a local college back in 1980. We have CNC and manual mills and a lathe as well which makes it nice for those fun personal projects when designing items for my motorcycles.

I have a small line of parts for Suzuki motorcycles which ship throughout North America and the world on a weekly basis. It's fun to see your designs on bikes in Russia, Australia and Brazil.

We grew with demand. Always go where the demand is. We learned from working with inventors it is very hard submitting a new product into the market place and having it get picked up and bought. Find out what people want first. In fact your best bet is making people comfortable, safe, and give them style while doing it. Don't try an item that is your pick. Give the public what they want as long as it fits your personal, moral, compass.

Sometimes I've found you don't need to make that item because it is not within your comfort zone and that's OK.

Not all business is good business even if they pay with "green" money.

Our company has grown because I never say "NO". If we don't do it in house we have partners who do it out of house and many times a company wants to come to us for "one stop shopping" so that we can supply the whole project and this has worked out well.

If however, we in our group, cannot best meet the need, more than likely we know someone who can.

By being diverse, you get to play in many mediums of material and processes. This gives you a great appreciation for what modern manufacturing methods are in existence but also those nearly forgotten that many times will still meet the need in the U.S. for making a nice product with a good price that is repeatable and from a source you can depend on.

I enjoy business, manufacturing and those who make things. I'm always open for discussion.

Scot Farley, Principal Designer at F3 Industrial Design

I love it when I get to interview somebody who is not only incredibly passionate about what he does but has the knowledge and expertise to back it up. Scot Farley is one of those rare people who live his dreams everyday and has blue arms because he keep pinching himself to make sure he is really awake!

Scot Farley is the Principal Designer and owner of F3 Industrial Design which specializes in "first to world" products and start-up projects.

He's the guy you want to talk to if you have an incredible idea and want somebody

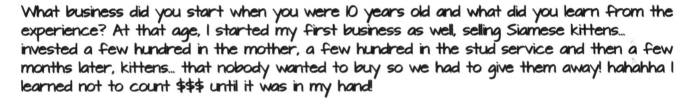

with the contacts (investment to manufacturing) and expertise (design to marketing) to help you bring your innovation to life in a profitable manner!

Visit his company at http://f3id.com

What business did you start when you were 10 years old and what did you learn from the experience? At that age, I started my first business as well, selling Siamese kittens... invested a few hundred in the mother, a few hundred in the stud service and then a few months later, kittens... that nobody wanted to buy so we had to give them away! hahahha I learned not to count $$$ until it was in my hand!

I lived on a farm in those days and although it is something I couldn't do these days, I had a business trapping possums.

We had a lot of orchards nearby and the farmers had a real problem with the possums eating all of their fruit as they were in plague proportions. I had a look at the existing technology of trapping and knew I was going to have to find an alternative. The animal was trapped by the leg in a steel "gin trap" and had to endure a lot of pain until the trapper came around and killed it. Animals that were left or forgotten about died of starvation, which was a sickening state of affairs.

I knew that the orchards needed protecting but couldn't use those traps if I was going to be involved in the industry. I researched the options and found a company making a product that was far more humane and so I purchased some of these and kept the possums under control that way.

I reinvested the profits back into buying more traps to build the business up to include a number of farms and although I never intended to become rich from the process, it taught me a lot about managing business finances and the rewards you can attain if you are willing to go without in the short term to achieve a longer term goal.

One of these and if I am honest, probably my single motivating factor in those days was the ability to buy my own motorbike, which was a pretty fun reward as a then 11 year old.

Although the business ended soon after I bought the bike, this ability to plan for the long term was a very important one for me to learn and I am still wired that way today.

You had incredible academic success while attending Queensland's University of Technology in Industrial Design. How important was that schooling for you at the time and how large of a role did it play in your entrepreneurial / design career?

It's funny but I've never really been that academic and in fact I had to go back to night school to even get into University. Once I started the course I did really well in it because I was so passionate about the industry it would lead me into.

I worked really hard and even though I was looking after my younger sister and brother, playing rugby and working two jobs. I still got great grades in a notoriously heavy duty course. I remember I was vying for the Dean's award with another student, and when running from work to the library, I got a stabbing pain in my chest that knocked me off my feet.

I decided there and then that I would stop pushing myself so hard and dropped back a few gears. The other guy got the award but the fact is that no-one has ever asked me about my grades since I left Uni.

I am a firm believer in a more balanced education that incorporates working in the chosen field so you can get the practical experiences that will help you in your career and in fact it was my work experience was what got me into my first job and the grades were secondary.

I don't believe the education process helped me with the Entrepreneurial side of my career at all. I believe I was born an entrepreneur and I actually think the education stifled me in that area quite a lot.

With entrepreneurial endeavors, you are always looking at the big picture and the education made me focus back into the detailed work and the two are really at odds.

I am able to make the distinction these days and am using both skill sets to develop some new and exciting ideas.

122

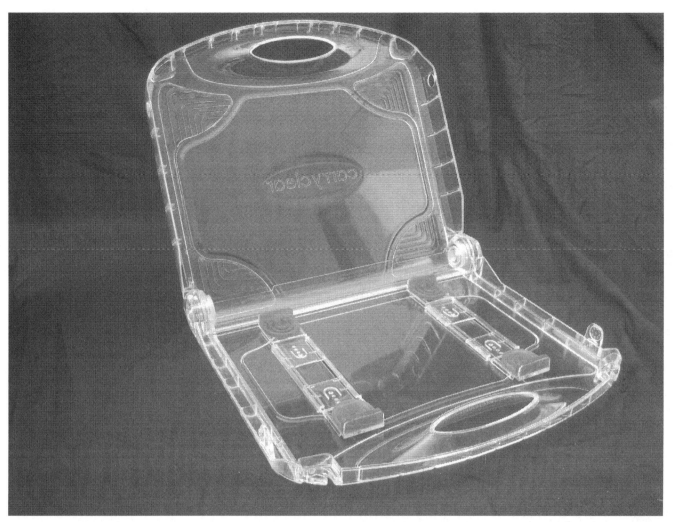

What lead to you to begin your own industrial design firm, F3? How did you come-up with the name and find your first clients?

I always had an end goal of having my own company and there was a lot of writing on the wall that my employer was going to eventually outsource my position. I figured I wouldn't wait for that to happen and decided to make the jump and figured he could then use me as a contractor.

Unfortunately this didn't work out as I had expected as he had never really intended to outsource the Design work. So from that point on, I was starting from scratch. This was a difficult time, I won't lie, and I had to live on a fairly meager wage until I found my feet.

Luckily this didn't take too long and I ended up taking a look at my strengths and realized the competitive advantage I had was that I am an Inventor (very different from an Industrial Designer) and also an experienced Industrial Designer.

I am extremely passionate about Invention and its ability to make positive change in the world, and I used this passion to create a niche in the market and focused on Inventors and start-up companies that my peers call "D" grade clients. I made these my "A" grade clients and learned how to service their needs.

Working for Inventors and Start-up's forced me to become very efficient and I developed a specific set of skills and strategies that allowed the projects to achieve their goals quickly and with very little re-work, which is otherwise common in the Research and Development industry.

I found that by using stage gates at every step in the development process and being ultra critical in this process meant that there was very little re-work if any at all and this alone could reduce the project costs and lead times dramatically.

These strategies and my new skill sets were also very beneficial to commercial clients and, as the company progressed, I developed a blend of Inventors and Commercial Clients.

The name F3 comes from the three fundamental aspects of design you need to get right in order to develop a successful product. The Form, Fit and Function of a product, the three F's are there to remind me to always get the fundamentals right and this will ensure the product suits its application.

You have a number of very nice projects on your website. Which kinds to you prefer working on? The complex mechanical ones like Exterior T5 Luminaire or "simple" ones like the Squattle water bottle?

Thanks for the positive feedback on the site. Unfortunately I can't put all of the exciting new developments up for reasons of confidentiality but there are a few there that show what I do.

In answer to your question, I am far more excited about the Squattle type projects than the more engineering based products simply because the Squattle was a first to world type endeavor while the lighting projects are more just ingenious ways of packaging existing technologies.

Both types of projects are challenging in their own way but to come up with a brand new idea that has never been seen before, really takes a lot of thought and is very challenging but also very rewarding.

The Squattle project was an annoying one actually and, in fact, it progressed a long way further than the image on the website shows. But despite the shear genius in it, it has never made it to market. Having said that, the research from this project had a major environmental benefit and changed the way liquids are packaged forever.

It uncovered that by eliminating the head space (air between the fluid and cap) you could extend the products shelf life considerably and this ended up being adopted by the packaging industry across the board, becoming best practice and saving billions of liters of otherwise wasted product and this is something I am very proud to have been a part of.

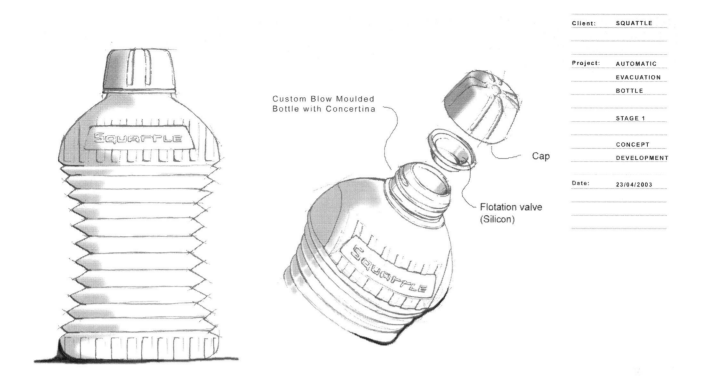

Custom Blow Moulded
Bottle with Concertina

Cap

Flotation valve
(Silicon)

Client:	SQUATTLE
Project:	AUTOMATIC
	EVACUATION
	BOTTLE
	STAGE 1
	CONCEPT
	DEVELOPMENT
Date:	23/04/2003

INDUSTRIAL DESIGN

Phone (07) 3395 6951   Fax (07) 3395 7356   Mobile 0414 853 267   Email scotf@f3id.com   Suite 3 / 620 Wynnum Road Morningside Queensland 4170

What is a "100 year change project" and what role did you play in them?

100 year change products are otherwise known as disruptive products and they come about when you take an industry that has been doing things the same way for hundreds of years and improve on their technology to turn that industry on its head.

A good example is Apple's iPhone. While everyone else was still making phones with physical buttons and limited functionality, Apple threw all of that benchmarking away and took the harder path of actually developing a phone that used new technologies and formats to enhance the user experience to the stage that other systems became obsolete and they gained a major share of the market by taking this line.

I actually have a project of my own that is an 8000 year change. It is a fishing sinker (www.kliksinkers.com) that you can snap onto your line instead of having to cut it, fit a sinker and then re-tie it to your line again.

It has an outer case that encapsulates a dense insert (i.e. lead or similar) and allows it to be added to and taken off your line at will so you can change weights as required, quickly and effortlessly.

The ball sinker has been in its standard format of a spherical lead ball with a hole through it since the Egyptians used them to hold their nets down 8000 years ago.

I am also working on a new packaging solution that will revolutionize the way brewers deliver their carbonated beverages. I can't disclose this one yet but it is getting close and I am hoping to have it on the market in the not so distant future.

These sorts of projects normally require a high level of Invention in order to achieve the disruption and that is what sets them apart from other design projects. I have done this for many clients over the years and the rewards can be incredible.

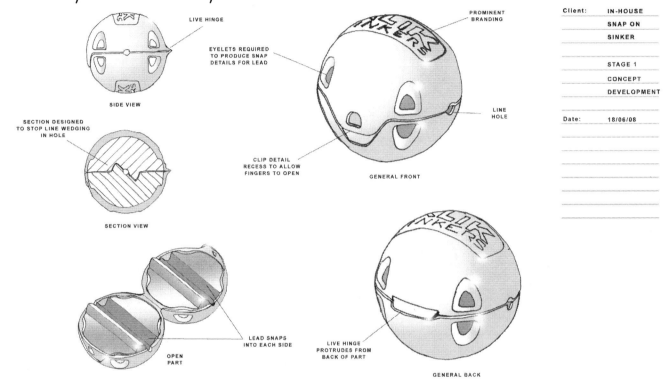

Phone (07) 3395 6951 Fax (07) 3395 7356 Mobile 0414 853 267 Email scott@f3id.com Suite 3 / 620 Wynnum Road Morningside Queensland 4170   1

Being based out of Australia, do you apply for US patents first followed by an Australian one? How are their rules different?

Good question. It depends on the product but generally I take advantage of the grace periods offered by what is known as a provisional patent, which isn't country dependant.

This means I can apply for a provisional and then, once it reaches its term, I can apply for a single patent in any country (where they are offered) or apply for a Patent Cooperation Treaty (PCT) that allows me to basically reserve the right to attain patents in multiple countries at a later date.

The Provisional Patent is an unpublished document but it sets a priority date from when you apply that allows you to develop the technology and get deals in place before you need to commit to a standard patent in individual or multiple countries.

As it isn't published, it allows you the flexibility to re-submit the provisional without having disclosed the art (information about the technology) and losing your novelty, which is incredibly useful if the development is taking longer than expected or if you haven't secured a deal/partner to help with the commercialization.

The disadvantage is that you lose your original priority date but, in my opinion, this is better than risking cash flow issues down the track or continuing with a patent that is based on a product that isn't meeting the brief.

PS: Please note that I am not a professional Patent Attorney and only use this strategy after considering many other factors, some of which may make the strategy too risky to employ.

My advice is always to see a professional Patent Attorney before making any decisions on Intellectual Property Protection but to do your research to make sure that you are using a strategy that will be best for your personal situation as one size does not fit all when it comes to Patents.

What are your views on patents in general? Is it best to focus your time and money on "first to market" or on the patent (provisional or full) first? What are your views on the recent change in the USA from "first to invent" to "first to register"?

I believe that Patents can be a very strategic aspect of a project and that is why I have tried to learn as much about them as I possibly can. I have great attorneys and, together with my product and commercial knowledge and their knowledge of the Patent process, we can normally use them to very good advantage.

There are a number of strategies that need to be employed to ensure they do not cause a project to fail because of their financial drain on a start up but if they are managed correctly, they can be very beneficial and sometimes crucial in the success of a business.

Knowing this there are always exceptions to the rule and sometimes projects simply do not suit a patent and you are far better off spending the money on marketing in order to flood the market and get your brand recognition to carry the company.

I believe that, in order to patent a product, it needs to be very unique or you will never get past the examiners as there are thousands upon thousands of ridiculous ideas in the system that can be used to site prior art and knock your product out.

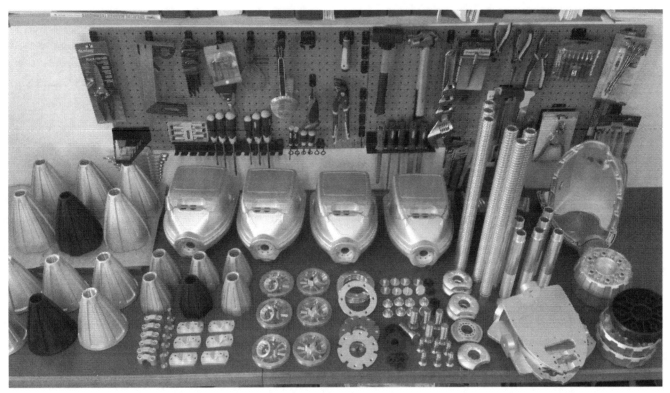

This is a result of the lack of vetting that allows anyone to apply for a patent on just about anything and this I believe will be the downfall of the system as it is being cluttered to choking point by what can only be described as doodlings of ideas that have no conceivable chance of ever amounting to anything.

I think the first to register law in the US will now cause the system to become more like our own with companies being forced to register before they can prove their ideas on the market.

Personally I thought the old (US) system was fairer on the original Inventor and the new system favors secondary (copy cat) type manufacturers and this will not be good for original products that need the chance to evolve without being copied as soon as they are released.

What are some things that inventors normally overlook when it comes to manufacturing their product for mass consumption? Are there some common issues with designs coming out of other firms in general that you have to rectify on a regular basis?

The biggest mistake I see Inventors make is to run with the first solution they come up with. Unfortunately a lot of Inventors have identified a problem and solved it but they have only solved it on one or perhaps a few levels.

They put this product on the market and it goes well for a little while until someone sees it, likes the idea and develops a product that does the same thing in a different way, meaning they can apply for a patent in their own right.

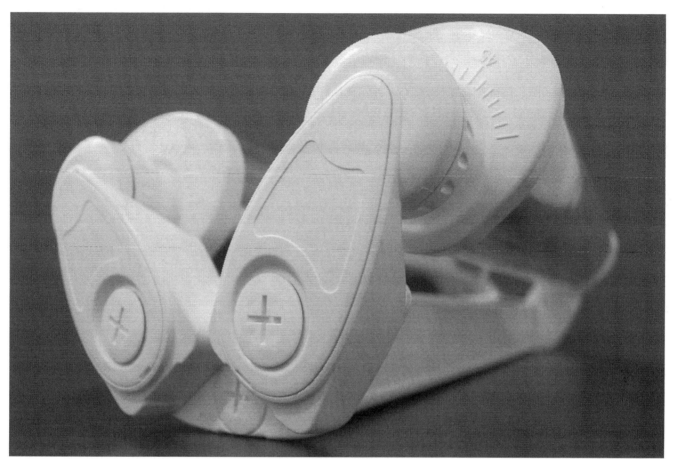

Because they have learned from all of the original Inventors mistakes they normally end up with a better product at a cheaper price and this allows them to quickly secure a major part of the market share, which can be devastating to the original supplier.

It is very important to evolve the product to a point of near perfection before it hits the market. It needs to be as refined as possible so it has the least number of components possible, is easy and cheap to manufacture, is easy to use and does not cause any OH&S issues, appeals to the market visually and achieves all of its functional requirements perfectly.

Unless you are qualified to do this then, unfortunately, employing a professional to about the only way you have any chance of achieving this.

On the flip side, the investment you make on an Industrial Designer usually pays for itself many times over once the product is manufactured. In many cases, the cost of employing an Industrial Designer to evolve the product will be more than offset just in the savings on tooling that has been eliminated through the refinement of the product and the removal of parts.

The other big cost that people neglect to account for is the initial order and inventory involved when you have an unrefined product that has too many parts. Each of those parts needs to be ordered in quantity (usually minimum orders are 5 000 parts or more) and paid for as well as stocked, assembled and shipped. Every part you remove saves you money for the life of the product and that can really add up.

How can an inventor (or manufacturer) compete against others that don't follow international copyright laws? You might have an awesome invention, most likely manufactured in China, then discover a little while later that they've been running another production cycle for the local/international market without telling you at worse or offering blatantly unfair compensation at best? What can an inventor do to protect himself in these cases? I don't want to single-out Chinese manufacturers specifically as this happens everywhere but, from my understanding, if you have an Australian or American patent, that doesn't cover you in China or any other country, right?

It's a hard one to answer and it comes down to human nature and trust. You can either throw your hands up in the air and say I'm not going to play or get in there and if you are copied, try and deal with the best you can.

Unfortunately it is very hard to bring anyone to justice when it comes to Intellectual Property as I have discovered personally and also through the experience with some of my Client's projects. The funny thing is that in all of these situations, the perpetrators were actually Australian and the Chinese were simply acting on instruction without any knowledge of the breach.

When you travel to China, you see everything you can imagine being copied and sold within the country but the Government there has been coming down hard on anyone who is selling this product back into countries that have a strong patent law as it inhibits the growth of their manufacturing industry.

They have actually spent a lot of time and money implementing a strong Patent culture within China and their patent system is now quite sophisticated.

And no the Australian and US patents don't cover you in any other countries but they cannot (by law) manufacture in their country and ship those products back into the countries you have cover in without breaching your patent.

Anything else you'd like to add?

I honestly believe that we are set to become one of the leaders in innovation here in Australia if we can learn how to integrate Invention and Inventors into mainstream business.

Our background is in farming and combined with our isolation we have been forced to diversify our skills and adapt what we have to suit our needs.

This along with a generally high level of education puts most Australians and New Zealanders (I imagine Canadians also) in a unique group primed to invent new and unique solutions to societies problems.

I think it is time for manufacturers, who are still trying to compete against the manufacturing giants in China making "me too" type components and seeing their companies slowly disappearing before their eyes, to take a step back and re-direct their remaining resources towards unique and protectable products that can command much higher profit margins and start selling these products on the world stage.

There are hundreds of these ideas around if you take the time to look but unfortunately a lot of Western companies are unable to integrate them into their businesses.

This is mainly because most large Western corporations are now run by board members as their original owners have passed on or retired.

Most boards are generally risk averse by nature and so are more likely to vote against these disruptive new ventures than for them due to the fact that they are very difficult to map out and so, in a lot of cases, the decision comes down to a gut feeling, which a board would find difficult to justify to the shareholders.

This often leaves it up to the Inventor / Entrepreneur to develop them on their own, which leaves them short of resources and sometimes the strain of this means some never get to market.

If we can combine the inventive/disruptive ideas and the businesses, then manufacturing in the West still has a fighting chance and we can start to turn our economies around while gainfully employing our citizens.

Thanks for the opportunity to discuss what I do and I hope some of what I have said helps your readers to get their projects off the ground.

Dr. Henri-Jacques Topf, Owner of Schneider Prototyping

I find it interesting how some people that I request an interview from, take weeks if not months to get back to me while others have just a few hours turnaround!

What's all the more fascinating though is that generally, owners of large multinationals are quicker than local small shops! Efficiency and passion may be a key in the success these huge companies have achieved in the global marketplace. He got back to me within hours!

His company, Schneider Prototyping, has been in the prototyping industry from the very beginning and has grown tremendously under his leadership.

Visit them online at http://Schneider-international.net

Back in 1991, what made you want to start Schneider Prototyping GmbH and where did the name of the company come from? Today there are many companies offering rapid prototyping services but back then, the whole idea was very much a novelty that few employed.

Back in 1989, we were shareholders of Cubital, one of the 2 pioneering companies in rapid prototyping, today the IP of Cubital is in Objet, that merged with Stratasys some time ago. After one of the board meetings, the idea developed to use one of these machines in order to set up a service bureau and serve the European market. After finishing my studies one year later this is what I did.

The name is from our sister company back then. I never wanted a company named afer me, that would have been awkward.

Which services do you provide yhat are the most popular or most widely used by your production centers? What types of 3 and 5 axis CNC machines do you currently employ in your operations?

We do about half of our business in metal castings (mostly fully machined and documented) and in plastic parts. RP is only about 7% of our sales.

For new machines, we have a tendency to buy DMG, as we feel very comfortable with them and have good experiences for many years. 5 axis machining is one of our core technologies, today more so than RP.

You currently employ over 200 employees across your production centers. How do you go about recruiting the best and the brightest and what are some of the challenges with doing so across different cultures and languages?

Usually head hunters/recruitment agencies. We don't find the different cultures an issue, maybe because of my personal background (I am French, being born in Germany. My wife is Israeli, born in Russia and my children live in UK. I was always a world-citizen). Most of our communication is in English. We are not poets, but we all manage to make ourselves understood in English pretty well.

The most important thing is TRULY understanding that different cultures/races/religions are neither better nor worse, only different. After this you need to accommodate, to the personal advantages and disadvantages of people.

Over the past few years, you acquired and opened-up new operations around the world - following the growing needs and demands of your customers with plans of entering the Indian and Singaporean markets shortly. How do you go about investigating if there is enough demand to open a new production facility and how long does it normally take from making a decision to actually opening an office?

We have already entered the Indian market and have now 4 branches in India (Delhi, Chennai, Pondicherry and Pune). Usually, I go there and talk to people. I truly believe in talking to people. It is MUCH more informative than reading research compiled by someone in some office.

Usually about 3-6 months. We actually know where we will go next. It is more a question of not overstretching our resources.

What is it about Schneider Prototyping GmbH that differentiates it from other rapid prototyping companies? What is your secret allowing you to experience such explosive growth?

The main issue is our extremely broad range of technologies. We have all of these technologies in-house in our own production. This allows us to advise our customers impartially as to the best technologies. It also allows us to avoid problems very early on.

We know from our own experience, what can go wrong. And our customers appreciate that we can give them the full service, from RP over prototyping of plastic parts and metal castings up to low-volume production in injection molding and metal castings, in many different technologies.

METAL

Plaster casting | Aluminium

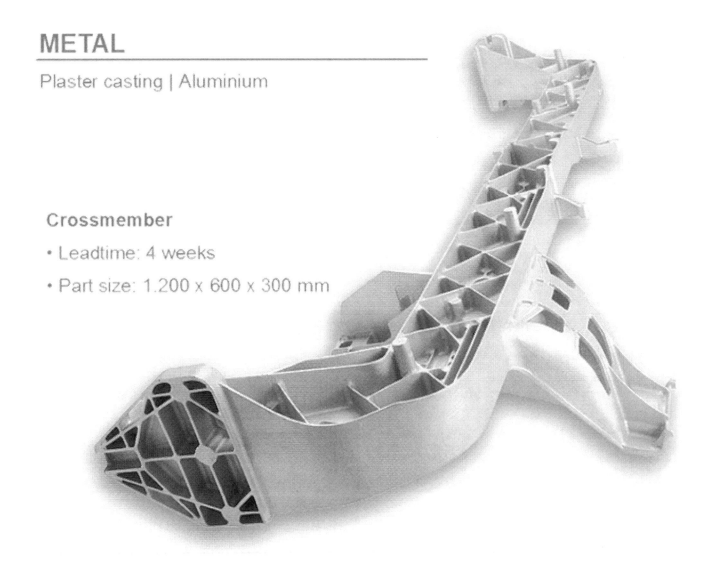

Crossmember

- Leadtime: 4 weeks
- Part size: 1.200 x 600 x 300 mm

How much has the rapid prototyping industry changed over the past 22 years? How do you see this market changing over the next two decades?

Tremendously in some ways and not very much in others. Today RP is routine, reliable and price driven. 22 years ago it was exciting, unreliable and technology driven. But most of the media hype about "3D-printing" is not really so new and could also have been done 15 years ago.

The new 3D-plotters are unreliable and their products are useless, in our context of industrial technical prototypes. This is of course different for someone with other needs but this will change, as the technologies develop.

The market for rapid manufacturing will grow a lot, but this will be driven by the machine manufacturers, not so much by service bureaus.

Already now the machine manufacturers enter the low-volume production market, squeezing out their former customers with lower prices and larger capacities. But the material cost will remain high and I do not see this to enter mass production.

Low-volume high-cost markets (military, aerospace, medical, robotics, ...) will be heavily influenced though, and of course it will be a great tool for inventors and educators all over the world, enabling normal people to do many things, that 10 years ago only big companies were able to do.

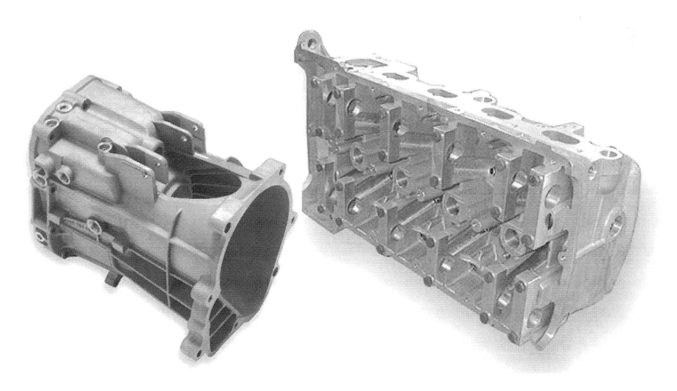

135

My Argument for Design Relativsm

Measurements aren't required, they are a hindrance to creativity and only impeed our minds due to their complexity and scale. When measurements are gone, our mind is free to image relativity instead, which allows your imagination to run wild.

To me, through the years of teaching myself how to design relatively, it occured to me that using instinct and imagination is more liberating than complex mathematical formulas and proven construction methods. We've live on instinct far long that we have on numbers and to me, they are a more fluid and faster method of production.

Here is a very simple problem that relativety solves using "new" technology and materials. Say, I'm 7ft tall, I will never find a car I can drive as the proportions are made for somebody who is 6ft tall. Unless I'm independently wealthy, driving a car is a luxury that I would never be able to enjoy as the amount of maths required to augment even one small part in a car requires every other part to be modified in kind. Using measurement relativism, that person would only need to increase the car size by 20% and they'd have a working car as the model would be 3D printed to take-in their dimensions and the "wall thicknesses" would have also been augmented to account for the new size. You don't need to scale the whole model, only the parts that directly affect a user. This opens up a whole new world of customization that I'm sure consumers with means (at first) would jump to. 3D printing metal and circuit boards is already possible.

If you ask painters when they are drawing what scale they are using, they will tell you they are simply rebuilding what they see in front of the canvas onto the canvas using what "feels right" without a measurement or ruler in sight. If you ask children how long something is, they'll use their bodyparts, not pull up a tape measure with inches or mms. Of course, the application of this design method doesn't suit every need. Measurements have their place in incredibly complex engineering such as tools and manufacturing of widgets but as 3D printers gain a foothold in both resolution and speed, those complexities will start to disolve, and I believe, lead to a revolution of design relativism.

When I first started along this journey in 2008, I did so knowing full well that the current world of woodworking was just too complicated. It was as-if it was a field built by people wanted to create barriers and measurements are by far the biggest one. Look at any "wood design" book and you'll see endless lists of measurements, from materials to tolerances. Compare that to this book where you see only a small black cube. Which is easiest to work with and design for?

You'll also notice that I do not use any exterior hardware. As 3D printers can build using different material properties right in the model, I think this will open a whole new world of simplification in all our lives. I want a door that fits in the door frame, I'll be able to 3D print that door solid and opaque with transparency and strength where I most need it and hinges that are part of the door and frame all in one shot.

Not only that, I'll even be able to integrate internal mechanisms so only my biomechanics can open it and which change randomly based off my unique chemical composition. No need for an eye scanner.

I've had people ask me on more than one occassion why they don't see me anywhere in the woodworking world. The reason is simple, I'm offering a very different method of building and thinking about design that's unfamiliar.

I'm not going down the route of "vested interests" as I don't believe there are any in the measurement world, what I think the issue is, is that people aren't use to "new" ways of thinking of centuries old building methods.

They like knowing their wood is a quarter inch thick and requires holes every 5 and 7/8ths that's exactly 1/8 deep with a circumference of 3/4 inch. They like a world where you need to use nails, screws and other hardware to keep things together. Glue is MORE than adequate for the vast variety of projects, even those you can drive on like my Wooden Big Wheels found in this book.

What I'm saying is that I just hope that this book helps open your mind to a new way of designing the world around you, where what you think can be done without being bogged down by endless material selections or just what's available at the local lumberyard.

This book may be filled with "toys" but I've got more ideas and time to build far larger and complex projects using the philosophies that I've developed. I'm eager to start designing furniture and more driveable projects which will give me the skills and resources required to get into buildings and eventually architecture using my system of thinking... all this can be done, without a measurement in sight.

All you need to know is your unit and area you wish to fill with said unit, the rest just comes together. That unit can be anything from a stone to a hand... as long as you understand it.

Assembled 14 piece model dimensions:
L: 372 W: 420 H: 372 (mm)
L: 14-41/64 W: 16-17/32 H: 14-41/64 (in)

Material Thickness: 6 mm (1/4 inch)

Summary Design Notes

Establish build parameters

The client for this project wanted the bird house to be roughly 25 cm square (excluding the roof). So once I had my box within those dimensions, I started playing with some ideas. He also wanted it to have holes on three of the four sides.

Adding details

Birds generally can't just fly into a bird house. So building simple yet strong pegs for them to land on was the first order of business followed by a roof to keep some of the elements out.

Ornamentated roofline

The roof needed a little more detail to make it interesting so I added some ornamentation. At this point I realized that the holes in the front (and back) were square which didn't match the rounded edges of the roofline. Time to fix!

Rounding the holes

I played with several concepts but nothing seem to jive with me. I liked the rounded aspect at the top but sticking round circles just made this look more like a Pinochio face to me than a bird house.

Adding more details

I ended-up with a very simple design: here in the front hole, just a half-circle outlining the entrance. It's a very small subtle detail but adds just enough for me to be happy with the design. I did think of adding it at the bottom and integrating it with the peg somehow but that's just complicating what is a very simple design.

Detailed Design Notes

It has been a while since I designed a simple bird house. It's fun to redesign things with the knowledge I've gained over the past few years to see if the results are better.

Step 1: Model adaptation

First thing to establish is the size of the bird house I'm building; this model will be roughly 25 cm square with holes across three of the sides.

The sketch isn't too detailed as I want to leave lots of room to move things around and evolve.

The challenge with this model will be making sure the interlocking parts are strong enough to hold everything together and yet make them easy enough to use and intuitive when it comes to building the final bird house model.

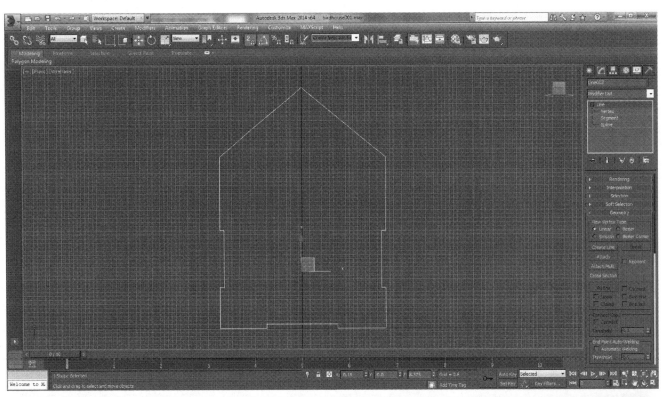

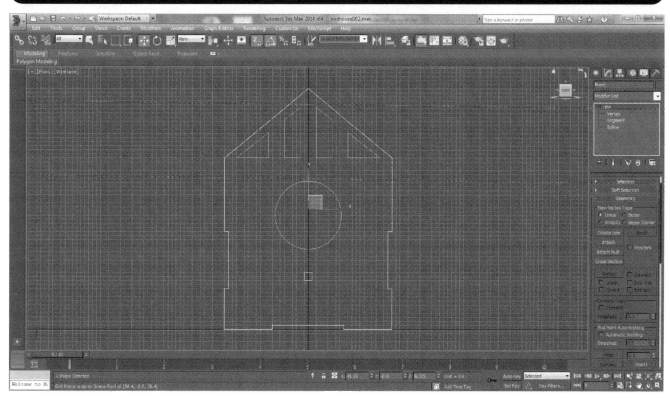

Step 2: Image top of this page
I've now added a few additional details to make this model slightly more interesting. If I were a bird, I'd like to have a skylight or a way to see through and inside the house without actually being on it while flying in.

Step 3: Image next page top
The house now has four sides, three of which with a hole and one with a solid back to protect against the weather. These options are easily modified in the 2D exported files, so customizing this to suit your needs isn't an issue to suit your liking and environment.

Step 4: Image next page bottom
I have one doubled-up peg going all the way through on the sides and one coming out in the front that is locked into place after being glued to the inner wall. I also dropped the side walls down to give me room for the roof to slant all the way down.

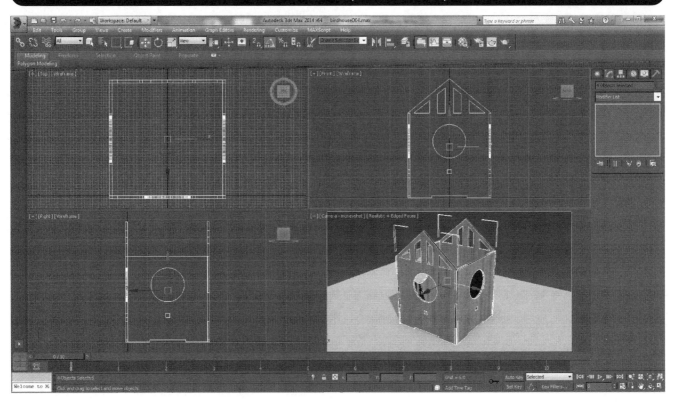

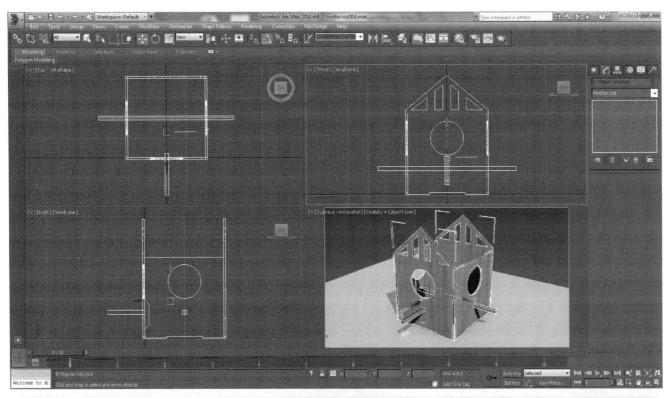

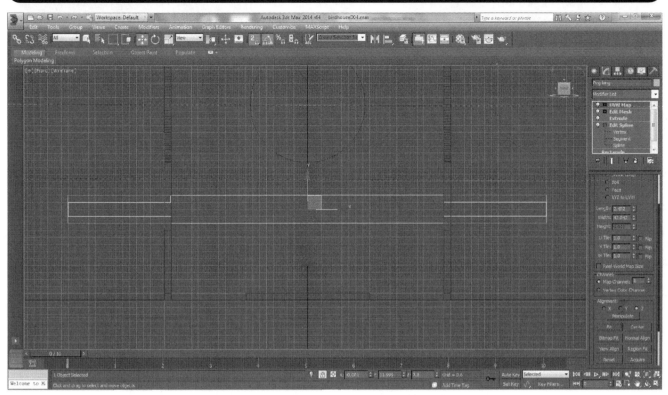

Step 5: Image top of this page
The peg that's going all the way through on the sides has been modified to be locked into place so both sides can now be tightened. This helps to increase the strength of the overall bird house.

Step 6: Image next page top
The base is finished and I made a slight lip in the front for easy positioning and the roof panels are identical so the builder doesn't need to worry about which goes where.

I think I have too many holes in the top and they are too large so I'm going to segment them differently. These holes also double as a method to hold the entire bird house in a tree by having a string go through the sides.

Step 7: Image next page bottom
I added a little ornamentation to the side of the roof. Again, this is easily removed in any 2D editing program so the fact that I have additional details doesn't really detract from the model as it is modifyable without needing any extensive skill sets.

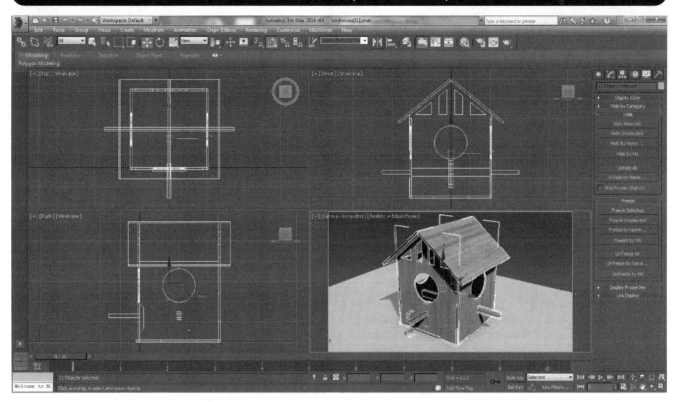

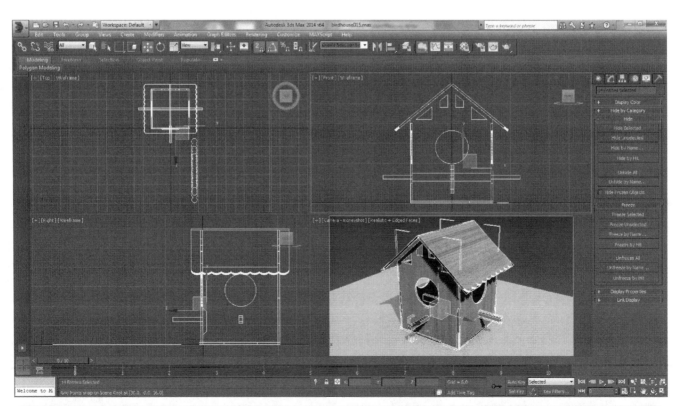

144

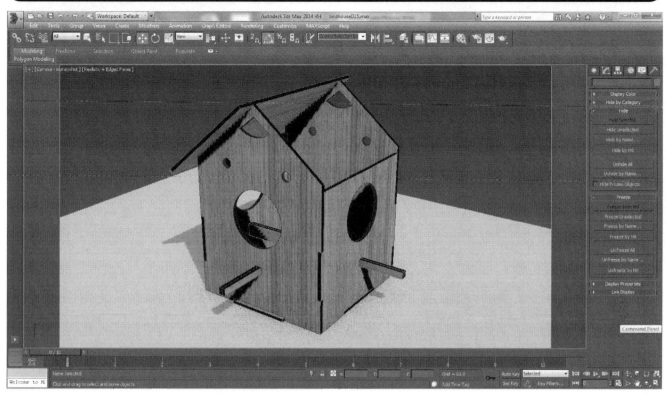

Step 8: Image top of this page

I found that the square window holes in the top were still too large and didn't match the roof line so I got rid of them and made them rounded instead. This also makes the hanging rope central to the entire bird house. It's more stable now!

I still find this a little boring, so I'm going to add a few more details, which can be easily edited by a person buying these plans on CNCKing.com.

Step 9: Image next page top

I think the design is almost perfect but I do see one problem, the bottom. I have one layer of plywood but if this is hanging from a tree, it might wear down and fall out as I don't want to use nails or screws for this design.

The simplest solution to this is to build a holder that glues into place on the side going from one side to the other that locks into the design itself so that, even if no glue was used, the base would still remain in place. At the same time, this will increase the aeration in this bird house.

Step 10: Image next page bottom

Having a locking mechanism like this makes perfect sense. Slide it up and left (or right) and add a little glue. I've now dramatically increased the strength of the base, it will never come off unless the bird gets a pick axe and shovel.

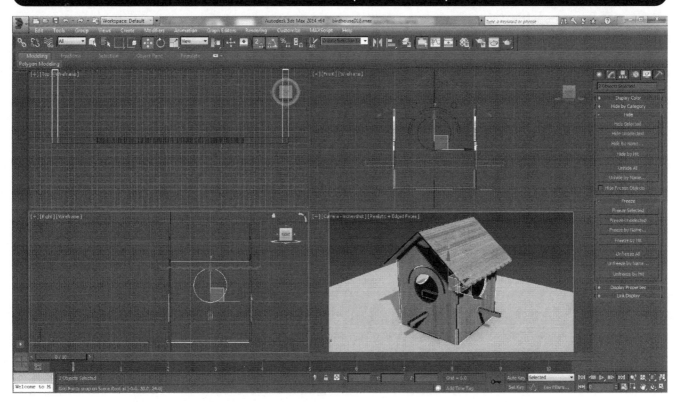

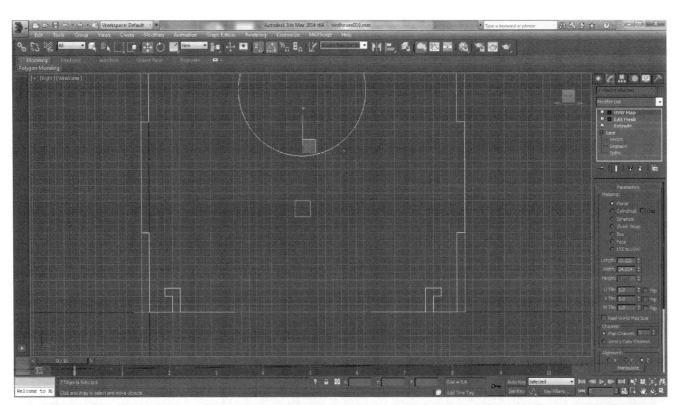

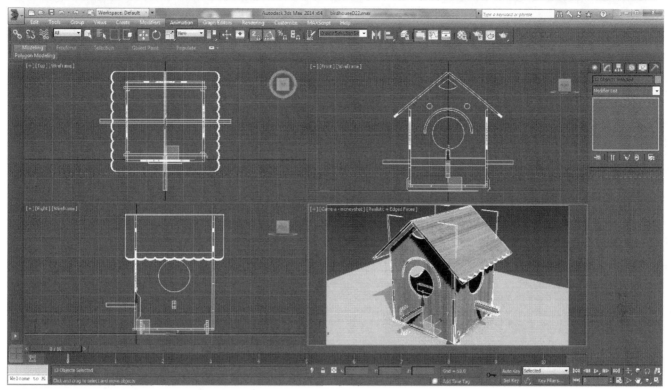

Step 11: Image top of this page.
I think I'm done. It looks good, it is strong being re-inforced from inside out and outside in. If I were a bird, I'd get a morgage for this house for sure, hopefully monthly worm payments aren't that high!

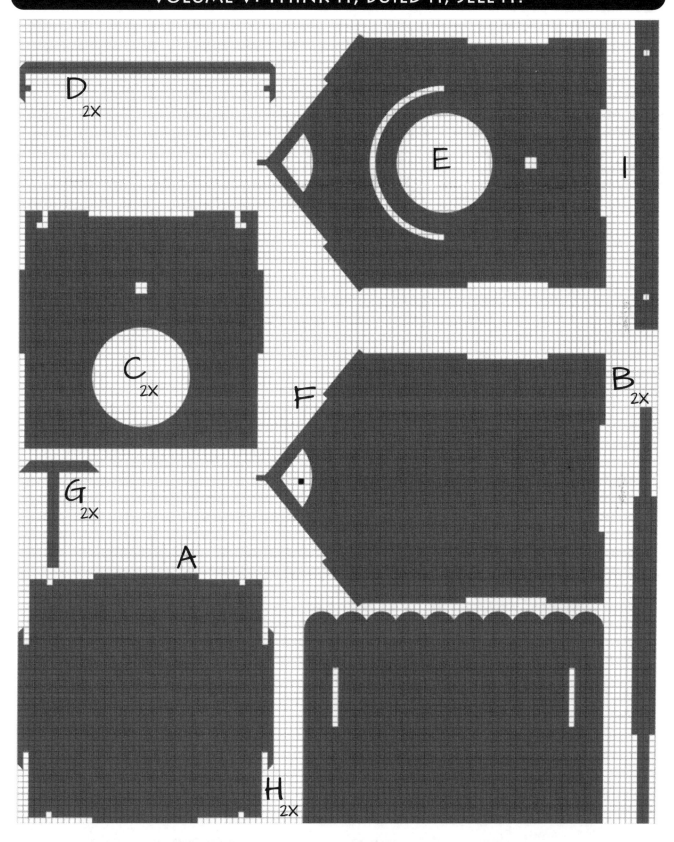

Step-by-Step Assembly Instructions

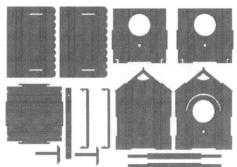

Step 1: Label and check inventory
Once you have all the pieces in front of you, the process of putting them together is no different from assembling pieces of Lego.

Label, using a pencil, the various parts and double-check your inventory. Take your time and enjoy the building process! Before jumping to the glue, be sure to do a dry run.

Step 2: Build the foundation
Start by laying down a part A (bottom panel) followed by two parts B (long pegs) in between both parts C (side panels) followed by bringing-up from the bottom and knotching to the left and right a part D to lock everything into place. Apply glue where the various parts intersect.

Step 3: Complete the sides
Slide and glue into place part E (front panel) and F (back panel) with parts G (front pegs) sliding into the front.

Allow to dry overnight.

Step 4: Perform some fishing touches
Slide and glue into place both parts H (roof panels) followed by part I (roof block) in order to prevent the weather from going through the roof.

There is no need to apply any preservatives or paint; feel free to sand any sharp edges down. ENJOY!

Can this model be CNC routed?

This model was built in a very specific manner, to help outline the design differences between a CNC laser and CNC router. This model could be laser cut no problem, having 6 mm of material widths across the bottom and the pegs doesn't pose an issue as there is no need for hold down or pushing/pulling forces on the piece with the laser.

There are two ways this model could be CNC routed but it would require a few design modifications.

The first would be parts B and D, there is only 12 mm of material long, by the time you add tabs, that goes dangerously narrow. This will be very prone to break using a 1/8 straight double-flute CNC router bit. So, these parts would need to be beefed-up.

Another thing you could technically do is cut this project using an even smaller bit, this would be my last choice because the smaller the bit, the less heat discipation there is between the material and the bit itself and the more forces put onto it during the cutting process. What does this all means? Basically, you need to cut things slower at a higher RPM and even then, it will still be more prone to break going through 6 mm plywood.

Other than those two parts, the rest could be savely cut with a CNC router though I'd probably increase the width of the roof block as, again, by the time you add tabs, the material widths are getting uncomfortably narrow and will be more prone to break.

If your answer is "who cares if a 10$ bit breaks" then you need to read my last volume (V4) as more often than not, you also have to throw away the board and reset things up again as a small bit fragment may cause the "new bit" to break where the old one did.

I'd see no problems at all cutting this with a plasma cutter or CNC waterjet at a slightly larger scale either for a metal version.

Bird House E

The first bird house was a success, the customer was happy and so were the birds, but then the customer wanted a slight variation so that bird would have a veranda going around the house where bird seeds could be placed. It's an easy modification.

As everything was fine with the first design, I just concentrated on fixing-up the bottom. The interlocking parts at the bottom need to be removed.

Remember, if this is hung, the string will go through the front and back portal. I made it so the roof doesn't need to be overly supported. This is not true with the current base once I removed the bottom interlocks. Easiest solution is to make little holes for pegs through the bottom of the current floor that interlock through another sub-floor with raised sides to create the veranda. This way, everything I've designed thus far is completely the same for the client. They've already built this once, building the same once more will save them time.

After building the veranda, I realized that I can actually get rid of the floor above it completely and just have the walls fall into it, then apply larger interlocks! By putting one floor above the other in wireframe, I have all the information I need to make a perfect floor as I know where the walls slot into.

By making all the fence units identical, all you need to do is stagger them around all four sides to complete them. Makes assembly far easier!

This design was also a great success with the customer. There are a few further modifications I'd like to do to this house, mainly around adding more density by having more than one home in it but that will be something I'll design later.

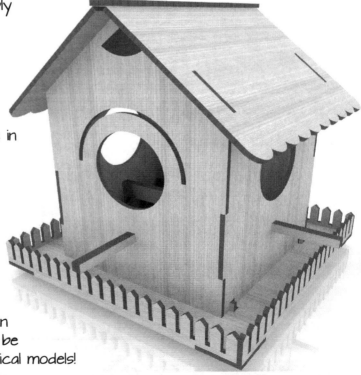

In the meantime, in hindsight, I guess I should have added small holes in the verandah because when it rains, the water really has nowhere to go.

There is always a modification that can be made to a design, experience can't be underestimated along with testing physical models!

Bootylicious Shoeholder

Assembled 28 piece model dimensions:
L: 528 W: 504 H: 1040 (mm)
L: 20-25/32 W: 19-27/32 H: 40-15/16 (in)

Material Thickness: 6 mm (1/4 inch)

Detailed Design Notes

I have one pair of shoes and one pair of sandals. When they wearout, I go out and buy a replacement and throw the old ones in the garbage outside of the shoe store. My wife on the other hand, needs dozens of shoes and it's becoming messy in the front foyer as a result... I need something to keep her shoes, boots and sandals in place without tripping over it.

As this is going to be for my wife, I'm going to build CNC router woman's boot holder as it has the height required for plenty of storage and the thickness to give my shelves a good level of depth. I also want it to double as a small table and a key holder. Without further ado, let's design then build it! By the way, if you wanted to make a cowboy boot holder, which was my first idea, the process would be identical with only a few changes needed to the silhouette. It goes without saying that although this model is going to be designed and cut for my CNC router, it can also just as easily be cut using a CNC laser.

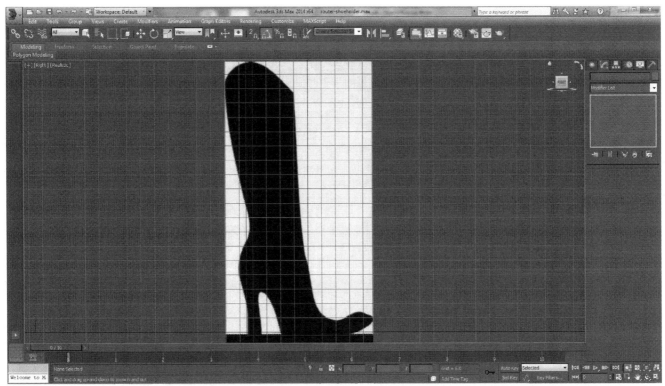

Step 1: Image top of this page

The first step is getting a reference silhouette that works within the parameters of my design. I built two boxes here, one shows me the maximum length and width of my CNC router cutting area - I will cut this out across three tiles using indexing - and the other is my silhouette. As this is going to be against a wall, I want the back to be flat. I will be making this slightly thicker as a result in the front as I have too much empty space and designing the shoe like the silhouette would just be a tripping hazard much like the shoes it will be storing.

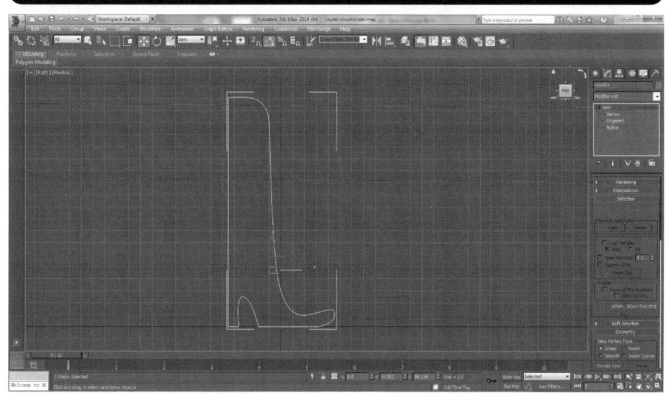

Step 2: Image top of this page

Now that I have my line drawing created, I no longer need the silhouette and I can modify the shoe to better suit the design and application I'm building this for. As this will have to be narrow, I have a few options. I can have a doubling or trippling of a shoe width to to create lots of shoe storage areas or, to make things a little more interesting... create this design to use both a cowboy boots on one side and a woman's boot on the other. This means, I have my storage area for MY two pairs of footwear and she has hers without mixing things up. This complicates the design but who cares, let's do it!

Step 3: Image next page top

The woman's boot goes all the way up to the knee but cowboy boots to mid-way up the calf, so we have a height difference. I'll put the cowboy boots on the outside with the woman's boots on the inside and I brought the cowboy boot down a bit so that it fits within two tiles from the bottom instead of having it go across three. This means it will be more accurate (I do my indexing by eye) and it isn't worth indexing a third tile that's mostly empty for a boot top.

Step 4: Image next page bottom

These shoes do have a different depths so what I'm going to do is give them the same. The first reason is that it makes the shelving easier to design for and esthetically, it will look better. I still have a few more modifications that are required to pull this off. I want the two line drawings to be more similar to one another, a few extra mm here and there won't be noticeable when this is built to full scale, especially when it's loaded with shoes and boots; so now's the time to make things mesh together.

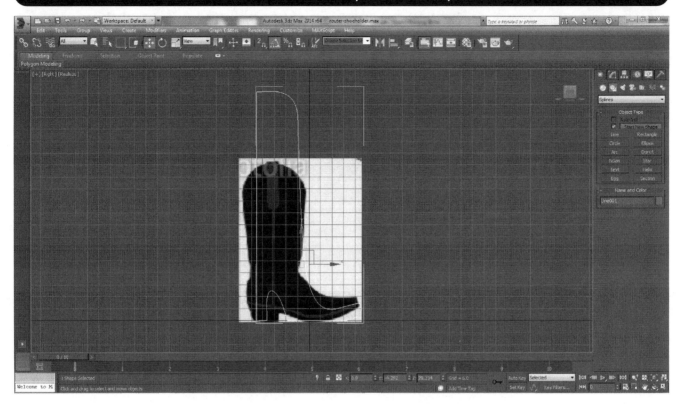

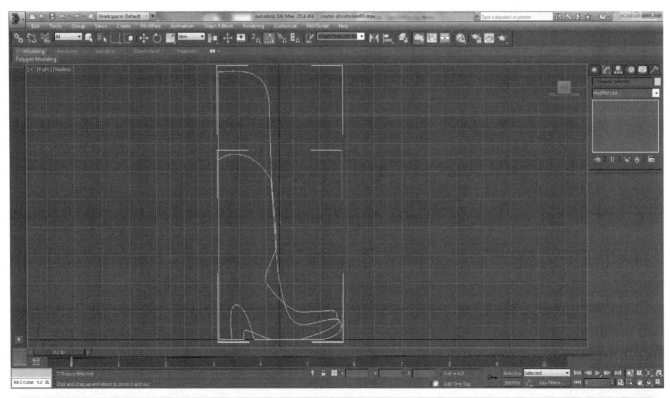

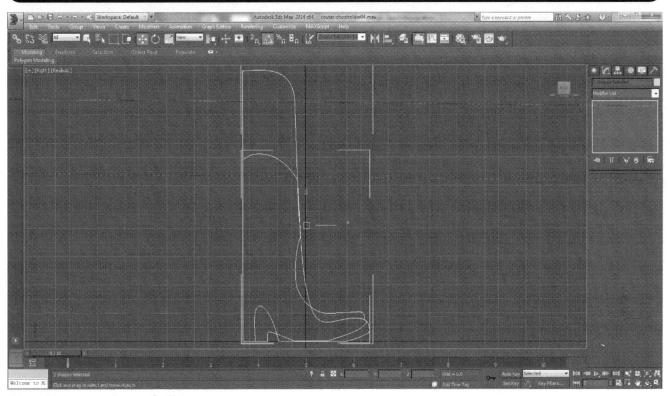

Step 5: Image top of this page

The boots are now much closer to one another depth wise. Unlike my kangaroo shelf, I want these silhouettes to have holes in the side, but first, I have to give these models some thickness to represent 6 mm material thickness. I measured my wood thickness and in this case it's 6.5 mm; so I'm going to give myself more tolerances along the length and width so that I can scale it up 10% without being off my maximum board size of 120 cm by 60 cm.

Step 6: Image next page top

After giving the boots some thickness, it would look pretty awful to have it like my original idea and generally, you put your pairs of footwear together, not in between other pairs.

As this will fit on the left of my front door, I'll have the higher boots on the left followed by the lower cowboy boots on the right. Reaching over to a lower ledge doesn't make sense if I'm going to store things on it momentarily before heading out. I also measured the width of two pairs of my shoes and if I give myself 30 cm, I have plenty of room.

Step 7: Image next page bottom

This is looking better. What I will do now is double-up the sides of each set of boots for strength and give them more presence. Once I have this sorted, I'll create the shelving. Also, by having the shorter boots next to the door gives me a method of hanging keys off the side of the taller boots.

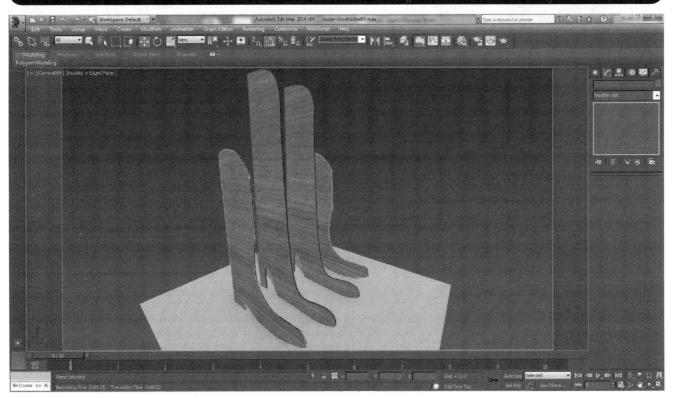

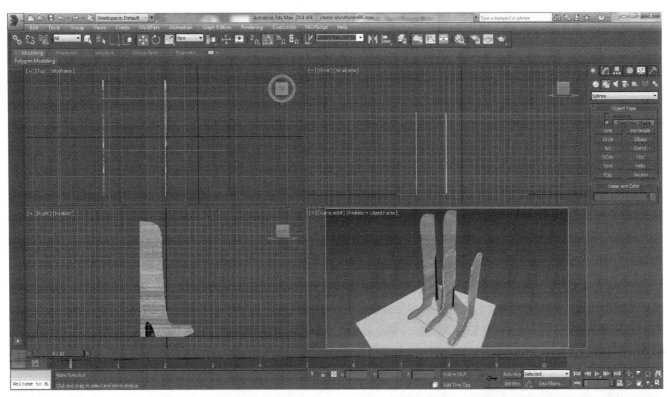

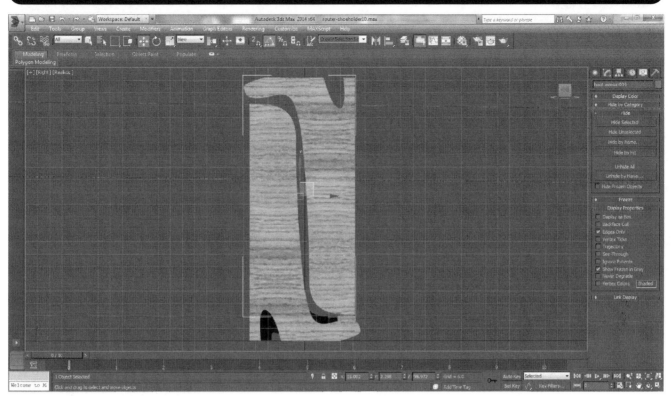

Step 8: Image top of this page

I want to be as efficient as I can cutting these pieces out and realized that if I rotate the cowboy boots 180 degrees, both boots could be cut easily from one 120 cm x 60 cm board with room to spare. I tried this as well with the taller boots and I'm just a few cms off from being able to this with those as well so I'm going to bring their height down a bit - something that won't be noticeable anyways - and be able to cut two on each board instead of one while wasting lots of room. The shelves are basically large rectangles, so this allows me to have four complete boards with only boots and then, another one or two, just for shelving and their relative supports.

Step 9: Image next page top

The difference may seem extremely minor but I've gained time by not having to cut out extra boards and money during the process. That's called being a SMART and EFFICIENT designer... wished I was always this smart and efficient!

Step 10: Image next page bottom

The boots are now set-up to be cut efficiently and the shelving spacing is now dead-on. The next step is to measure how "high" shoes and boots are in general and make the shelves fit within those vertical parameters. Looking good! My boots are slightly more than 60 cm across both boots. If I bring them in a bit more, this will mean I can cut them horizontally instead of vertically.

Why is this important? Well, it means I wouldn't have to tile them. I'd like to have one shelf go all the way through both sets of boots - it speeds-up the build process, dramatically decreases my piece count and makes everything stronger overall.

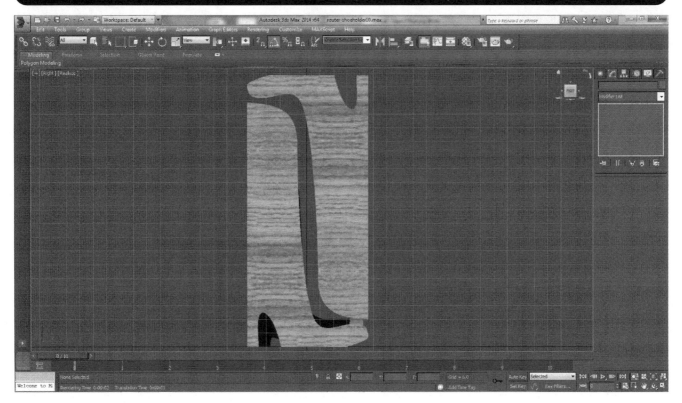

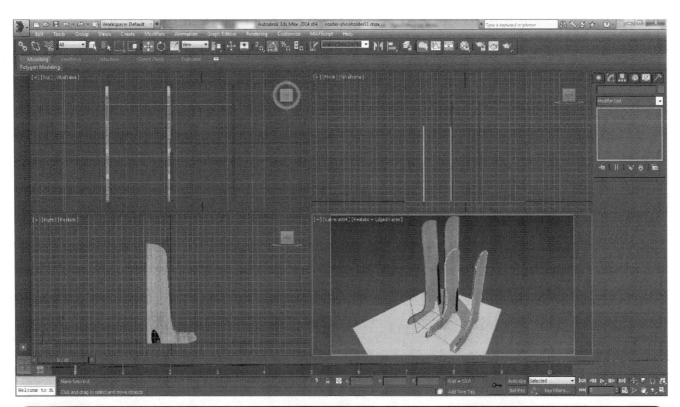

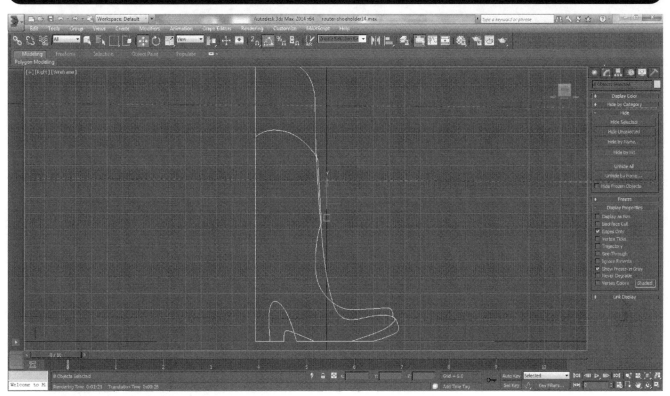

Step 11: Image top of this page

I'm not happy with the feet in the back. I think it's fine having two different set-ups but for the front, it just looks bad. When you think about it, there is no reason why the other boot can't be identical to the cowboy boot, but with a high heel and longer top. This would fix the esthetics and mean I don't need to double-up (four-up) the inside where the two boots meet.

Besides, I prefer the curve of the cowboy boot over the overly straight woman's boot, but as it will be higher, there is no reason why I can't make it extend a bit more towards the front as the curves would line-up.

Step 12: Image next page top

I really like this new set-up. There is a lot more symmetry across the board, I'm happy with the aesthetics and, measuring my shoes, I'd be fine making the shelves 5 cm high but as there is some variance, I'm going to go with 15.4 cm in between the shelves. This means at a height of roughly 120 cm; I'll have 5-7 shelves from top to bottom. If you need more room, you could easily double shoes up, but I think 5 pairs of shoes is more than enough unless you have more than one pair of feet. I fear that if I left more room, it would be a motivation for my wife to fill it up with more footwear!

Step 13: Image next page bottom

These are rough shelves to give me an idea of where to put my tabs. I don't need crossmembers because I have plenty of vertical supports (boot silhouettes) and footwear isn't the heaviest thing either.

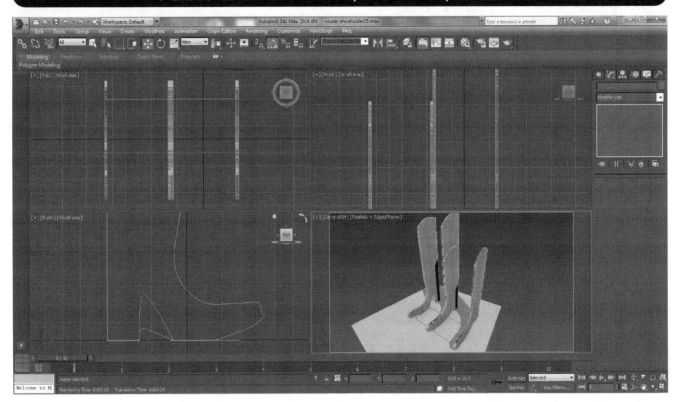

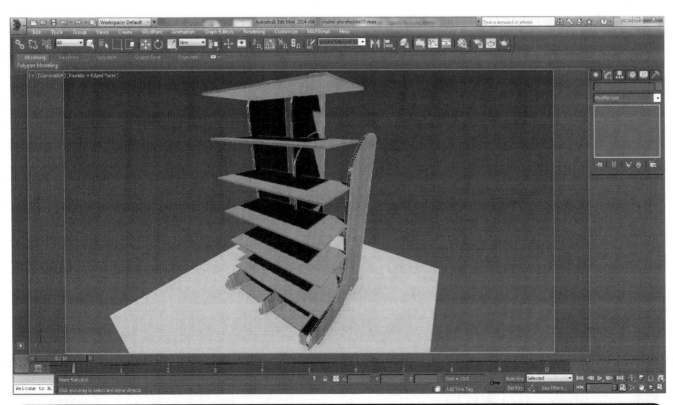

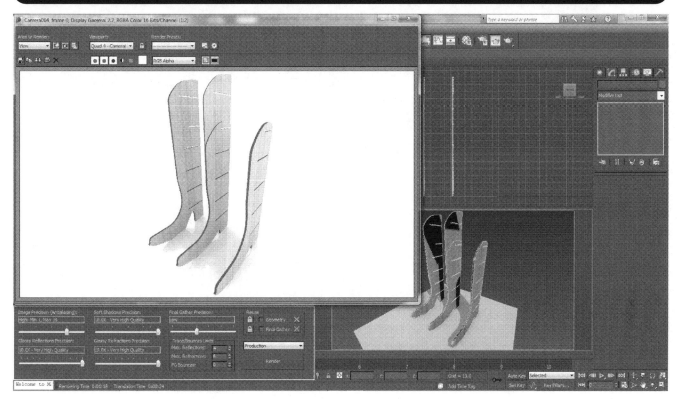

Step 14: Image top of this page

I build my slots going up both boots and deleted my temporary shelves. Looking at the pieces, the decision to use the same base boot design was a good one.

Step 15: Image next page top

The shelves are now in place. Looking at the model, I think the cowboy boot looks too similar to the top of the woman's boot, so I'm going to cut it down the middle a bit more. I'll also create a bottom base to this footwear holder as well, just to make the structure more stable. I don't have a backing as this will go against the wall and these aren't small things falling in the back - unlike the issue I thought I'd have with my kangaroo shelf.

Step 16: Image next page bottom

I now made each outside part full so you don't see the shelvings going through the boots, but I left the top as-is since I want to make a little cubby hole and key holder coming off the edge.

I see that I screwed-up the second shelf from the top: the first one needs to be full-sized while the other remain small. That's another area I'll transform into a box for more little things.

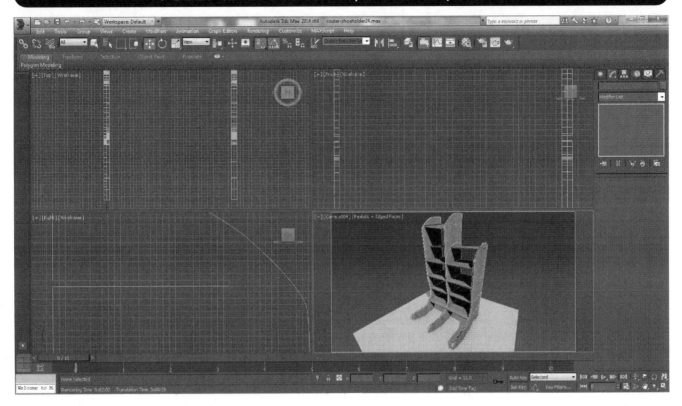

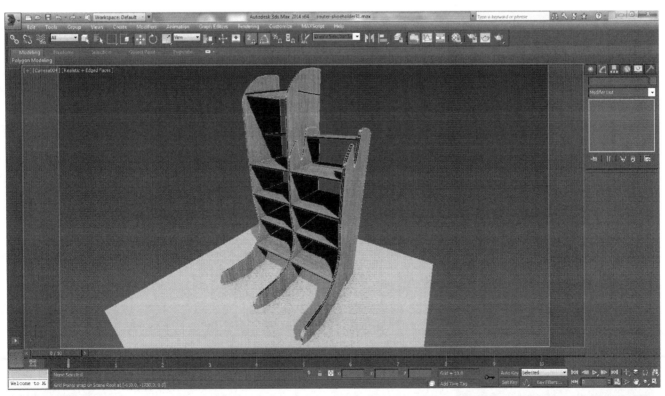

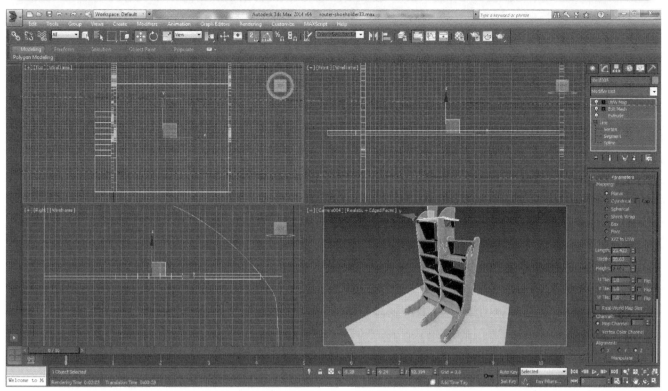

Step 17: Image top of this page

Now that the top is fixed and better thought-out, I'm going to focus on the bottom. Like real shoes, originally I thought of adding a sole but that's kinda hard now as the foot is raised off the ground, so I'll try to figure something out that looks good and adds more depth down below.

Step 18: Image next page top

I'm going to work a bit more on the base and, looking at the model, it seems a little flat due to the boots, what I'm going to do is add another layer on the side to fix this and make it a little more interesting. This won't add much if any strength so it's purely cosmetic.

Step 19: Image next page bottom

Adding the shelf on the cowboy boots is looking good. I built a shelf slightly higher going through the top boot for keys and small items but now that I think about it, it's redundant, so I'm going to remove it, but I do find the model a bit boring, so I'm going to make some inlays and windows.

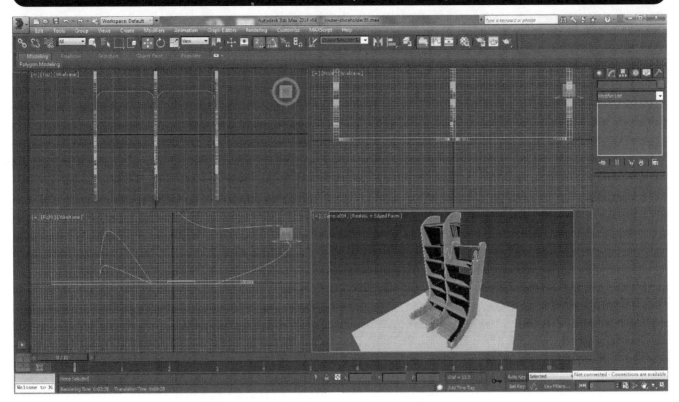

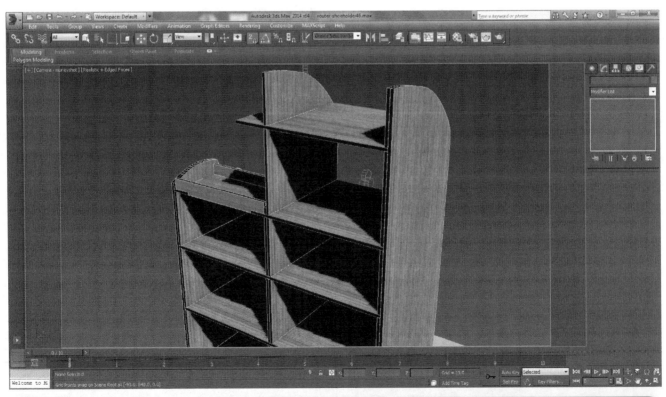

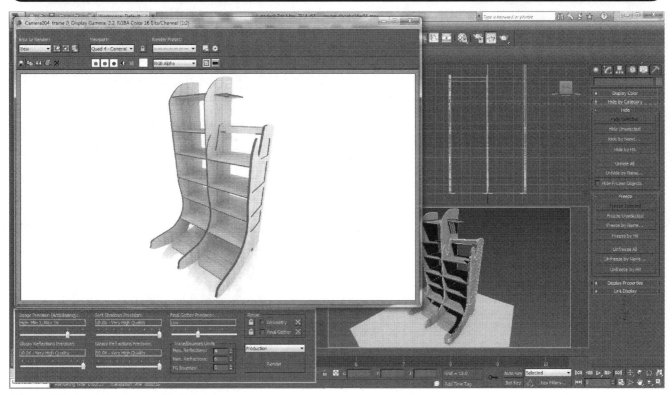

Step 20: Image top of this page

I think that looks far better now with the windows on the side. I placed them strategically so you still hide the shelves. I'm going to do this on the other side, the taller boots, as well. I still don't like the foot area though, I'm thinking of making them a drawer instead.

Step 21: Image next page top

I like the extra depth I've created using this silhouette. What's especially nice about this is that it just adds visually a lot more to the model that was there before. Now I have to fix-up the bottom somehow.

Step 22: Image next page bottom

After a bit of going back and forth, I've decided to make wooden shoe shelves that just slide into the base. So that means they can be used for shoes or other items of choice like gloves, hats etc.

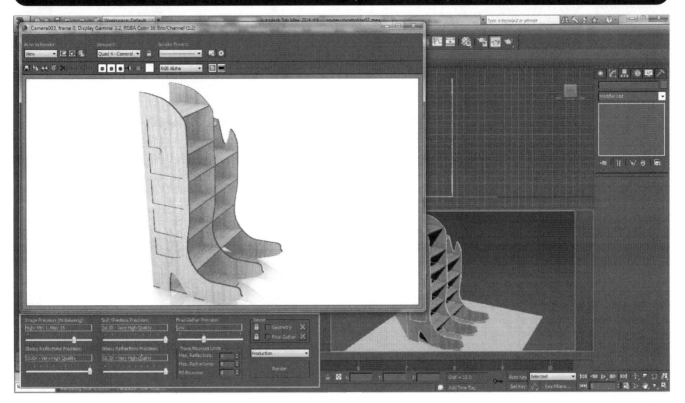

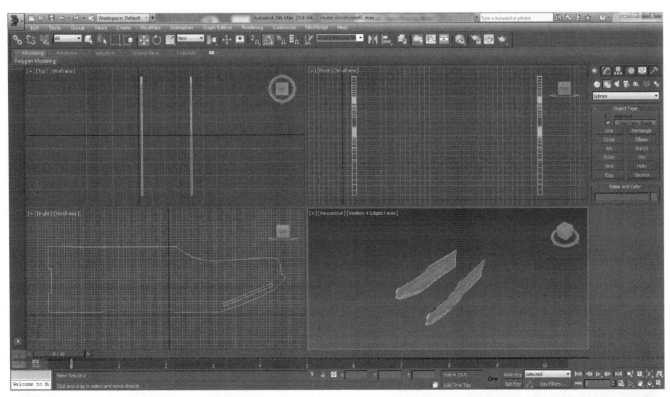

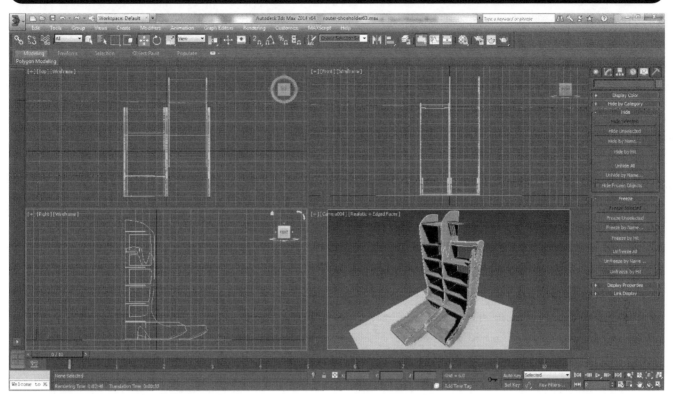

Step 23: Image top of this page

What I've done is create a design feature that was troubling into a functional one that actually will be used. These drawers are HUGE; which is perfect for putting lots of things and they also fit great in the whole shoe holder. I'm happy with this design - let's make the cutting files!

Step 24: Image next page top

I broke-up the model into individual pieces. It's always a surprise where a model looks like in 2D after working it for so long in a 3D environment. It's pretty neat and makes me appreciate people who work in 2D exclusively to make a 3D model. I really don't know how they do it!

Step 25: Image next page bottom

Once I got rid of the 3rd dimension on my model pieces and exported the file to Adobe Illustrator format, I then measured my wood as everything is relative to wood thickness. My material is 6.5 mm thick so what I did was scale the entire drawing up by 10%. Having something slightly larger is better than having them slightly too small.

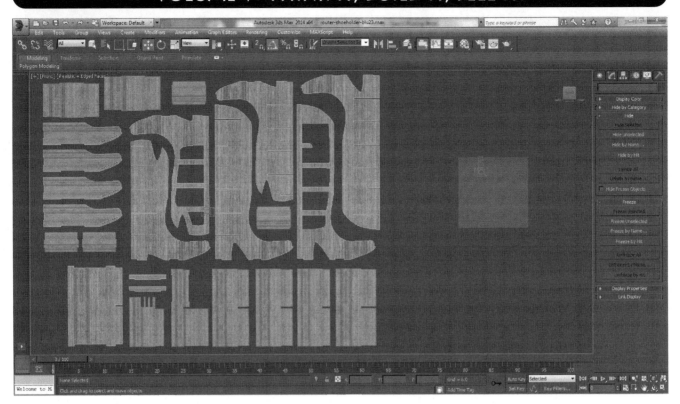

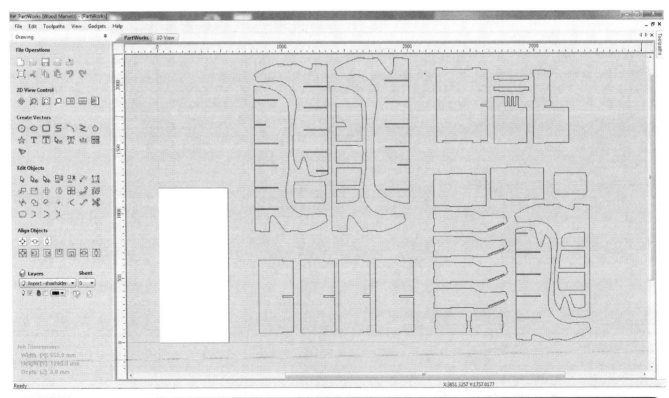

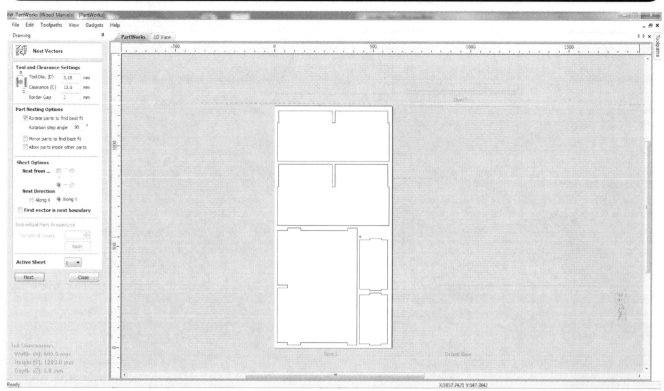

Step 26: Image top of this page

A slight problem... my height is fine when I increased the scale of the largest boot up by 10% but I completely forgot about the width. I'm a few mm more than what I can cut on my ShopBot Desktop, so what I have to do now is go back to my 3D model and shave-off a few mm from their length.

This is yet another reminder to me to get a full sheet CNC router ASAP! Tiling is something I'm proficient in, but you still have limits to content with. This is why I tell everybody getting a CNC machine, regardless of type, get the biggest damn machine you can afford and then some!

Step 27: Image next page top

I've shaved off 30 mm from the side of the boot; it will give me plenty of room and not really cost me as much in the grand scheme of things. You can see the original line on the left and six squares over the new boot line. I have to update all the parts across the model to reflect this change. Although this is overkill, I prefer to do this change once than twice.

Step 28: Image next page bottom

My shortest shelf is now 200 mm, which is fine for my wife, she has small feet, but not for me. I want to extend the shelves out a bit more so what I'll do, is make the front come out a bit more. So now my shortest shelf is 216 mm which, when increased by 10%, will make it just under 240 mm which is more than what I originally took off from the back while keeping the design virtually identical. By having such large feet, I know it can hold weight without tipping over either. So I don't need to add a bunch of additional weight to keep it steady.

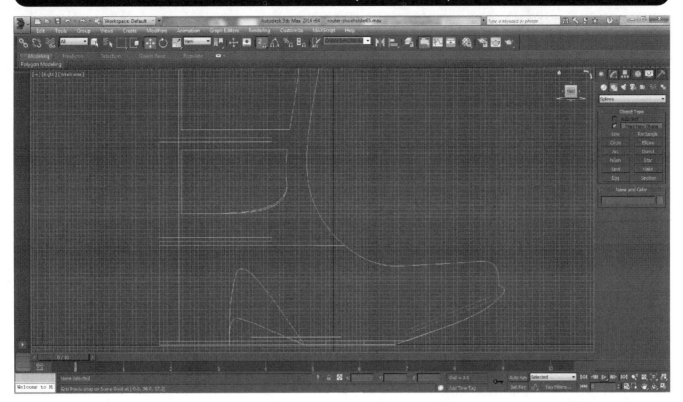

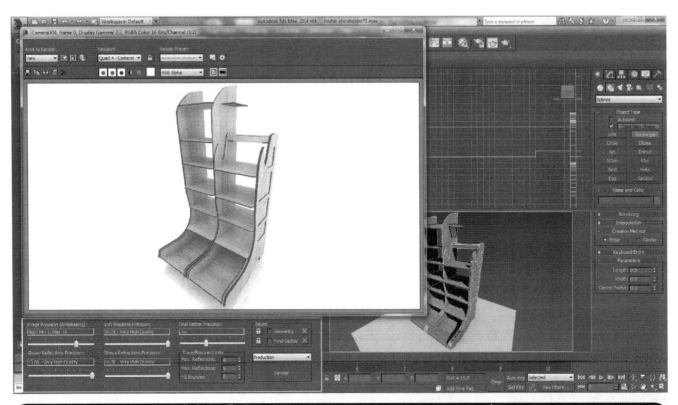

Step 29: Image top of this page

I do feel, while I'm making these changes anyways, I should add a stop to prevent the shoes from scuffing-up the back wall. This will be up against but I don't want these to be dark holes as a result, so I'm going to create a very open stop.

This requires more modifications to my design, but I think it's worth it. I'll also add a stop for the bottom shelves, so you can't push them all the way through.

Step 30: Image next page top

I've added slots on both sides of the back shelves so that something can be glued right against them securely. This will strengthen the overall design and prevent shoes from going all the way though the back as well as the bottom drawers.

Step 31: Image next page bottom

Do you see the problem in this screenshot? The bottom drawers are too long and go into the back shelving I created. This is the power of a digital design process because I can create things that aren't possible and fix them before ever cutting my first board.

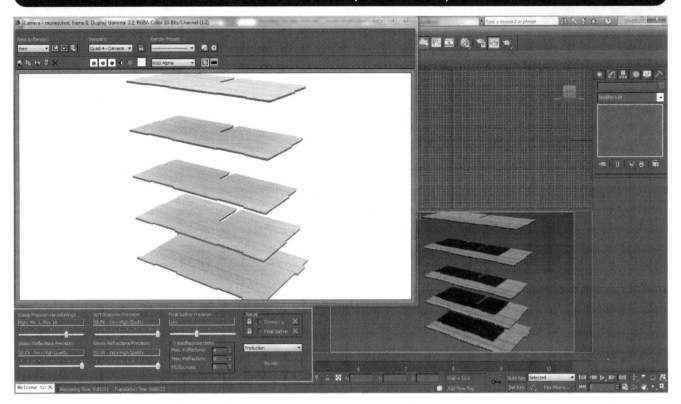

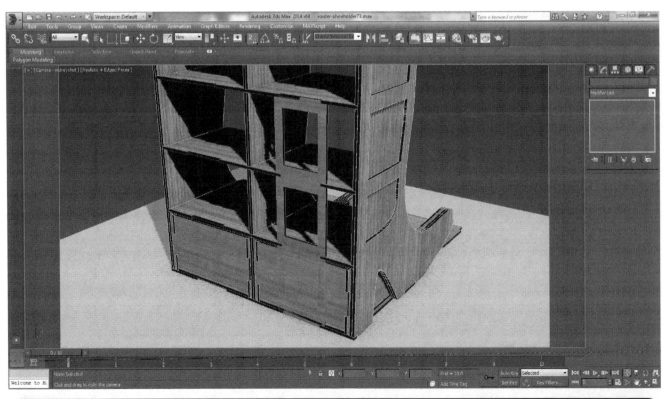

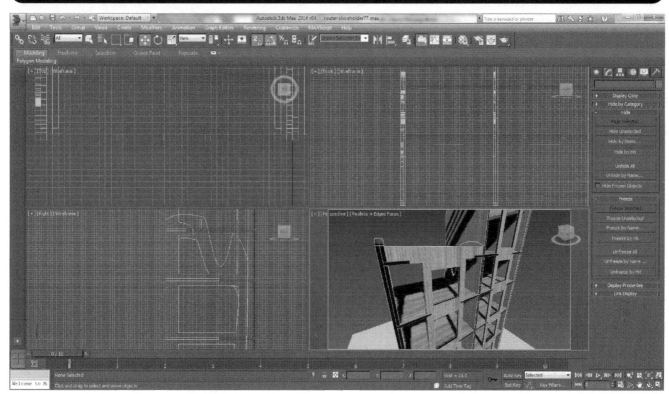

Step 32: Image top of this page
I took the opportunity to streamline the lower shelve's top. Making one of the back stops also make-up the actual back of the box. So, although I created four new pieces to this project, I managed to streamline one of those out of the model while making another unique piece so assssembly is all the easier!

Time to break the design up into individual parts and make the cutting files!

Step 33: Image next page top
Everything is looking great so far. I have my original files on the left and my new outlines on the right. I can now export it into Adobe Illustrator, rescale correctly, then export the new file to PartWorks.

Step 34: Image next page bottom
I have to manually fix all the nodes across all the parts so that I can add the tool paths and fillets to all the inside corners. The entire project fits across seven sheets measuring roughly 600 x 1200 mm, so it's a good size project that should cut pretty quick as it's only a total of 21 tiles.

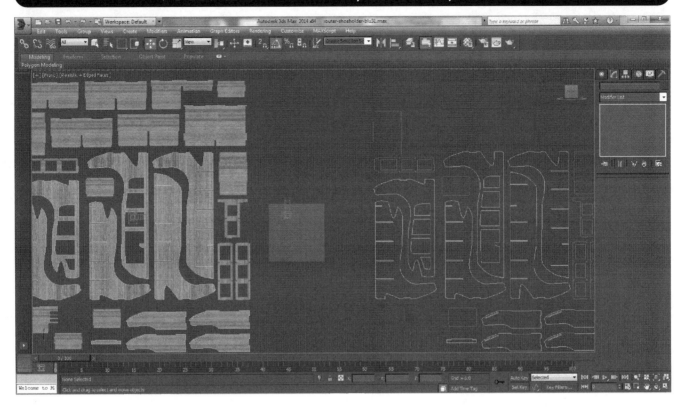

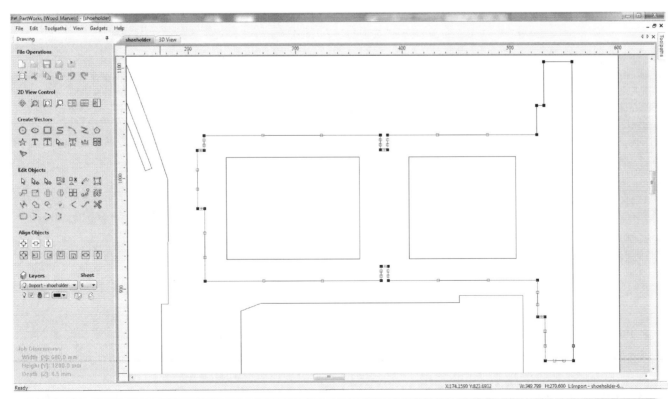

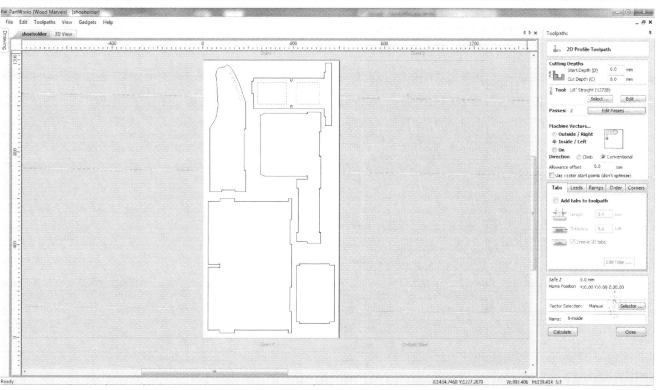

Step 35: Image top of this page

The tool paths go pretty smooth on this project as I'll be putting the screws along the sides - I gave myself a border of I cm which is plenty to hold the larger sheet size in place. A trick I discovered that allows me to cut through boards about twice as fast as normal as I've removed an entire tool path and screwing/unscrewing workflow.

Summary Design Notes

Establish model sizes

After modeling the boot style I wanted to use for this model, I had to deside the size of the overall model and material thickness I'd use to accomplish the build. I generally use 6 mm for CNC table router and 4 mm for CNC laser, though I buid-in some variance depending on what's locally available.

Adding shelves

Once dimensions had been established, I measured the length and width of my shoes to see where my shelving should be located for optimal placement.

Adding a base

Not part of the original concept behind this model, but I decided the bottom shelf should actually be able to slide in and out for things not used as often. As such, I had to perform a couple of build modifications to make this possible and the entire structure strong enough to support it all.

Adding a drawer

Now that I designed sliding drawers, I went back on top and further refined the key holder (part sticking out from the top boot towards the right side). As this will be next to the door, it might as well have more than one purpose.

Adding details

To prevent shoes from falling behind the model, I created a piece of wood that both supports the shelves, keeps everything square.

The entire model is very strong now and ready for a variety of uses!

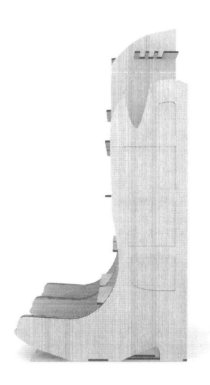

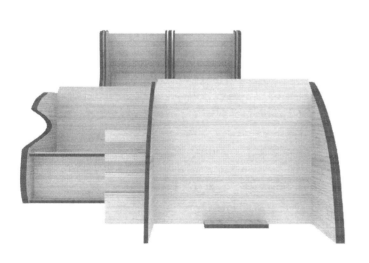
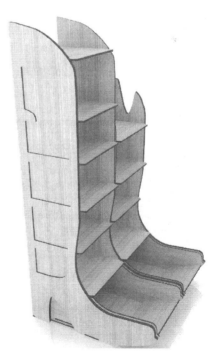

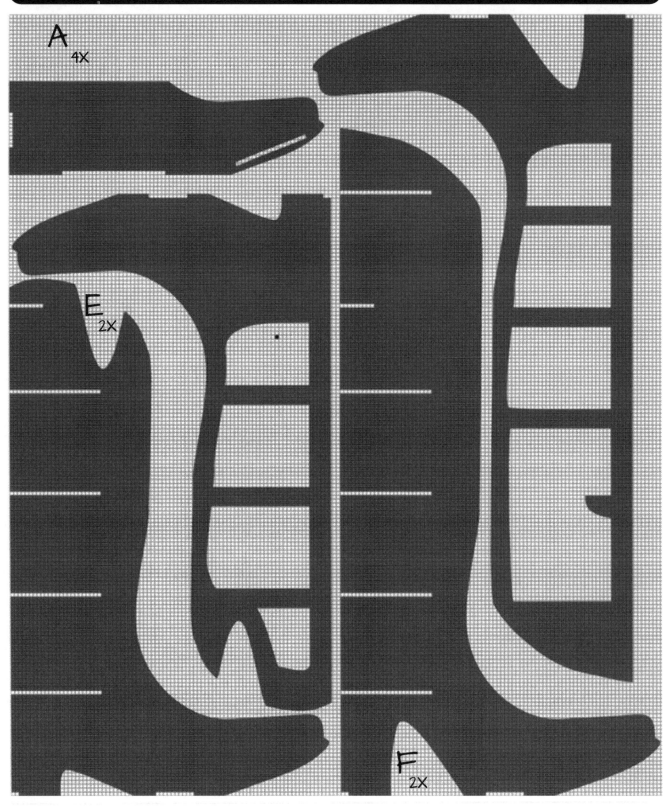

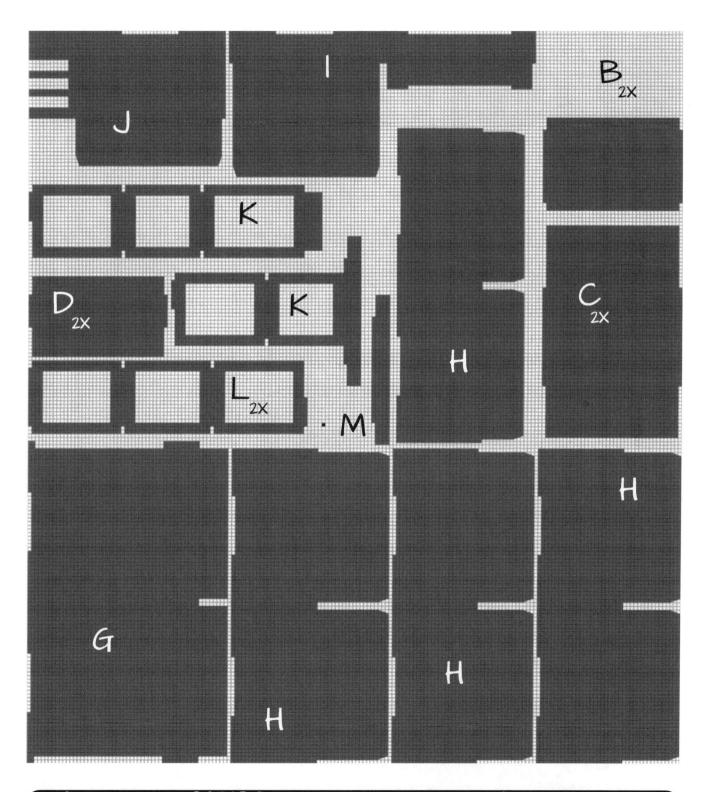

Step-by-Step Assembly Instructions

Step 1: Label and check inventory
Once you have all the pieces in front of you, the process of putting them together is no different from assembling pieces of Lego.

Label, using a pencil, the various parts and double-check your inventory. Take your time and enjoy the building process! Before jumping to the glue, be sure to do a dry run.

Step 2: Create the drawers
Inbetween two parts A (shoe silhouette), slide and glue into place from back to front, a part B, C and D. Allow these to dry overnight.

Step 3: Add the side panels
Slide and glue into place both parts E (short boots) and F (tall boots) over part G (bottom plate).

Step 4: Add shelves
Add the various shelves (H) so that they follow the outline of the boots with part I followed by J to build the top. Apply glue where the various parts intersect and allow to dry overnight.

Step-by-Step Assembly Instructions

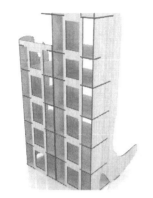

Step 5: Add back supports
To prevent shoes from falling out the back or marking the back wall, add the parts K (top support lattice) above both parts L (bottom support lattice).

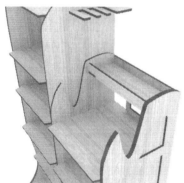

Step 6: Add front stop
Onto the top of the smaller boot, add part M which will form an area to put coins and other small things.

At this time you can glue both detailed ornate boot sides onto the completed model.

Allow to dry overnight.

Step 7: Perform some fishing touches
There is no need to apply any preservatives or paint; feel free to sand any sharp edges down. ENJOY!

Croc Box

Assembled 11 piece model dimensions:
L: 296 W: 296 H: 308 (mm)
L: 11-21/32 W: 11-21/32 H: 12-1/8 (in)

Material Thickness: 4 mm (1/8 inch)

Summary Design Notes

Base dimensions

I was tasked with making this box fit within a 30 cm cube space, so I made my base fit within those dimensions. Once that was established, I started with adding vertical slots to divide where each working drawer would extend into.

Add drawers

These drawers would be identical in both the front and the back of this model, so once I established the working dimensions of one, I was able to mirror the parts to form the other. This is why it's important to use symmetry as much as possible in a model so the build process is efficient.

Add second floor

While building this box, I had to pay careful attention to the sides and supports, so I built it up vertically by making parts intersect one another for added strength. I also decided on a doubled central column so that there was extra strength in the model overall.

Adding pivots

At the very bottom there are working drawers followed by an open space so, on the top, I wanted to make something that could be spun around. I build-in tight tolerances with plenty of supports so that friction would prevent it from being too easy to spin while creating plenty of contact so that it didn't tip.

Jaw hinge

The jaw hinge added another unique feature to this organizer, I had to make sure that it was placed optimally so that, open or closed, the movement made sense and the teeth aligned properly. If I moved the hinge just a centemeter up, down, left or right of its current position, the jaw wouldn't work.

Detailed Design Notes

There are a few features of this design that warrant extra attention as they may not look obvious from the start, but make a very important contribution to this working Croc Head Organizer design.

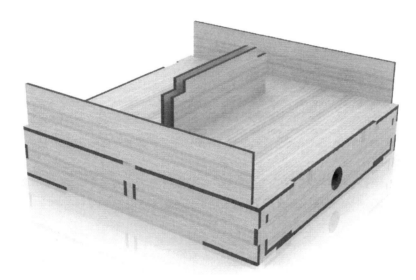

Support through the bottom to the top
The more pieces you have in a model, the weaker it becomes, so it's important to have as many large pieces that intersect with other large pieces as possible.

What you see in the above picture are solid side panels that are supported vertically and horizontally by both the base and the middle partition. The partition "glues" the base to the second floor and the third (not shown) by going both through these floor boards and at the same time provider for some surface area for the vertical sides to lean against.

The two holes on the side provide a guide so that even with little glue, there is a snug fit for everything to fit together.

The drawers are meant to come completely outside of the model on purpose (unlike the Spinning Gear Box) because they slide directly on the base instead of being elevated onto vertical guides - having glue all around the box and with drawers in place would have made it too easy for the drawers to also get glued in place.

Large spinning surface

As I build all my models to require no exterior hardware, having pieces that spin around can be challenging especially if you only have gravity as your guide. In this case, you'll notice an extra large circular area with crossed inner supports.

The purpose of having such a large surface area is to make sure that when the model spins around, there is plenty of contact with the base of the Croc Head and the organizer underneith. If this is made too thin, it's too easily tipped.

Another important feature is that I had to make sure that the round circular plane didn't move and was locked in. Glue can accomplish this (as it has) but having crossed members in the middle also provides an incredible amount of support.

The middle area is elevated slightly further to intersect with the hole at the bottom of the Croc Head. You want both of these circular supports to be as large as possible without being evident unless they are meant to be a noticeable visual of the model.

Building in this manner allows just the right among of friction to prevent the whole head from spinning too effortlessly while providing enough contact to make sure that even if objects aren't evenly distributed on or in the head in either it's open or close position, they don't cause the head itself to fall over.

Hinged Jaw

The last important aspect of this model I want to focus on is the head itself. You'll notice that the hinge is 2/3rds of the way from the start... how did I know this was the optimal area for the hinge to be? I tested it virtually until I found the perfect spot to place it.

As I wanted to keep the piece count of this model at an absolute minimum, I wanted the vertical slots in the head to be both supportive and play a roll in to the keeping the jaw aligned. In the back, I made the support come out a bit more through the lower jaw to provide a method of supporting a round ring that would lock into place into which you slide the upper jaw section.

This poses one problem: the jaw can come all the way down in the front as the upper jaw is wider than the lower one. To solve this issue, I made the vertical slot in the front also come out from the jaw but instead of holding a hinge divide, it was meant as a block to prevent the jaw from going further.

I had to do quite a bit of virtual testing until I had the jaw and both slots in their optimal area to make this entire head work properly.

The teeth, by the way, are identical on both the upper and lower jaw on purpose to speed up the design process and actually have slight groves to make them even more jagged like shark teeth.

Product Renders

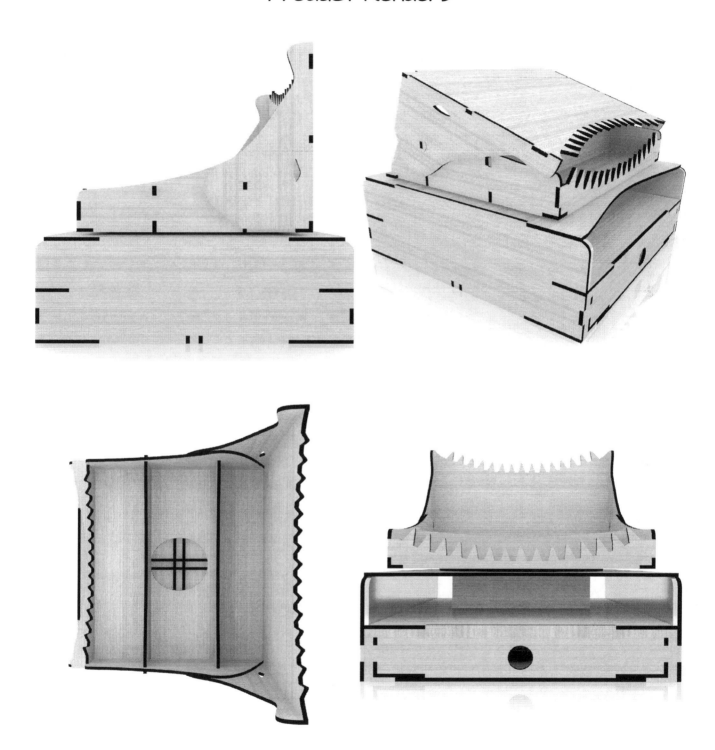

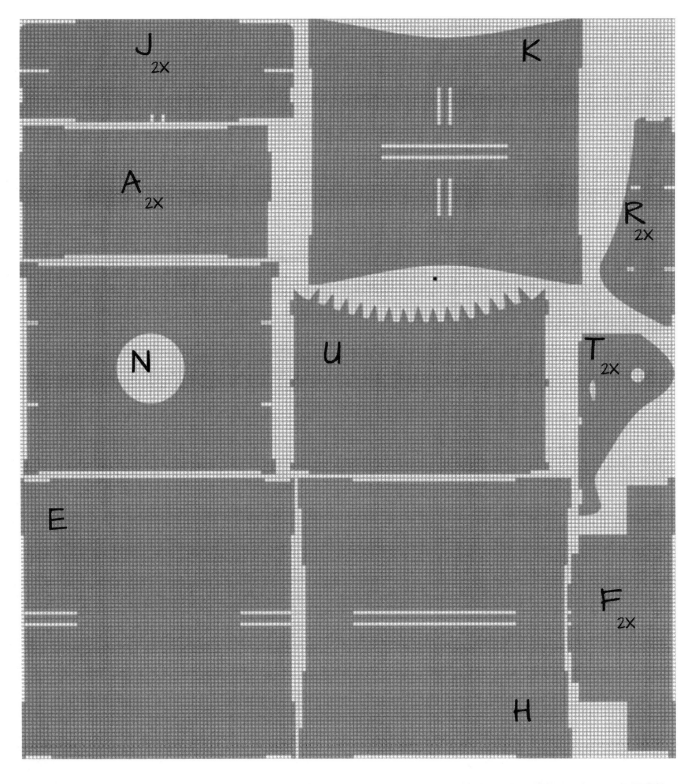

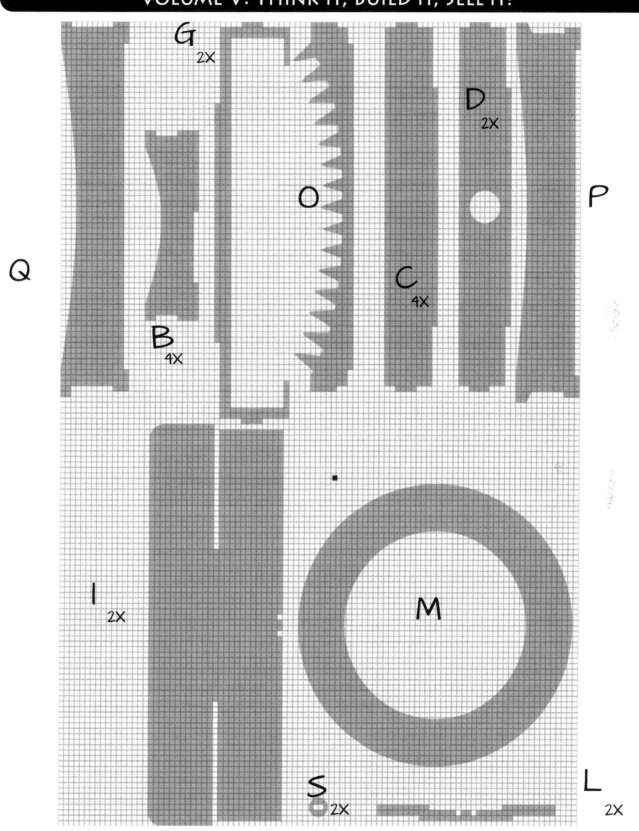

Step-by-Step Assembly Instructions

Step 1: Label and check inventory

Once you have all the pieces in front of you, the process of putting them together is no different from assembling pieces of Lego.

Label, using a pencil, the various parts and double-check your inventory. Take your time and enjoy the building process! Before jumping to the glue, be sure to do a dry run.

Step 2: Build the drawers

Start by laying down a part A (drawer base) followed by a part B on both sides followed by a part C (no hole) on the back of the drawer and a part D (hole) in the front. Use glue to keep the various parts together and allow them to dry overnight with clamps.

Repeat this process again so that you have two identical drawers.

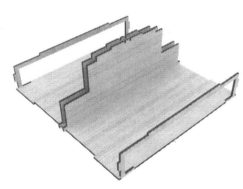

Step 3: Build the base

Slide and glue into part E (base), both parts F (vertical supports) followed by a part G (drawer hole) on both ends.

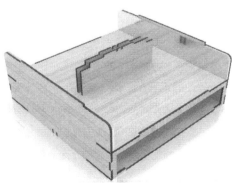

Step 4: Complete the first floor

From the top, slide and glue into place a part H (second floor) while on both sides, slide and glue a part I (mirrored acrylic) followed by a part J (solid cap).

This is where you can use your creativity. Cut out holes on the sides of part J to create added depth to your design.

Step-by-Step Assembly Instructions

Step 5: Complete the second floor
You can now drop and glue into place part K (top cap) followed by both parts L (cross members) and then a part M (circular support).

Allow the entire box to dry overnight.

Step 6: Start the lower jaw
Using part N as the base, slide and glue into place, from front to back, parts O (lower teeth), P and Q. Apply glue on the various intersecting parts.

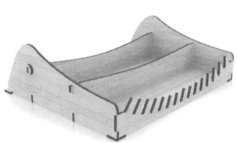

Step 7: Add the hinge
Onto both sides, slide and glue into place a part R (side panel) followed by a part S (end cap).

Allow the lower jaw assembly to dry overnight before proceeding to step 8 as you don't want the upper jaw to glue to the lower jaw.

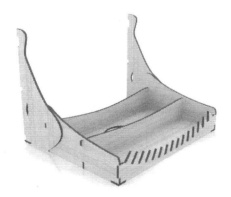

Step 8: Start the upper jaw
Slide into place without glue, a part T (upper jaw) onto both sides. Make sure these parts relatively easily rotate over part S (end cap).

Step-by-Step Assembly Instructions

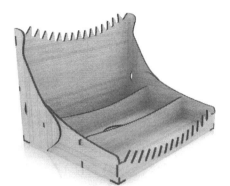

Step 9: Finish the croc head
Using glue to keep part U (top jaw teeth) together with clamps until the entire croc head is dry.

Step 10: Perform some finishing touches
You can now slide into place without any glue, the two lower drawers in the base and the crock head on the top.

Now, let's convert this CNC laser model into one that's easily cut using a CNC router - specifically, my awesome ShopBot Desktop!

Detailed Design Notes

This CNC table router Croc Head Organizer was modified to test the jaw mechanism of the laser cut version. The original laser was designed to be cut using 4 mm (1/8 inch) thick material, but I wanted to make something larger and had some 7 mm (9/32 inch) laying around, so I scaled it up to suit my ShopBot Desktop.

There were also a few areas where making it purely on a table router would have caused some issues, so scaling the entire drawing up solve those in one fell swoop.

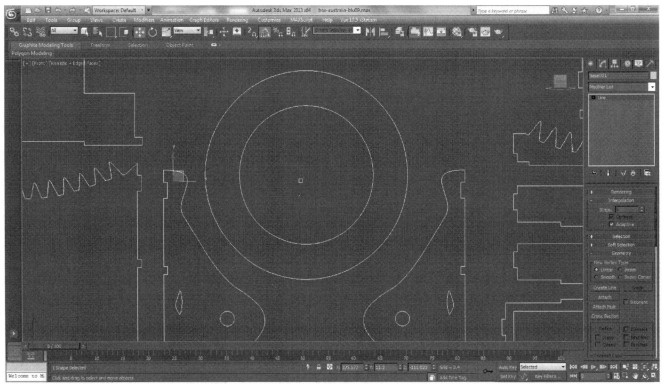

Step 1: Image top of this page
As this design is already made for a CNC laser cutter, I need first to export all the files into a vector format so I can proceed with converting it to be cut with my ShopBot Desktop instead of a laser cutter.

Step 2: Image next page top
As you can see, there are quite a few pieces that make up the laser version of this model.

Step 3: Image next page bottom
But what I want to do is focus on the little square I created within 3DS Max, as all my projects are based on wood thickness. All I need to do is scale this square to equal what I'm trying to achieve and everything will work perfectly. This square is 10.16 mm square.

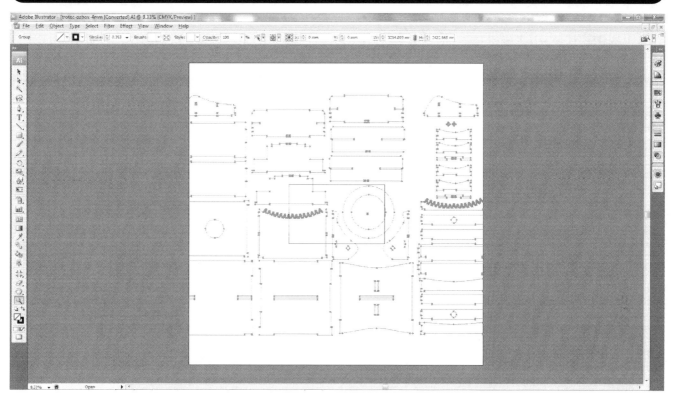

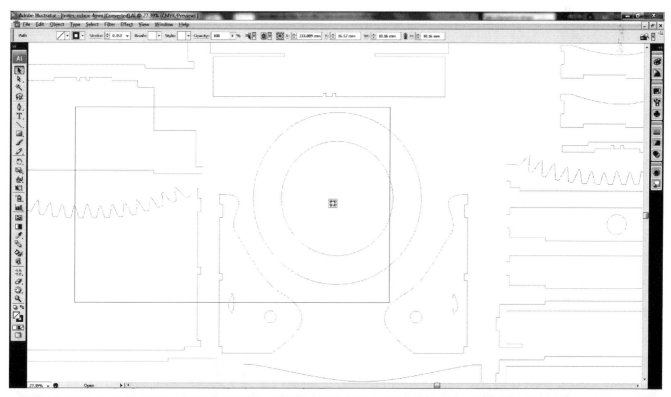

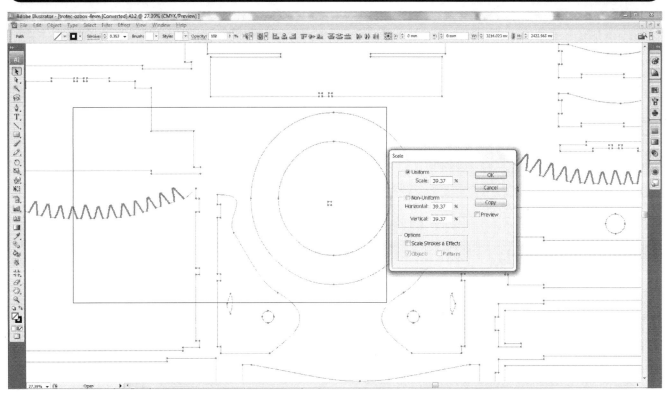

Step 4: Image top of this page
10.16 x ??? = 4 mm thus 4 / 10.16 = 39.37 so 10.16 x 39.37 = 4 mm I want if this was to be cut with my laser (as per original design).

Step 5: Image next page top
You'll see the rectangle in the background; this represents my board size, in this case I'll use 400 x 500 mm.

Step 6: Image next page bottom
But in this case, my wood thickness is 7 mm, not 4mm. So it's time to scale the whole drawing up using the same equation: 4 mm x ??? = 7 mm thus 7 / 4 = 1.75 using the same little square I had earlier so everything is dead-on.

I now have a small problem: the bottom boards making-up the drawers are simply too large to fit on my table router (one of the disadvantages of having a desktop model is a smaller cutting surface).

There are a few other issues with the drawers that would probably cause me some grief as well, so I decided only to test the top so making one modification, removing the inner hole on the base as the head of the croc won't need to rotate if it's on a flat surface.

I know the drawers are fine, it's the hinge aspect of this design that I really want to test anyhow.

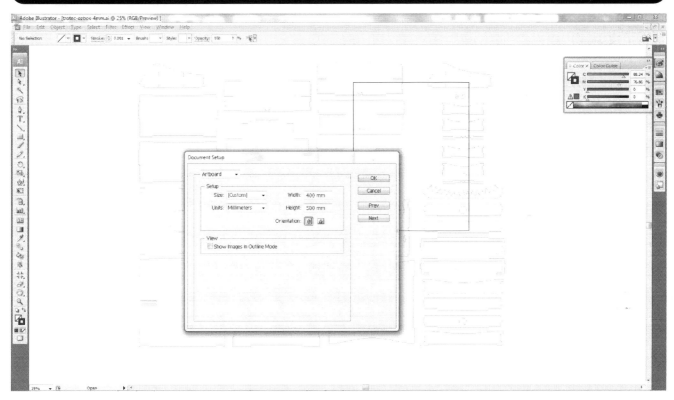

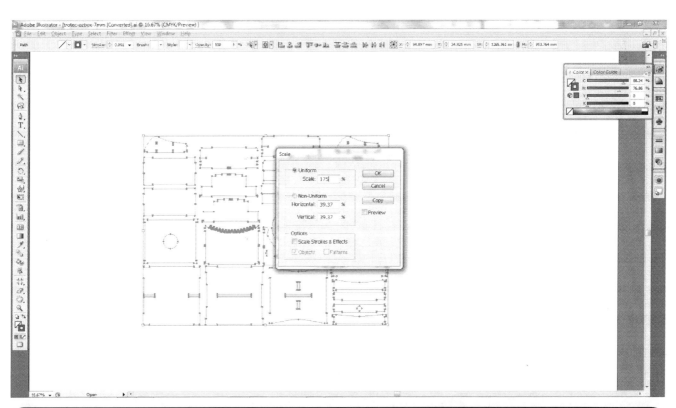

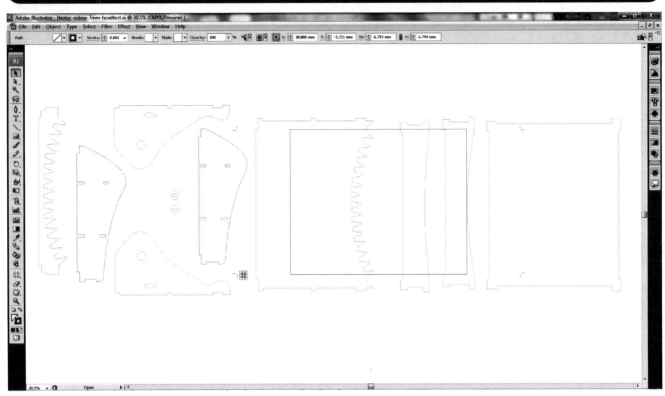

Step 7: Image top of this page

I want to use a minimum of glue, so I further scaled the drawing down by a fraction of a mm. I also deleted all the parts that wouldn't take part in this test (the drawers under the head) so that I wouldn't get confused as to what is and isn't part of this project.

Step 8: Image next page top

Using the rectangle I established in Step 5, I began laying out the individual pieces. I always start with the largest piece first as this is my limiting factor.

If I lay out all the smaller pieces first then realize that my scale is wrong (it won't fit the board), then I wasted lots of time optimizing lots of files. If I can find this problem NOW I save a lot of time.

Step 9: Image next page bottom

It's just a matter of laying all the pieces out on different virtual boards in Adobe Illustrator which will then be imported into Partworks for the dogbones and tool pathing. This includes pockets for the hold down screws, inner and outer profile cuts.

I've now created all the tool paths for this project. As you can see, the preview looks perfect and it's time to cut this project out!

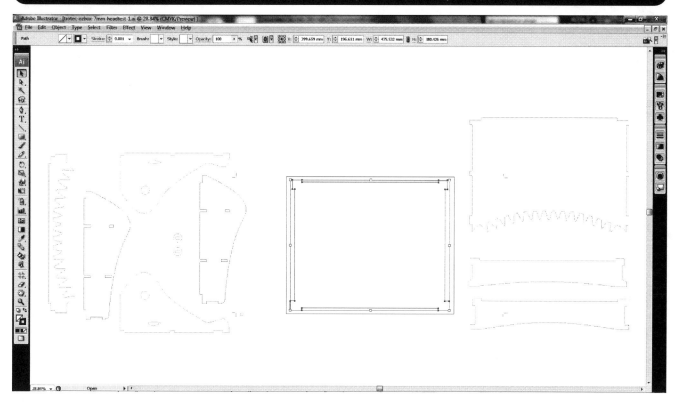

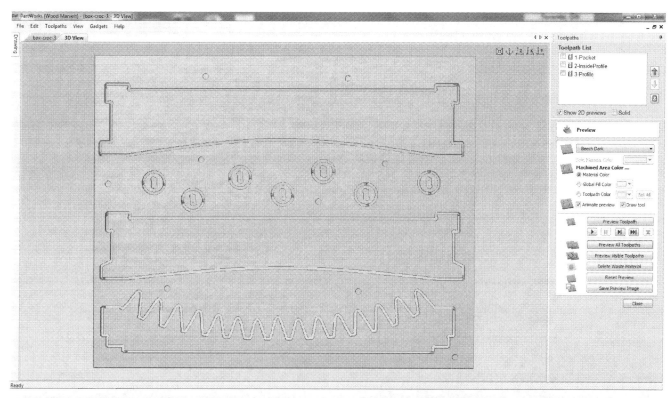

The cutting went smooth - I'm still mesmerized by how smooth such a powerful machine moves so effortlessly though wood. After cutting all the pieces out, I got my clamps and glued them all together.

I allowed the bottom jaw to dry first before building onto it the top jaw as I wanted to make sure the hinge wasn't tainted with glue dripping from above. In hindsight, I didn't need to do this but it made sense at the time.

I tend to use a lot more clamps than necessary, just like the screws I use for hold down. I found from experience that using too many is a better winning proposition than not using enough.

Once the upper and lower jaw were dry, I then tested the hinge mechanism and it worked perfectly as envision.

You will notice, I have a lot of sawdust on the table. The purpose of this is to make sure my models doesn't glue to the table. The sawdust absorbs the glue and is easily removed.

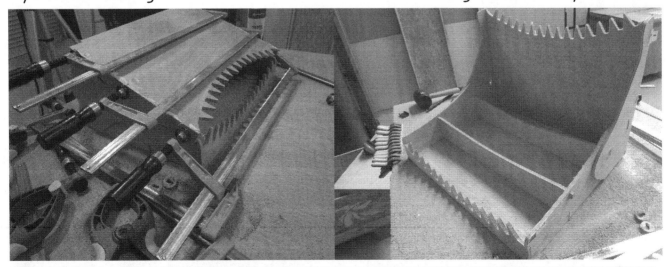

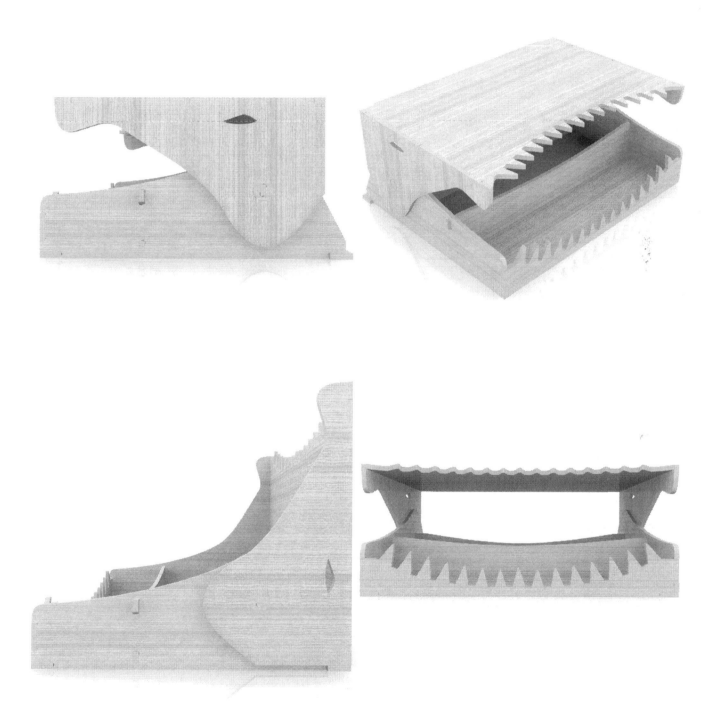

Testing Platform : ShopBot Desktop CNC Table Router
Bit: 1/8 inch straight double flute

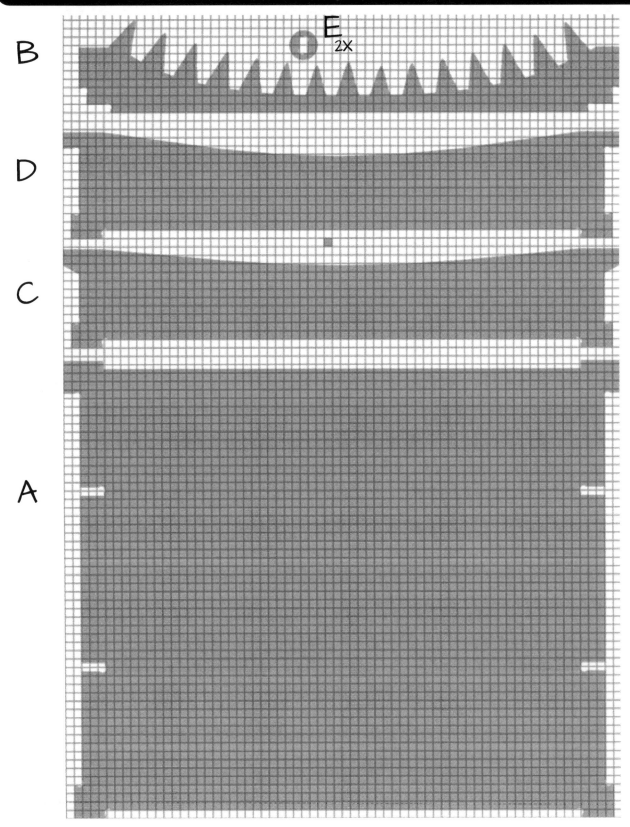

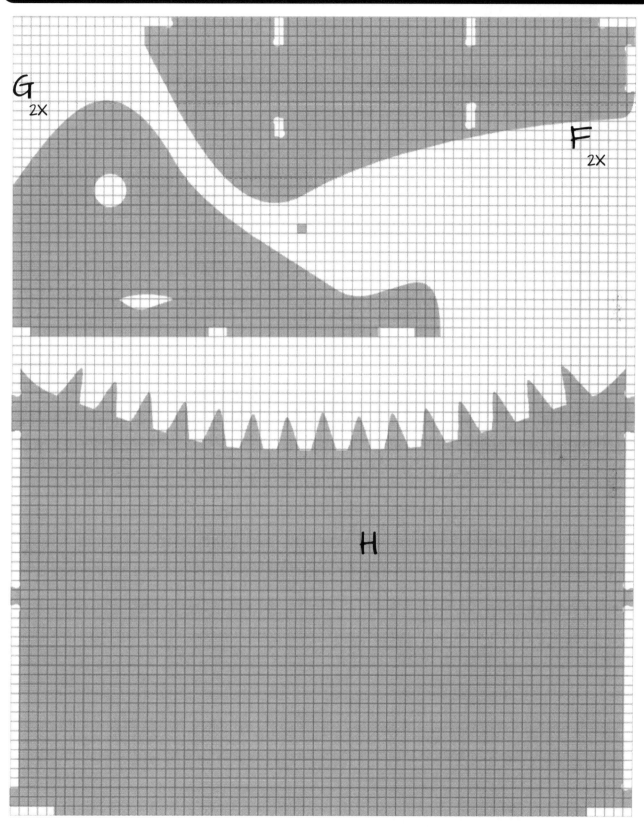

Step-by-Step Assembly Instructions

Step 1: Label and check inventory
Once you have all the pieces in front of you, the process of putting them together is no different from assembling pieces of Lego.

Label, using a pencil, the various parts and double-check your inventory. Take your time and enjoy the building process! Before jumping to the glue, be sure to do a dry run.

Step 2: Start with the base
Start by laying down part A, followed by glueing and sliding into place a part B (teeth) in the front followed by part C and D partitions towards the back.

Step 3: Build the lower jaw
On both sides, slide and glue into place a part E (lower jaw) followed by a part F (jaw peg). Allow the entire assembly to dry overnight.

Step 4: Perform some fishing touches
Slide on both sides a part G (upper jaw) on both sides and glue onto them a part H (upper teeth). While this part is drying, be sure to rotate the top so that it doesn't glue into place.

There is no need to apply any preservatives or paint; feel free to sand any sharp edges down. ENJOY!

Assembled 10 piece model dimensions:
L: 460 W: 350 H: 300 (mm)
L: 18-7/64 W: 13-25/32 H: 11-13/16 (in)

Material Thickness: 6 mm (1/4 inch)

Detailed Design Notes

After making my kangaroo shelving unit (found after this project in this book), I decided to salvage some parts of this project to make another one, a kangaroo laptop stand! I've been wanting to make this for a while for my own laptop which will hold it at an optimal viewing angle on my desk.

Step 1: Model Adaptation

As all my parts are already scaled to 6 mm, this saves me a lot of time - hence the salvaging process.

What I want to do here is make a reference box that's 30 cm by 40 cm as this represents the surface area I want to use for my laptop. This can be easily scaled up or down to fit your own laptop.

This is why keeping scraps of previous projects is important as you can use some of it to save time on other projects, whether it's for material testing with the CNC laser or seeing how much thickness is needed to fit within a specific customer spec.

By the time the stuff heads into the fire pit or the recycle bin, it's been well worn and used optimally across several projects!

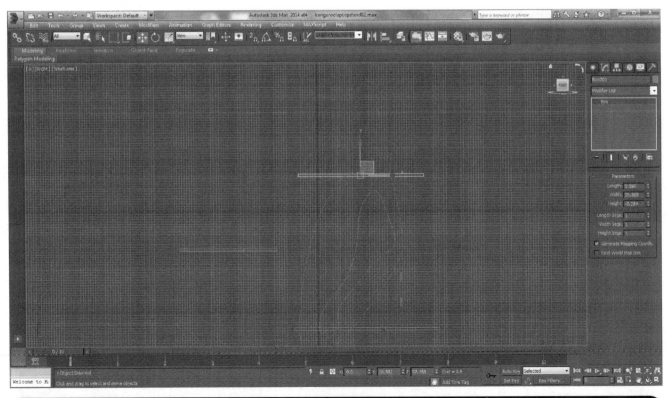

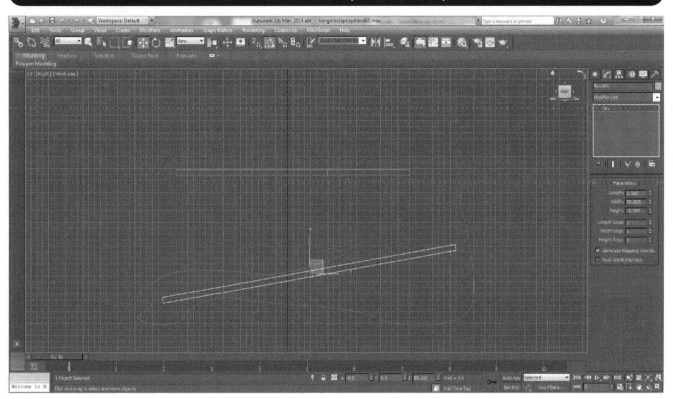

Step 2: Image top of this page

I had an arm that I merged using a boolean operation with the head to form the side of my laptop stand. I have kept a separate head as I want to have a little depth on this project visually speaking.

The advantage of having a large side is that it reduces glare and instills a little privacy when working in an office setting especially with such an attractive laptop stand!

Step 3: Image next page top

I have my reference length in the middle of the screenshot. I'm modifying the shelf with a smoother front than my kangaroo shelf and giving it two inserts into the sides instead of one in the middle as this will have a lot more weight (static and variable) than the shelf unit.

Step 4: Image next page bottom

Like the shelving unit, I want to double-up the sides so that I can hide where the boards intersect so I'm leaving a space between the head and arm assembly on purpose to remind myself later.

Now that my shelf is the correct width, I'm going to give it some holes to help dissipate heat from the laptop better and make it look a little cooler in the process.

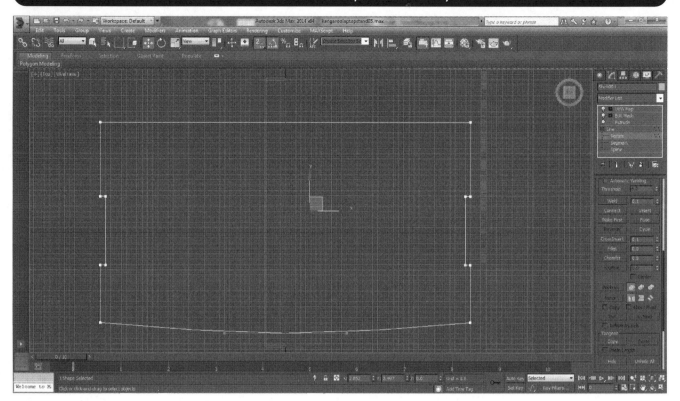

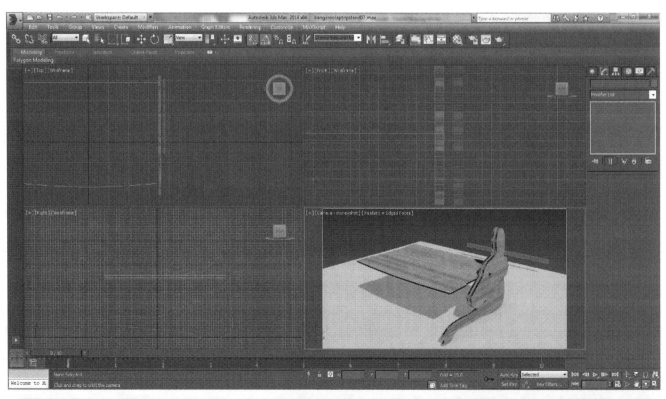

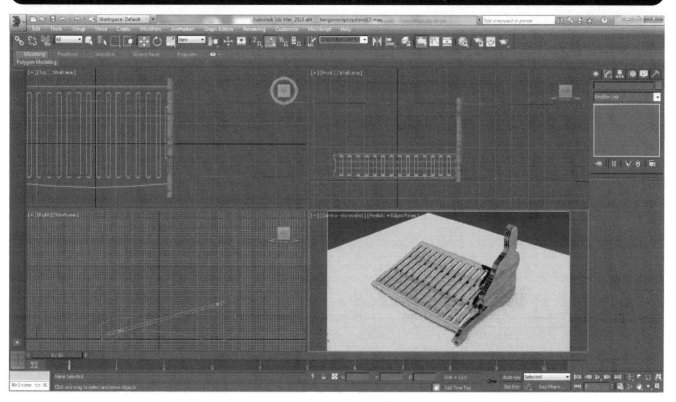

Step 5: Image top of this page

I've now angled the bed that will hold the laptop 15 degrees and made slight changes to the arm so that I will be able to completely hide the interlock behind a doubled-up set of arms - one with guide holes and the other without, like I made for my Kangaroo Shelves earlier.

Step 6: Image next page top

The model is looking great, I added cross sections underneath to keep the platform rigid as some laptops do have quite a bit of weight.

There is one problem with this model though, the laptop would slide down as there aren't any blocks in the front to prevent the laptop from sliding off.

Step 7: Image next page bottom

I added a large section out back to keep the kangaroo laptop stand square and made the platform symmetrical with peg holes to hold the laptop in place.

I need to add some pegs on the front to keep it from sagging over use.

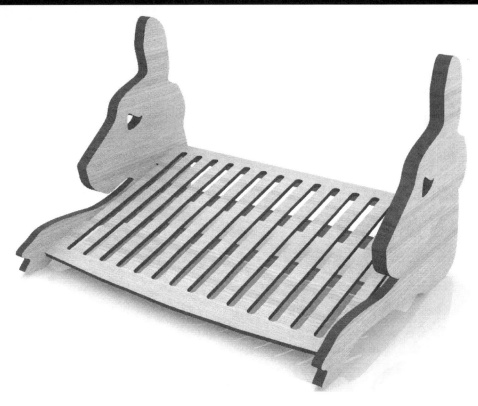

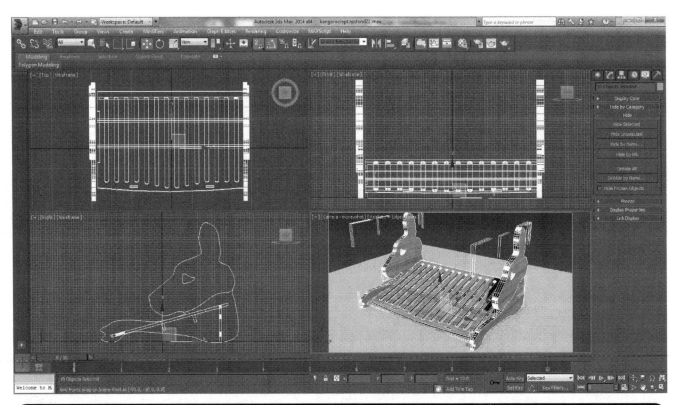

Step 8: Image top of this page

The pegs are supported from underneath with a piece of material going a good length of it, supporting the entire platform at the same time. They are also out of the way of your wrists when you type on the laptop, so just about any size laptop should fit fine on this.

Step 9: Image next page top

I exported the laptop stand and split it up into its component parts, converted into 2D splines to be exported into AI for further processing.

Step 10: Image next page bottom

I scaled my drawing perfectly and split up the parts across four 400 x 500 mm panels. The next step is saving this file and exporting it to PartWorks.

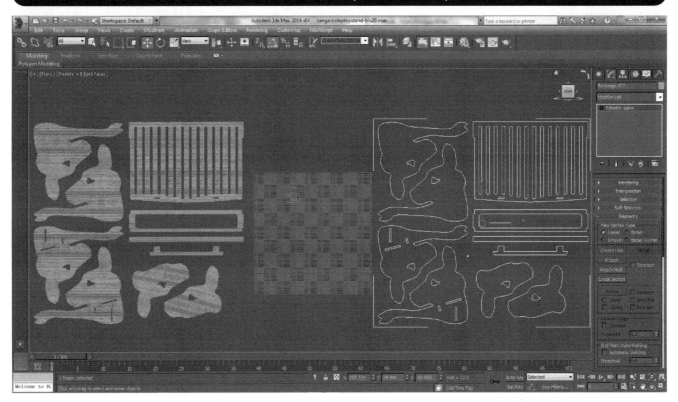

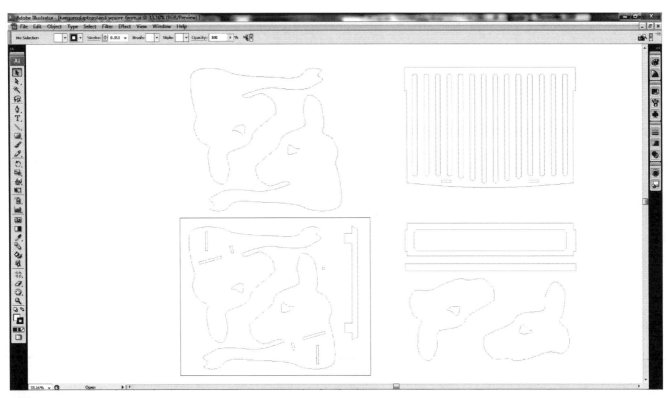

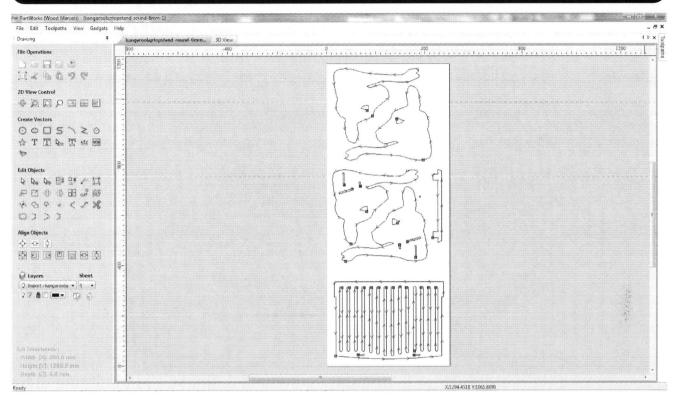

Step 11: Image top of this page

I really enjoy cutting sheets at length instead of smaller cut ones. Not only is it faster but I find it a more efficient way of working, so I'll do the same with this project.

The problem with tiling is that it's such a fun way to work, that going back to non-tiling methods feels like going backwards even if, in this case, it really isn't needed at all as none of my parts need to be tiled across multiple sheets.

I did all my tool pathing and exported the relevant files - next up cutting!

Product Renders

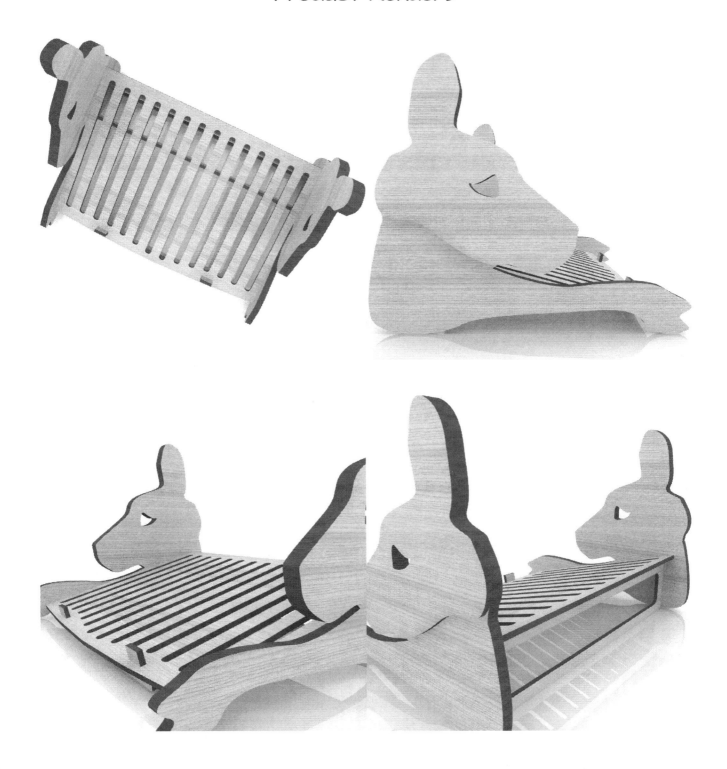

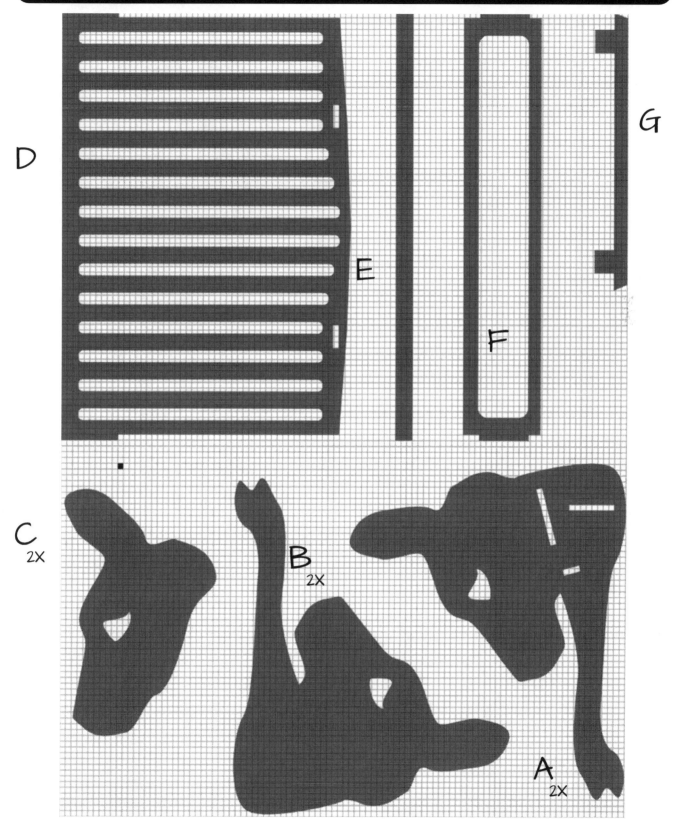

Step-by-Step Assembly Instructions

Step 1: Label and check inventory
Once you have all the pieces in front of you, the process of putting them together is no different from assembling pieces of Lego.

Label, using a pencil, the various parts and double-check your inventory. Take your time and enjoy the building process! Before jumping to the glue, be sure to do a dry run.

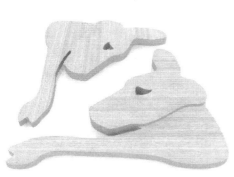

Step 2: Create side panels
Start by laying down a part A (holed body) followed by a part B (solid body) followed by a part C (head only) applying glue where the various surfaces meet.

Step 3: Complete the base
Slide and glue into place in between the two assembly you built in the previous step, parts D (laptop base), E (long peg) and F (square windowed peg).

Step 4: Perform some fishing touches
Slide and glue into place part G (laptop stop) in the front and let everything dry overnight.

There is no need to apply any preservatives or paint; feel free to sand any sharp edges down. ENJOY!

The Build Process

Building this model was very straight forward because it only had a few pieces and based off what I learned building the Kangaroo Shelf earlier. The pieces are far more manageable and I gave myself some extra tolerances with the pegs, so they slid in a little easier than with the shelf.

It's amazing how much of a difference an interlocking piece fits within another when you have an extra 0.5 mm of play!

As the weather here is much warmer, glue tends to flow very easily on pieces. So I've gotten into the habit of using far too many clamps rather than not enough to keep things together, even when it isn't necessary.

This model came out solid, and works very well. The extra room I gave myself worked out perfectly because I didn't envision having to use the USB/power cables for a laptop! Sometimes, the best design decisions just happen to work for other reasons as well!

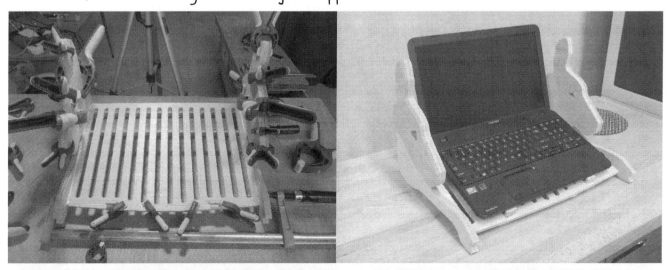

219

Assembled 70 piece model dimensions:
L: 296 W: 292 H: 296 (mm)
L: 11-21/32 W: 11-1/2 H: 11-21/32 (in)

Material Thickness: 6 mm (1/4 inch)

Summary Design Notes

Establish outline and scale
The first task is to establish the exact scale vertically of this kangaroo shelf. At the same time, I created two extra parts to give the model a bit more depth.

Adding horizontal limits
Although I could have made this shelf far wider, it would have required additional supports vertically and horizontally. To keep things in proportion, I limited myself to the maximum comfortable width I can cut with my CNC table router.

Adding shelves
Shelves are separated by about 180 mm, but this is very easy to modify. I built it in such a way that the bottom shelves are slotted into the kangaroo silhouette but hidden by the leg which helps with making something visually appealing.

Adding horizontal supports
The shelves would sag overtime unless I add horizontal supports going all the way across. I added two sets of these supports for each shelf to make sure that things remain strong over the long term.

Adding details
Small details like giving the head more depth by adding an extra one on both sides and locking the arms in place instead of making them swivel - an idea I was considering - help this shelf remain functional, yet easy to cut and assemble with a CNC laser or table router.

Detailed Design Notes

I've never designed a shelf here on CNCKing.com other than my first "Showcases" which appeared in my first two volumes. The reason is simple, they are easy to design so why bother teaching others how to make them? I happen to need some shelves through and what I find at the store is your typical boring shelf. So I thought, being in Australia when this design was in need, I'd design a Kangaroo shelf!

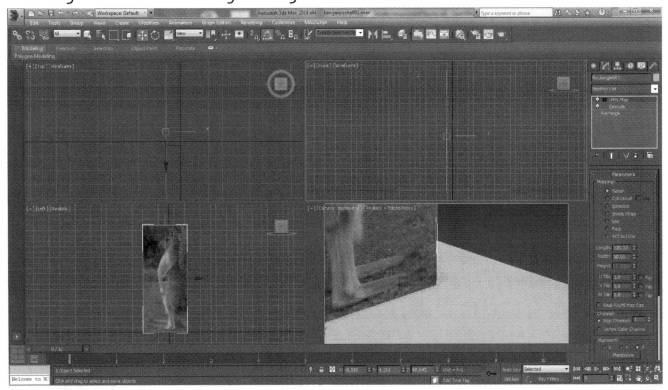

Model adaptation

Since I can't draw very well, I have to go online and look for a picture of a kangaroo standing that fits within my table router parameters which is 500 mm wide by 1200 mm high. After looking at a lot of pictures, I scaled one up to fit perfectly. Since a shelf is meant to go against a wall, the kangaroo is a perfect animal because I can cut off the back to be flat and the large feet in the front will keep it from tipping over.

I now have my kangaroo standing on a board that's exactly 500 mm x 1200 mm (the image size I made fits in with Photoshop) and then created a rectagle within 3DS Max of the same size, added the texture to the box. Tracing is now very easy. The grid is set-up to be 6 mm (each square in the screenshot is 6 cm) because I want to cut this with my table router using tiling.

My first tiling project was the Sydney Harbour Bridge and that was two tiles. This one will require three and I'll position it by eye because it went so well last time around.

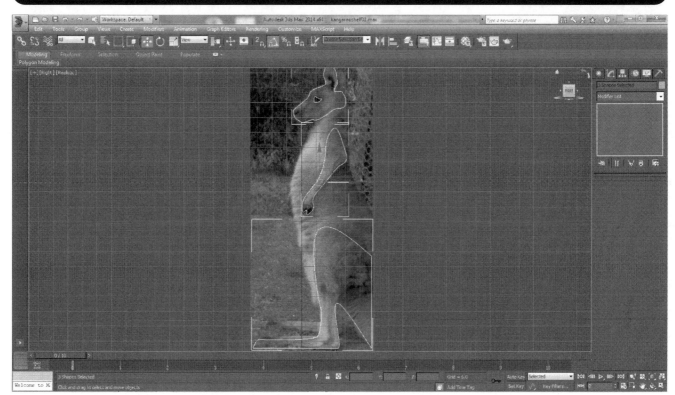

Step 1: Image top of this page

I want to make this shelf layered. Sure it takes longer to build, will require some extra guides and generally complicate the design for no real structural reason but it gives a model so much more depth.

I don't want just a silhouette of a kangaroo, I want it to have some depth as well though I'm keeping this at a minimum for easy assembly. Here I've built 2D splines, the first outer layer of the model, next step is outlining the entire kangaroo.

Step 2: Image next page top

Now that I have the entire kangaroo outlined - I added a bit more of a belly so I have a bit more storage space - I'm happy with everything so far. Keep in mind that this is a shelf. So I need to make my outlines perfect so that I have plenty of strength vertically to hold lots of things horizontally.

By adding this two-layers on each side, I've added some strength so that the shelf won't want to bend inwards if I put a little too many heavy items inside. I no longer need my reference picture, so that's gone.

Step 3: Image next page bottom

I've now extruded the model - looking great! I want my shelves to be 45 cm wide. So I have some good hold-down when table routing this design. So right now, I've just reflected what I've done and roughed-out the distance for the shelves.

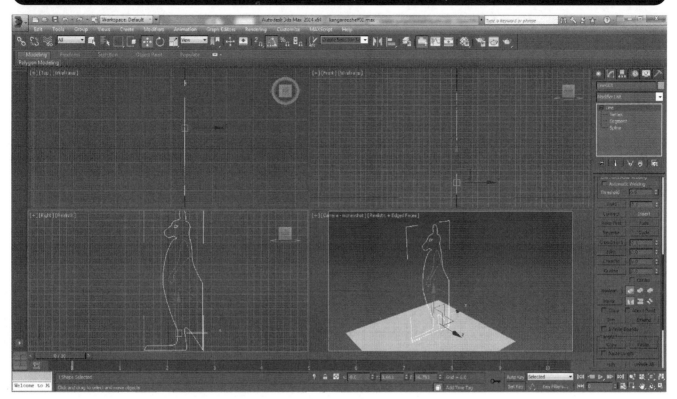

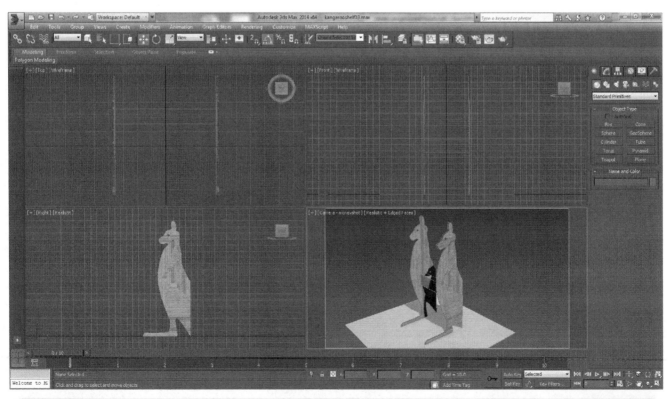

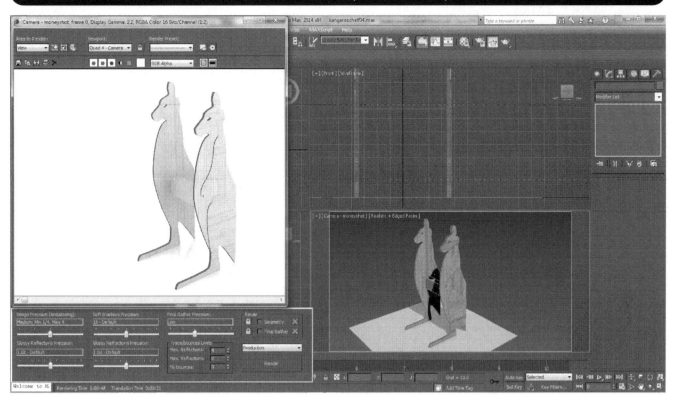

Step 4: Image top of this page
I have an ongoing concern about the vertical aspect of the shelf, so I double-up the entire kangaroo profile. So each side is now a solid 12 mm thick and I'll have the shelves going through both of them.

Of course, I will add vertical and horizonal shelves within the kangaroo, but I prefer to overbuild a model to have less problems down the road rather than underbuild them.

Doubling-up the kangaroo profile, for instance, will require a lot more work especially with tiling, but it's well worth it in my opnion.

Step 5: Image next page top
I want a strong base so that the first level of the kangaroo shelf to actually be on the floor. I've used the leg on the outside to hide the interlock I've created between the feet.

Step 6: Image next page bottom
I made each of my shelves about 18 cm high from the bottom up to follow the outline of the kangaroo with a bit of extra room on the upper head part. This raises another issue, putting things in shelves in the upper area may mean objects fall all the way through into the back, so I have to create some backstops to prevent this from happening.

You'll notice I rounded outer edges of the shelf to soften the look to match the animal.

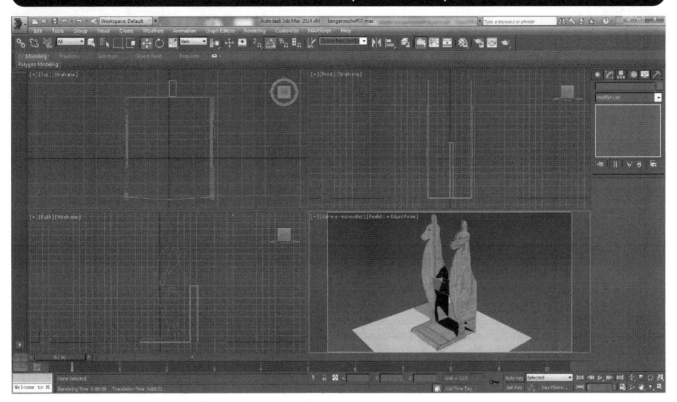

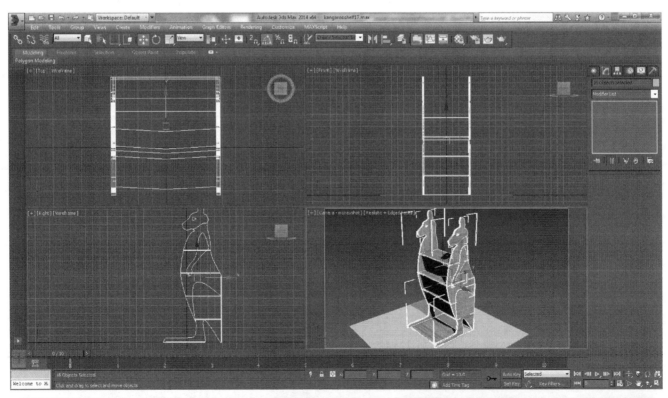

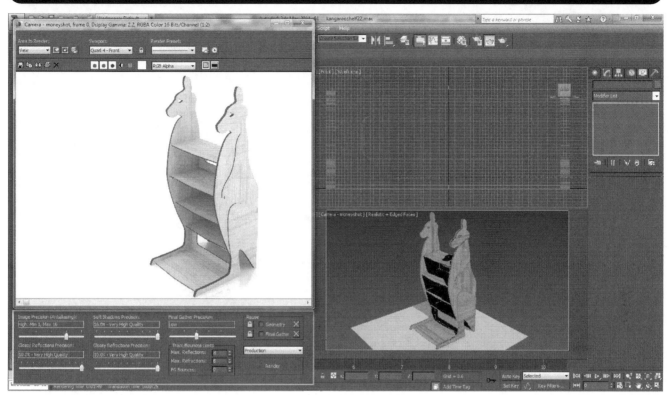

Step 6: Image top of this page

Now the shelves are supported on three edges so they can easily hold some weight and have stops at all levels except for the top where larger and flat items are more likely to be placed.

I converted the second from the bottom shelf to slide into place unlike the others which will be static because I want to add a hidden area in the tail section - it isn't a large area but most things worth hiding aren't that big to begin with, like diamond rings and cash. There is also one secret hiding spot in the back.

Step 7: Image next page top

I've fixed the shelves across the board to only go through one of the doubled-up kangaroo profiles so that they aren't seen protruding from the edge. The shelves also extrude "rounded' outwards from the profile by 12 mm to give this a bit more depth and smoothing lines of the project further. I'll now do a final review of the model to make sure the smaller pieces of this model fit within my 400 x 500 mm tolerances because I don't want to have tile parts just because I'm a few mm too large.

Step 8: Image next page bottom

I added two rows of under-shelves support in order to give them a bit more strength as they do extend almost 450 mm. Although these may not be needed, I might as well add them now rather than have issues later down the road which could have been easily avoided. Only thing I have left to do is creating all the tabs inside of the profiles for the shelves now that those issues are all resolved.

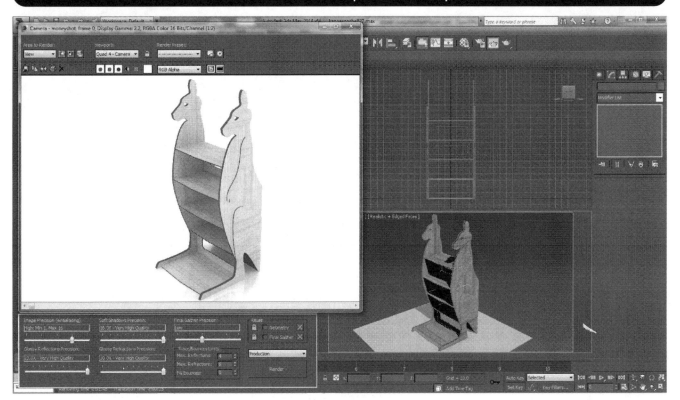

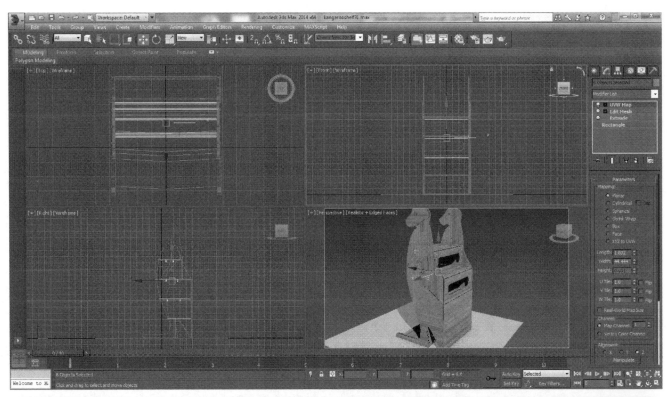

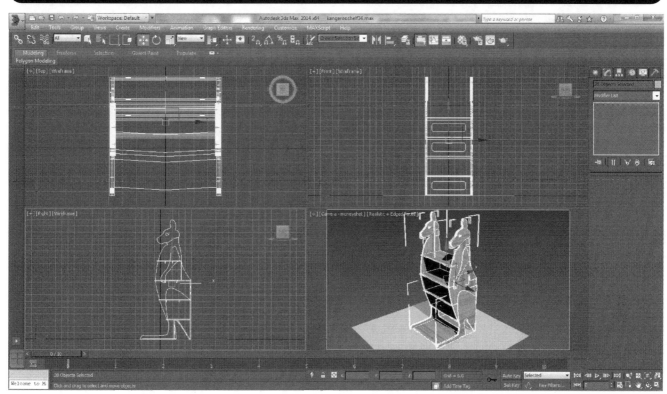

Step 9: Image top of this page
Everything looks good! I'm now going to generate the cutting files next, but first, I need to group all the parts and bring them into another file to separate all the parts from one another.

Step 10: Image next page top
After separating the individual parts, I get rid of the extrusion and end up with all my outlines which will be converted into toolpaths within PartWorks.

Step 11: Image next page bottom
As these files are rather large. I've separararated them into their rough cutting area so that when I export them, I know which files to duplicate and which not to. To save time, I'm going to try to use tiling for the entire project because it saves me from having to do two cross-cuts for each sheet.

This is why having a full-sheet router would be a dream because I could organize my parts across a far larger surface area. In all, this projec takes the equivalent of 21 sheets at 400 x 500 mm!

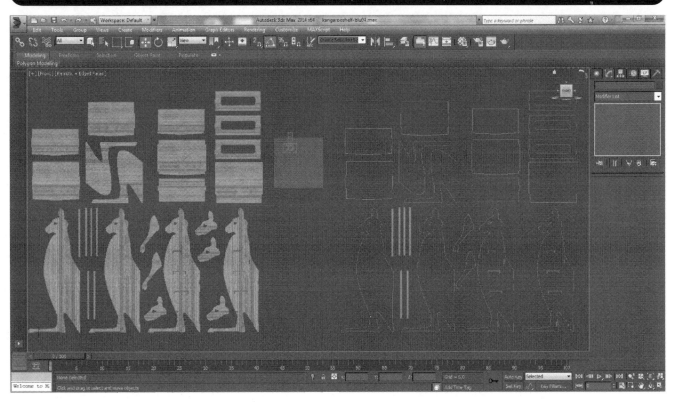

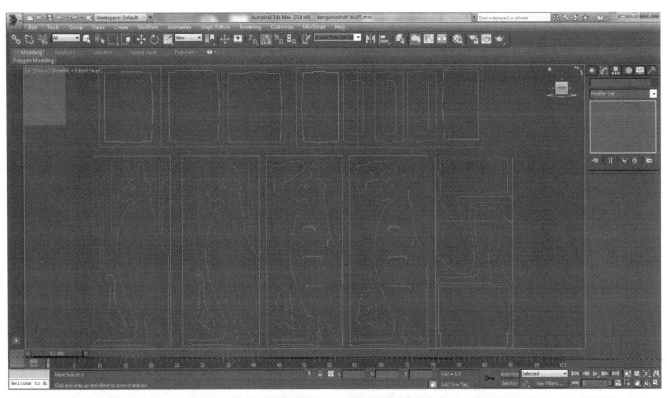

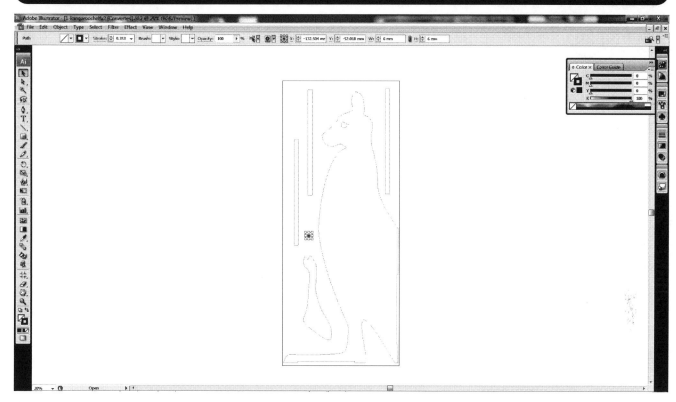

Step 12: Image top of this page

Once I scaled down my drawing so that the square I made in reference in my 3DS Max file down represent 6 mm, I know my drawing is perfect. I'll do the same for the other sheets, then export this into PartWorks.

Step 13: Image next page top

Tiling saves an incredible amount of time, but it also creates a headache because I have to stop, reposition the board, then cut the next tile. The issue with this is that each time I do this, I introduce a new area of potential error in my finished model since I place everything by eye.

These kangaroo silhouettes also barely fit on the board, so I'll have to pay special attention to my workflow for this project by probably cutting my board to be wider than 500 mm just so I have extra room on the sides to keep all the pieces together during the cutting process.

Another issue is for some of these tiles, I really don't have as much hold down as I'd like... tricky!

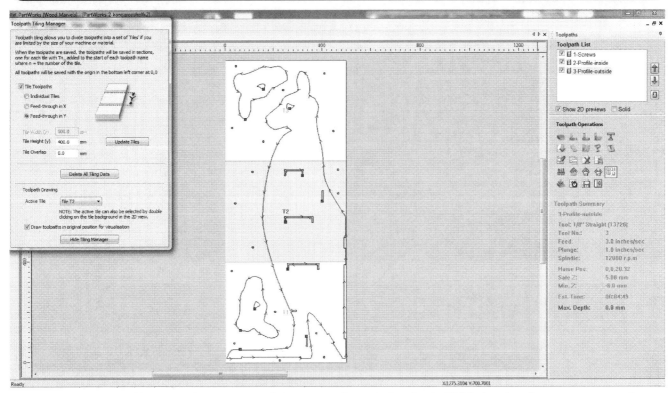

The challenge with these bigger models regardless of what CNC technology you use to cut them out with, is that you need room to store all the pieces and plenty of room around them when it comes to assembling.

Like the issue I had with my Wooden Big Wheels (in this book as well), you quickly realize the importance of space to turn things around and clamps of various sizes. This model was pretty straight forward because I tend to design things to use as few pieces (unique ones at that!) as possible.

Nothing worse than trying to assemble a project where pieces look like one another except for a slight variance in size or shape.

For this model, I could have made it far larger, but I wanted to limit the amount of "tiles" I used for this project, similar to my Wooden Big Wheels (CNC router version). For proof of concept though, making this at half scale would have been a breeze with either CNC platform.

Although my Trotec Speedy 400 flexx isn't a "full sheet" machine, my next CNC router will be, projects like this appreciate the freedom and ease of use that comes with having such a large platform to design for and cut onto. Same goes with plasma and other technologies out there, the bigger the platform, the easier a project becomes to turn into reality and the more efficient the whole project becomes.

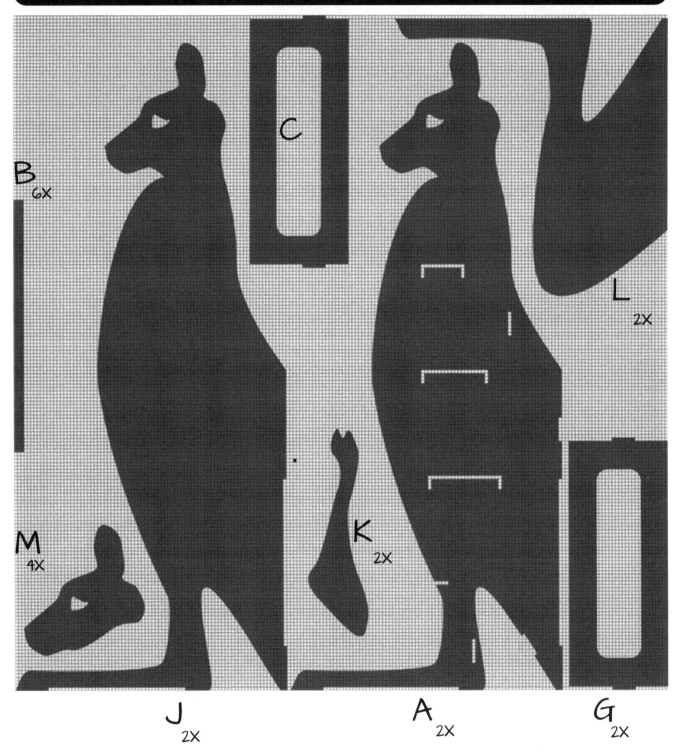

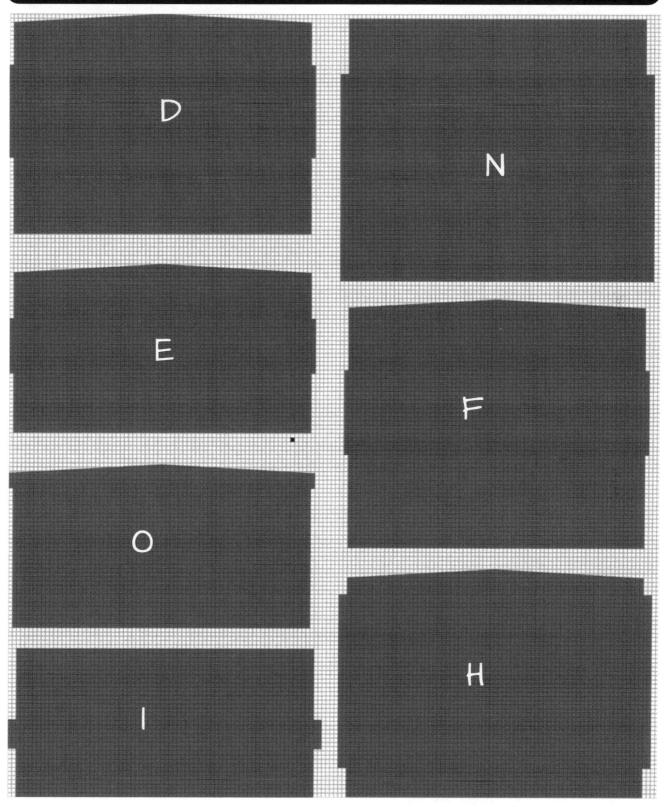

Step-by-Step Assembly Instructions

Step 1: Label and check inventory

Once you have all the pieces in front of you, the process of putting them together is no different from assembling pieces of Lego.

Label, using a pencil, the various parts and double-check your inventory. Take your time and enjoy the building process! Before jumping to the glue, be sure to do a dry run.

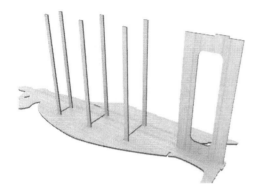

Step 2: Add supports

Start by laying down a part A (kangaroo silhouette with holes) followed by six parts B (shelf supports) followed by a part C into the back of the foot. Apply glue where all these parts intersect.

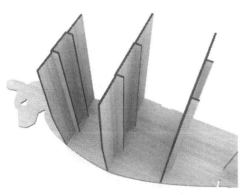

Step 3: Add shelves

Slide and glue into place parts D, E and F (shelves). The shelf at the feet comes out to reveal a hidden area in the tail, so that will be only slid in without glue at the end of the assembly process.

Step 4: Create shelve stops

There is nothing worse than putting things in shelves and having them fall in the back to never be seen again. This is why I designed stops to prevent this from happening in the back.

Slide and glue into place parts G (stops) followed by another part A on the top. Allow this to dry overnight so that you can easily stand it to continue the build process.

Step 5: Start the base
Slide and glue into place a part H (foot plate) between the feet and part I (back cap) in the tail section.

Step 6: Add arms and legs
Onto both sides, slide and glue into place parts J (kangaroo silhouette no holes) followed by a part K (arms) and L (hind legs).

Step 7: Add heads and backing
Slide and glue into place on the head all four parts M (heads) on both sides of the silhouettes while on the base part N (large stop) with clamps will make sure nothing falls behind while creating a safe hidden area in the tail section.

Step 8: Perform some fishing touches
You can now slide into place without glue, part O (shelf). There is no need to apply any preservatives or paint; feel free to sand any sharp edges down. ENJOY!

Build Lessons

I learned quite a bit from this project both designing and assembling it, the biggest is that I got tiling down. It's just amazing how I was able to accurately make something so big - the equivalent of 21 x 400 x 500 mm sheets (or two full sheets 1 200 x 600 mm).

I used MDF for this build and that's the first and last time I use this awful material with my CNC router! It's great for inducing headaches (I had one for 3 days!) and just makes dust everywhere compared to the typical marine plywood I use for my projects. I will say that it does sand very well and cuts very clean but this overpriced cardboard has no room in my future builds.

Other than the MDF headache, the build went very well. It's surprisingly strong considering how weak MDF is for structure (I'm using 6 mm) but that's, thanks to my supports, not the material itself. I used a lot of clamps while this was glueing and some parts moved a bit on me while drying... something I have to keep an eye out!

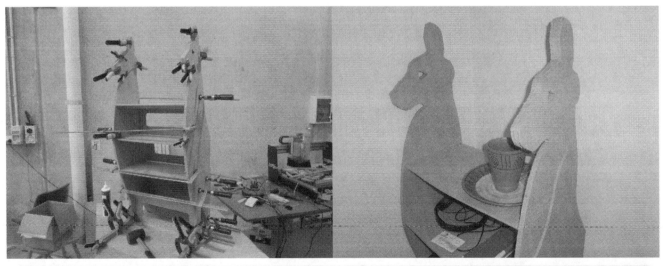

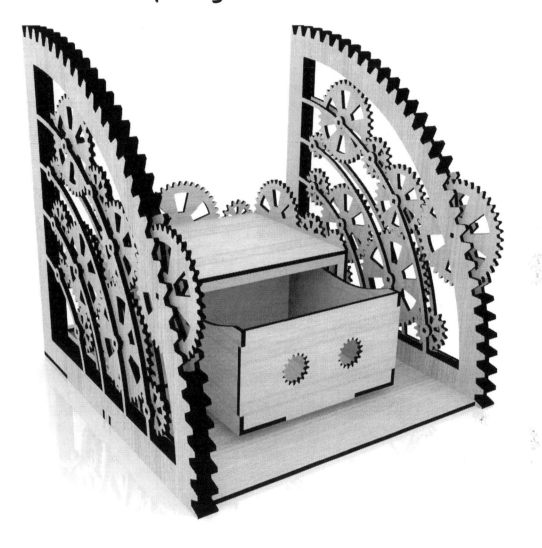

Assembled 70 piece model dimensions:
L: 296 W: 292 H: 296 (mm)
L: 11-21/32 W: 11-1/2 H: 11-21/32 (in)

Material Thickness: 4 mm (1/8 inch)

Summary Design Notes

Establish gear sizes

As this design was to originally use the same platform I established for the Croc Head Organizer, the next thing I had to establish are the gear ratios that this design was to have without any other distractions getting in the way.

Adding vertical gears

I wanted to make the gears stand-out from the rest of the model and, having them hidden on the side of a box, just didn't interest me very much. So I got the idea of putting the gears inside a massive gear which doubled as a side panel.

Add gear supports

The next challenge I had to contend with was how to hold the gears in place. After some playing around, I decided upon a thin arc strip with a hole for the gear knob to hold them in place. I also added an additional gear at the top that protruded from the large side gear to make spinning them an easy process.

Adding a drawer

After working out the angles and spinning ratios of the gears, it was time to build a drawer in between them. This box is the outline of what I had in mind.

Adding details

I now have a working drawer with a built-in stop, meaning that once it was built and glue into place, there is no way it can ever come OUT of the box holding it.

I added some additional gear fringes on the box itself to add a bit more visuals.

Detailed Design Notes

This design came about after designing the simpler Croc Head Organizer. I was thinking of using many of the same elements developed on that project and incorporating some gears and some additional personalization. It failed miserably.

Model adaptation

Adapting one design to fit that of another just doesn't seem to work well for me, the results are usually less than spectacular even in the best of circumstances. The problem I think comes about due to legacy visions for a model. I actually designed this gear box FIRST on paper, but got inspired with the Croc Head Organizer and followed that through to completion but then, I went back to this box and nothing looked good.

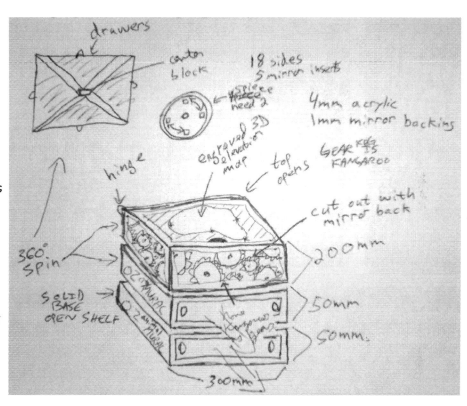

241

I was trying everything possible to make this gear box look presentable, adding engravings, staggering the gears then and adding vertical and horizontal elements. The more I tried to make something nice, the worse it looked. It was just ugly and I had lost my initial vision for this model even with the sketch. It was as if I was driving down a smooth paved road and all of a sudden, it became gravel full of potholes.

At this point, I knew from experience that the best thing I could do was completely rethink this model. I began to think of how I could IMPROVE this model but how I would have built it if I were to start from scratch. The idea of having working gears was a must-have for me, but then began to think of ways of incorporating gears within gears.

At first, I was toying with ideas of a floating gear in the middle of a larger gear, but I had to have this box fit within a 30 cm cube space and the gears would have had to be too small, and building it would have been challenging in the real world.

I then got the bright idea of simply using a quarter of a large gear and putting little ones inside. Figuring-out all the gear details wasn't much fun, but I got a working model virtually that made sense and moved properly.

The reason for the massive quarter gear was to allow me the opportunity to create both a strong structure on both sides of the box and, most importantly, provide something visually stimulating that really stood out but at the same time, allowed for plenty of room for internal play of the different gear ratios.

Holding the various gears in place using strong yet thin arcs allowed me to offer them being held in space in a way that made sense and allowed plenty of room for the gears.

I wanted the user to see the gears through the support - they needed to be minimal.

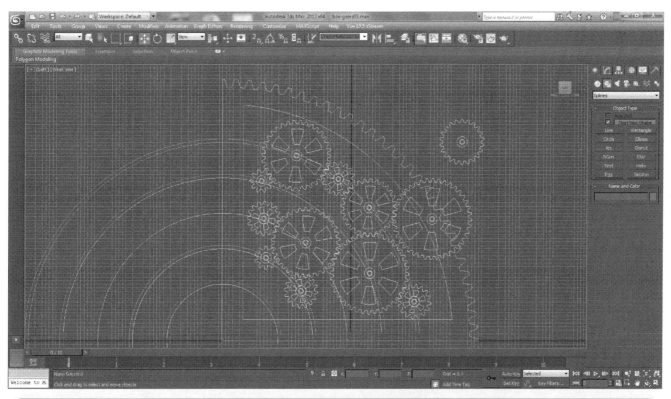

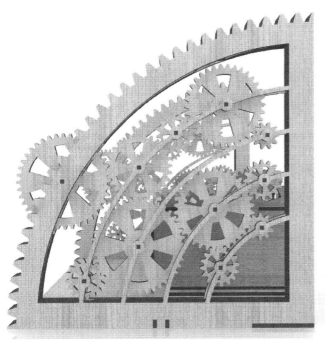

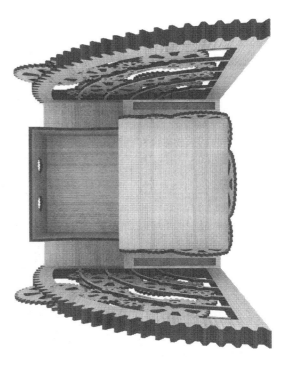

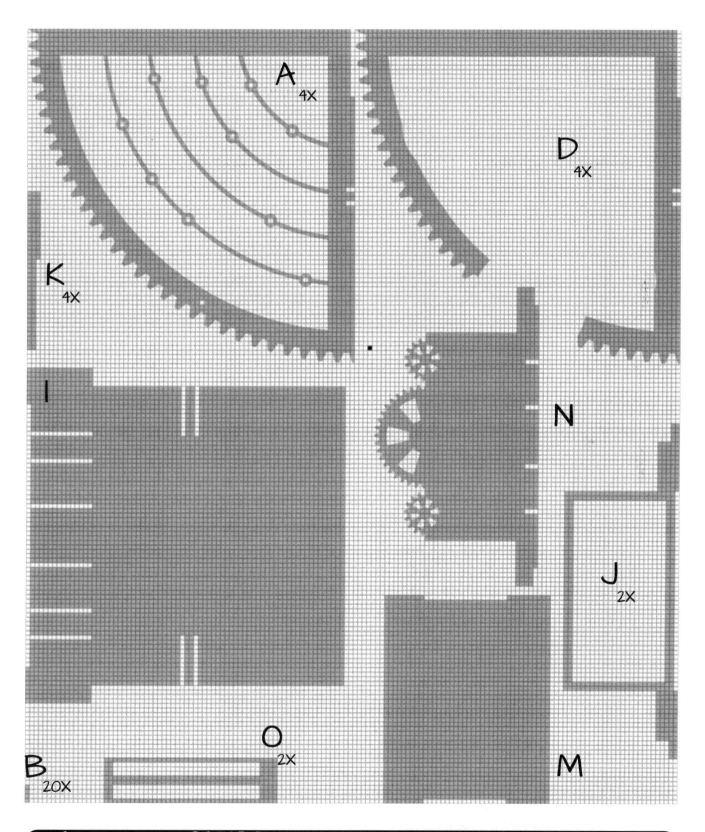

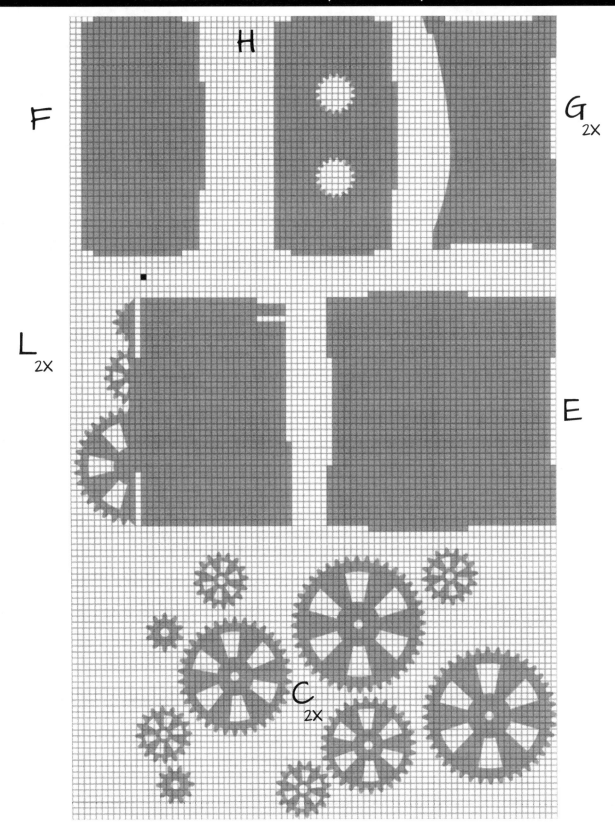

Step-by-Step Assembly Instructions

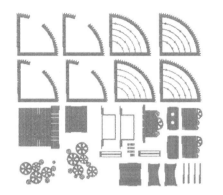

Step 1: Label and check inventory

Once you have all the pieces in front of you, the process of putting them together is no different from assembling pieces of Lego.

Label, using a pencil, the various parts and double-check your inventory. Take your time and enjoy the building process! Before jumping to the glue, be sure to do a dry run.

Step 2: Add gears to a side panel

Start by laying down a part A (full quarter gear) followed by ten parts B (pegs) followed by a part C (gear assembly). Only glue the pegs in place.

Step 3: Complete the side panel

Slide and glue into place two parts D (cut quarter gear) followed by another part A to cap. While the glue is drying, be sure to rotate the gears every once in a while to make sure that the gears don't glue to the entire assembly.

Allow to dry overnight.

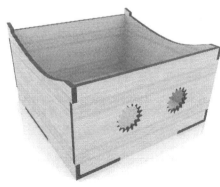

Step 4: Create the drawer

We need to glue the drawer together before inserting it into the model to make sure it can easily move once the rest of the model dries as it will be locked-in.

With a part E on the ground, slide and glue a part F in the back, both parts G on the side capped with a part H in the front.

Allow to dry overnight.

Step-by-Step Assembly Instructions

Step 5: Start the base
Slide and glue into place a part I (base) with part J (open drawer guides) with the assembly you made within step 3 on both sides.

Step 6: Add drawer details
Onto the base, slide and glue into place all four parts K (drawer guides) followed by an assembly made-up by both parts L (drawer sides) and a part M (drawer roof).

Allow to dry overnight.

Step 7: Lock the drawer in place
The drawer on purpose cannot slide completely out from the back, so it must be slid in through the back followed by a part N (backing) followed by a part O (slotted caps) on both sides in between the gear and drawer assembly.

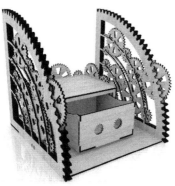

Step 8: Perform some fishing touches
There is no need to apply any preservatives or paint; feel free to sand any sharp edges down. ENJOY!

Assembled 11 piece model dimensions:
L: 296 W: 296 H: 308 (mm)
L: 11-21/32 W: 11-21/32 H: 12-1/8 (in)

Material Thickness: 4 mm (1/8 inch)

Originally designed in WoodMarvels.com Volume 3: Evolution of Wooden Designs and expanded upon in CNCKing.com Volume 4: Rise of the CNC ~ Ultimate CNC Design Course.

Detailed Design Notes

I've used my laser cutter texture for the CNC table router version of this model as it can be made just as easily with one but, more importantly, provide additional contrast for this model as it has lots of details that may be hard to see otherwise.

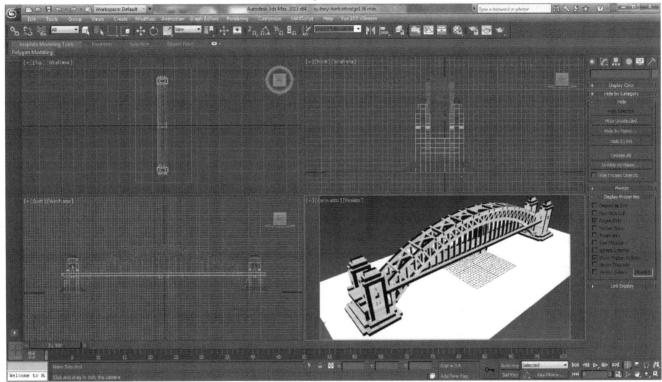

Step 1: Image top of this page

Although this model is going to be optimized for a table router (though you can laser cut any router model), I'm kepping the contrasting texture to help isolate problems that will happen during this design conversion process. Every aspect of this model will require some modifications and the more "help" and "pointers" to help isolate issues that may come-up with a table router, the better the final design will be.

Step 2: Image next page top

The first issue is resolving the biggest piece of the model first as that will present the biggest challenge since my surface isn't large enough to begin with. I have a total width (length in this case) of 48 cm, I can't exceed roughly 80 cm using 6 mm. Rather than rebuilding the entire model from scratch, I'll change thickness of that 48 mm from 6 mm to 4 mm, then scale it back up to 6 mm within illustrator. As such, 4 ---> 6 mm is a difference of 150 percent.

So, 48 cm x 150 percent = 72 cm with a height of 12 x 150 percent = 18 cm. This works out great because it means I can cut two spans at once since my maximum width (height of the model) is 50cm... this gives me plenty of space and hold-down possibilities.

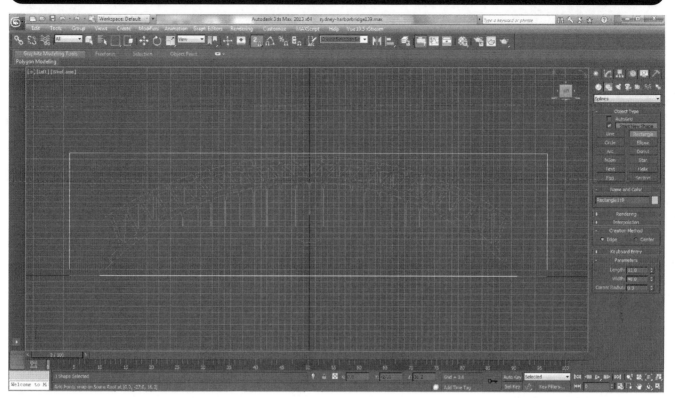

Step 3: Image next page top

As this model will be very long and built out of plywood, I want to make it extra strong. So the first thing I did here was remind myself that I want to double-up on the spans and change my grid parameters from 6 mm to 4 mm so references are easier to sort-out before going too deep into the design.

Step 4: Image next page bottom

This model is NOT CNC router friendly, it's borderline for lasers (in focus) but for a router that's ripping and pushing through material, these little strings of material are going to be ripped apart. The solution is simple, make them thicker and increase the amount of tolerance throughout the pieces.

One thing I can't help is the sharp inner corners, as a router uses a round bit, those will be rounded and adding dog bones would look horrible. Each square in the picture represents 4 mm and as you can see, the bridge supports are 2 mm.

When this design is increased by 150 percent (4 mm to 6 mm) that would make it 3 mm. Still too thin. As such, I'm going to increase them to 4 mm (which would be 6 mm once scaled).

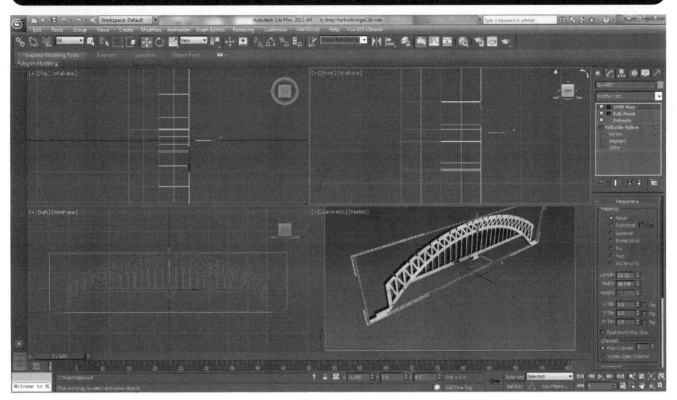

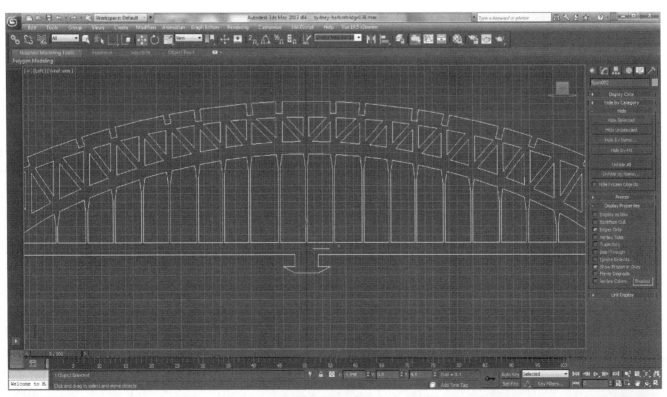

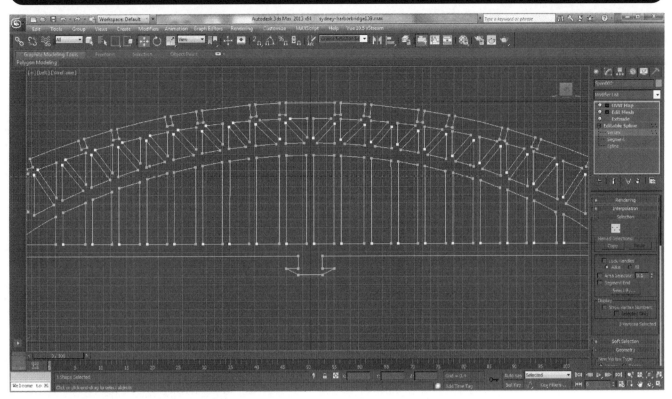

Step 5: Image top of this page

That's looking far better, now I need to fix-up the top. Because all of these inner shapes will be rounded, I'm not too concerned if they are close to one another on the middle part because that will be automatically steamlined by the router but the very top is a problem. If I add dog bones there, it will go through the lower holes so that needs to be brought-up. I also removed a few extra nodes on my mesh - something I've started to do since this model was originally designed.

Step 6: Image next page top

I've increased the height of the bridge and extended the sides to be slightly thicker just to make sure I have some extra stength built-into the model to lessen the possibility of it breaking apart during the routing process. The more tolerances you build into your model NOW the smoother things will go later.

Step 7: Image next page bottom

As I design all my models based on material thickness, these kind of thickness issues will reak havoc on the final design if I don't catch all of them. Although I work in a 3D environment, it's really 2D extruded to the material thickness. In this picture, you see a major problem.

If I layer a piece over the bottom step that's 4 mm (squares help for sizing), I will have 2 mm sticking out and intersecting the piece above it. Solution? Bring it down to 4 mm and review the model closely to catch all of these.

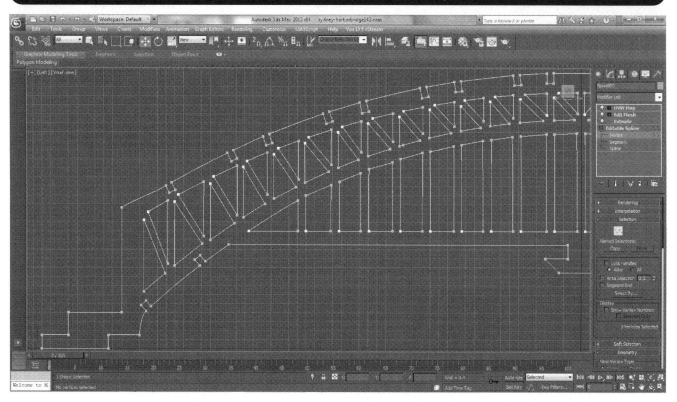

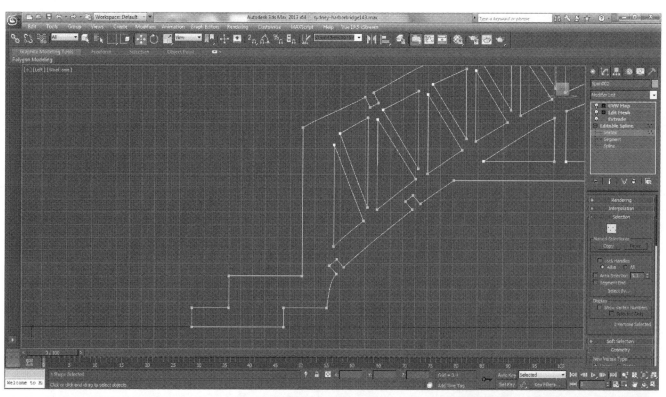

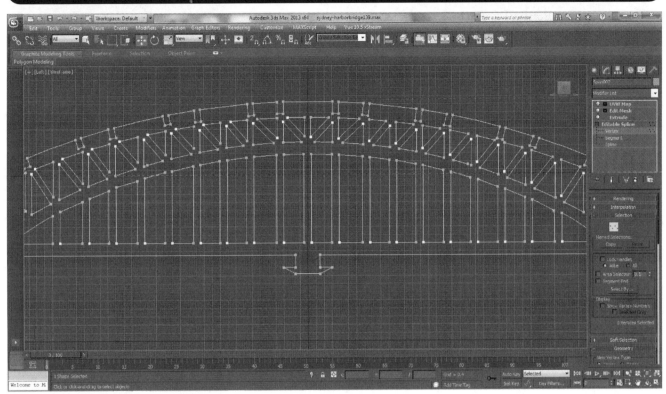

Step 8: Image top of this page

The model will already be highly modified simply due to the span doubling, but throw-in a 150 percent increase in size using the same material thickness and, what may "appear" easy and straight forward, has a lot of issues that could derail it in the real world. I went through TONNES of these issues with my earlier models, so I know what to watch-out for, but soemtimes they can be hard to spot until you cut the model out and build it in the real world for the first time.

As I've doubled the spans, I had to make adjustments to the road that goes between them in order to have it at the right width. I also further streamlined the spans themselves to give additional tolerances for a CNC table router.

Step 9: Image next page top

Here is one of many legacy issues I'll have to resolve digitally before fabricating the model. As you see, there is an overlap of the squares that are used in the middle of the bridge span to hold-up the road. There are two problems here, one is the overlap but, more importantly, the parts need to be made 4 mm instead of 6 mm as you see in the picture.

This is why it's vital that I created a grid that represented material thickness as otherwise, I wouldn't have noticed that the issue here is really thickness related more than positional. I also need to make some slight changes to the spans so that the bottom matches the grid pattern I've established in order to avoid potential issues with both sides of the bridge.

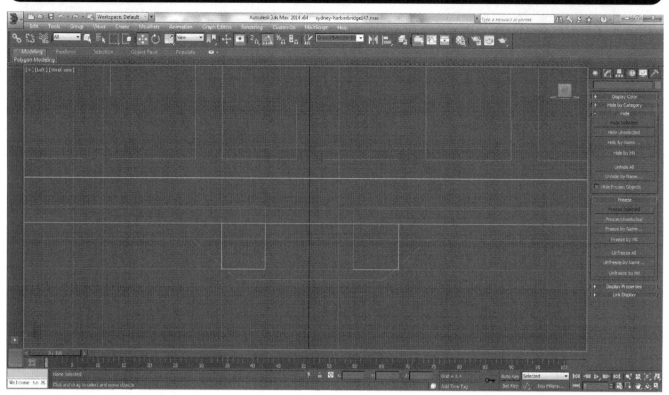

Step 10: Image next page top
Now everything fits perfectly within my grid pattern. You'll notice the top holes in the span don't match it. This doesn't matter as there are no intersecting parts to deal with, but I also increased the distance between the bottom of the span and the top where the holes begin in order to give additional strength to the model.

Each hole that's made weakens the model. I want as much wood as possible on the bottom as that's where the stress will be most shown.

Step 11: Image next page bottom
Now that I have the spans and roads / sidewalks sorted out, the next step is to work on the ramps on either side of the bridge. In order to save a tremendous amount of time, I deleted one side completely which I'll then mirror onto the other side.

This means I only have to edit ONE side to get it to work perfectly instead of going back and forth one side of the other which would only increase error.

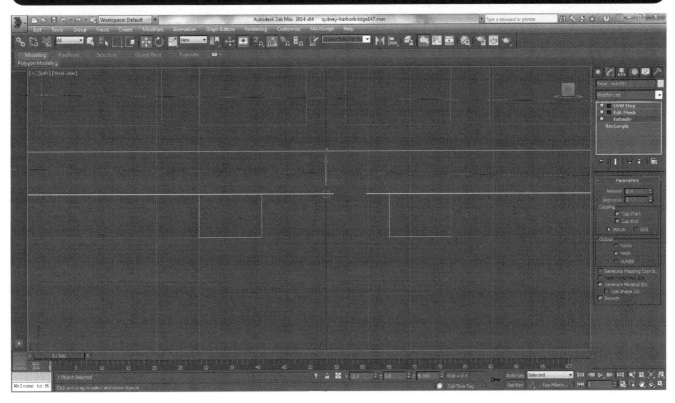

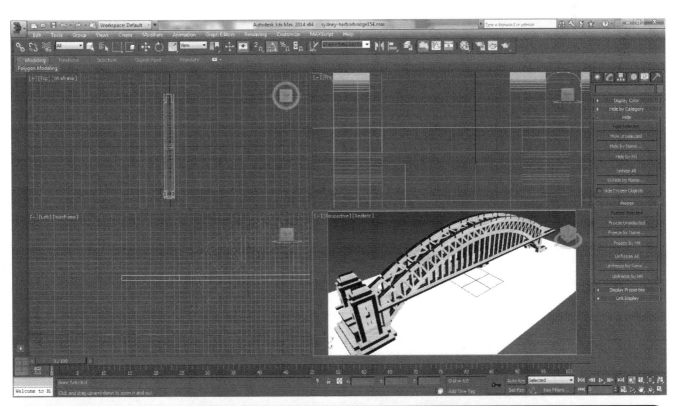

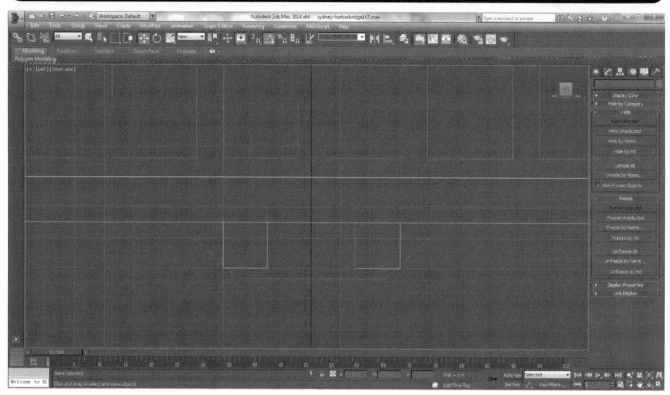

Step 12: Image top of this page

As you can see, most of the parts, after they are made 4 mm instead of 6 mm, fall out of my new grid format. If I didn't have this grid established early, it would be almost impossible to get everything fitting perfectly again as, in all three dimensions, I need to modify the parts to fit back together in a tight and working order. Since this is the first time I look at the model in this orientation, it also becomes clear that it's no longer centered (see black center line). To make my job easier from here on out, I'll have to move the entire bridge to the new center point - the reason is simple, it's easier to see symetry when you have equal parts on each side.

Step 13: Image next page top

Now we see a big problem that wasn't apparent previously: the spans aren't symmetrical with the road. This most likely occured when I doubled the spans, I must have doubled one on the inside and the other on the outside. Without centering the model, I probably wouldn't have realized this until far later in the redesign of this project. This may look trivial, but when you consider, this means the road isn't symetrical nor would the interlocks coming from the spans into the towers on either side, a tremendous amount of time has been saved already! I want the spans to be dead-on the grid at all angles - it's far easier to modify this now.

Step 14: Image next page bottom

Now that the entire bridge is symetrical onto a center point, the rest of the model will be far easier to modify correctly.

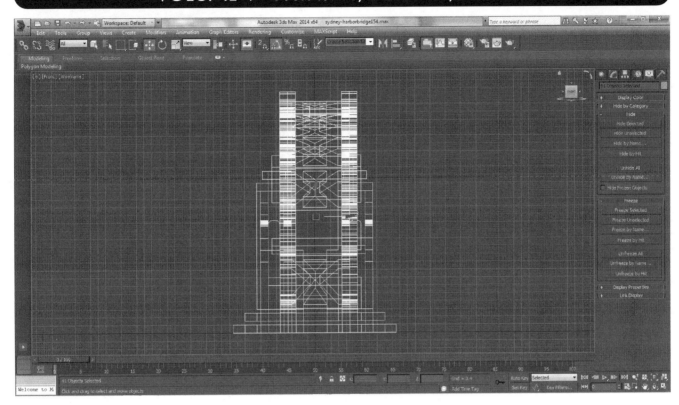

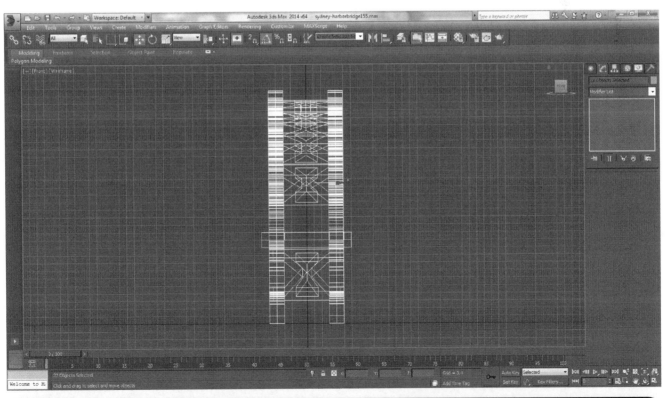

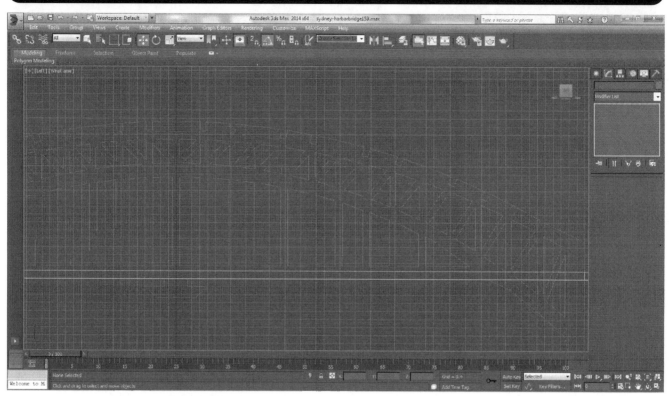

Step 15: Image top of this page.
Another point of contention that I have to deal with is the fact that the cross members are going all the way along the top of the double spans. Making them thinner (6 mm to 4 mm thick).

Step 16: Image next page top
Unlike the original model, I made both the front and back of the tower the same. This model was designed a long time ago and since then, I've learned that the more pieces I can have that are the same, the easier the cutting and assembly process is.

Although I could mark the pieces so they stood out, having two pieces that look "similar" isn't much fun when you have a pile of 50 pieces looking at being assembled.

Step 17: Image next page bottom
Looking at the tower, there are still lots of issues to resolve, as this is to be made with a CNC router, I built into the model lots of additional tolerances and also made the bridge wider in order to make the entire model all the more sturdy.

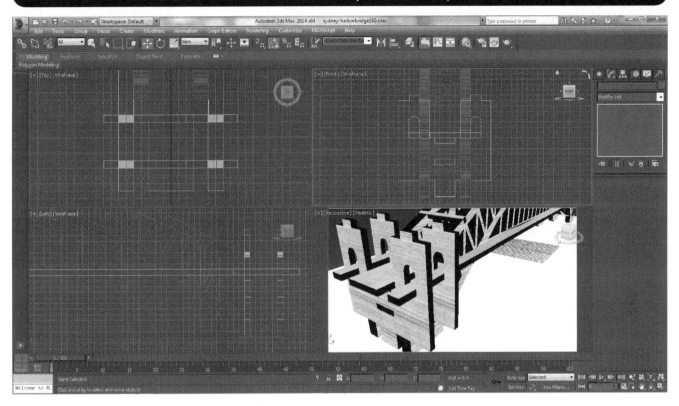

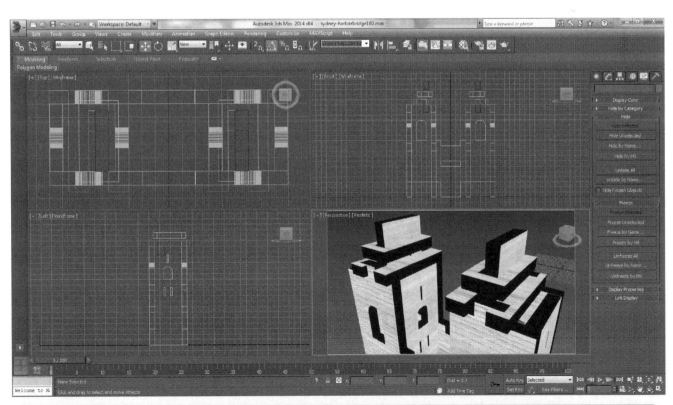

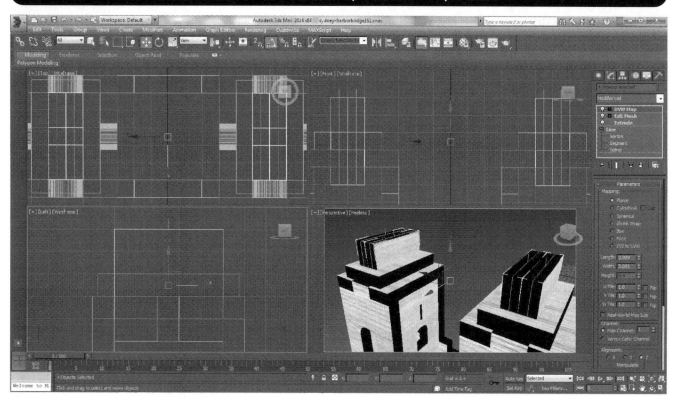

Step 18: Image top of this page

Now that all the top parts are aligned to my grid, I know that it will work when finally assembled. The tricky part of redesigning a model digitally to a different scalable material size is the endless small changes that need to be made in order to have a completed project come together in the right way once individual parts are locked together to form larger pieces.

Step 19: Image next page top

What you see here is impossible in the real world; the long side of the tower goes right through into one of the double spans - you can't have two objects occupy the same space except in the virtual world.

There are three obvious solutions to solve this. One is to move the spans out of the way by either making the road wider or thinner (affecting total span width), but that would require extensive renovations to the span cross-sections and cause other issues in the tower itself.

Another option is to have the intersecting span (only the inner span is affected) cut short to give room for the side, but that would cause stability issues that I'd have to deal with later or, the simplest choice, cut the side panel down.

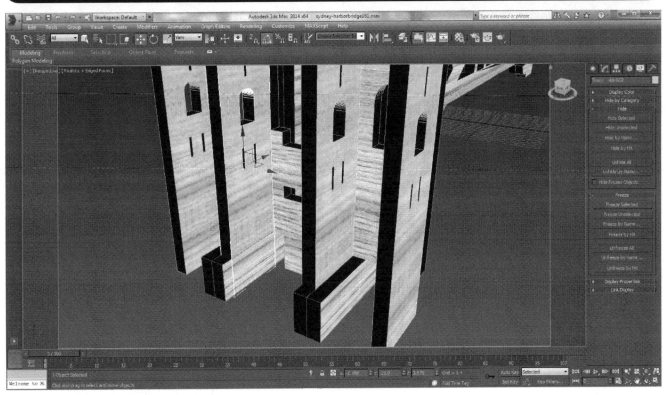

Step 20: Image next page top
I went with the third option, I've found that the simpler way is usually the best way. Now that this is resolved and I have the spans going through the towers along with the roads and sidewalks. I can sort out the issues at the foundation of the bridge which will be extensive as each of the parts you see in the picture will need to fit into the base securely.

Step 21: Image next page bottom
What I like to do for more complex models is to remove their textures so that any issues are easier to notice. In this case, the two base plates needed far too many changes. So it was quicker to just rebuild them from scratch to fit the new bridge platform.

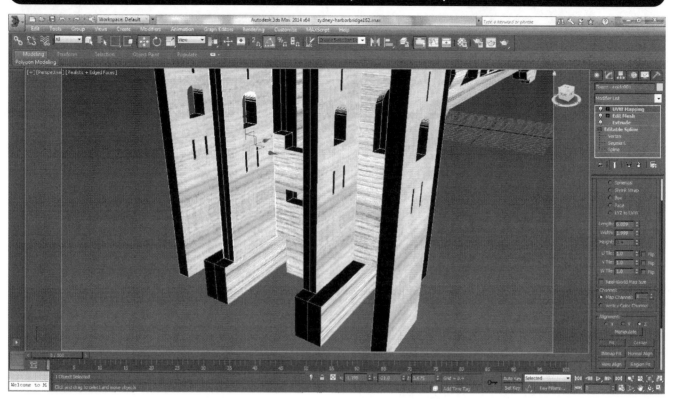

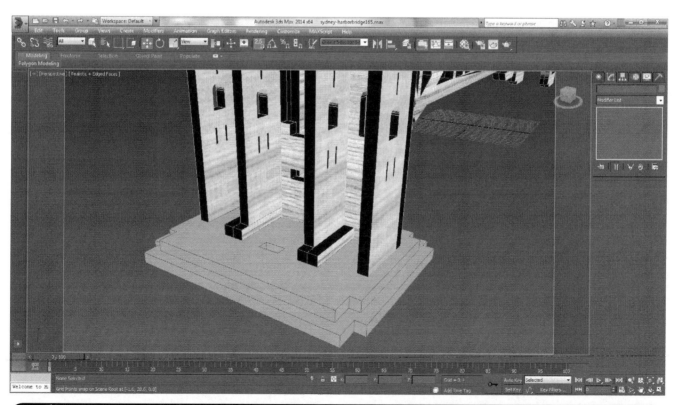

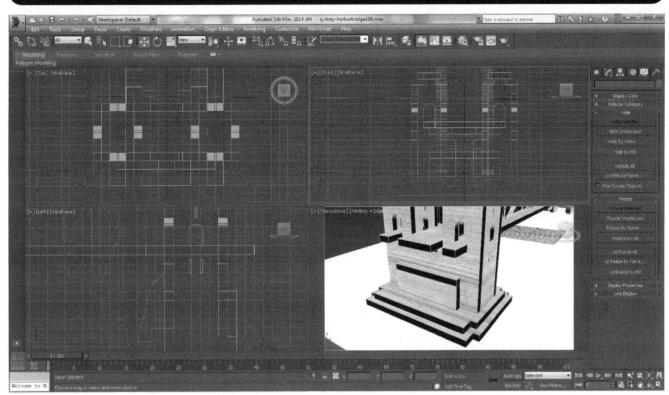

Step 22: Image top of this page

The front of the tower is now done with the last interlocking part. I just need to fix the interlocks that appear under the bridge span to make sure those pieces are all correct as well.

This is why it's important to build projects that don't use too many pieces - optimal design for application will save you a ton of time if any changes are required.

Step23: Image next page top

Now that the under the bridge details are sorted, I need to check each piece individually to double-check that all my interlocks are correct.

Step 24: Image next page bottom

After a few changes, it's time to render the project out to see how it looks - it's far beefier than the original laser model but this was anavoidable. It will also be far stronger than the laser version as well!

Visually, everything looks fine. So I can now clone the tower to also appear at the other end of the bridge and then export the parts to be cut with my router.

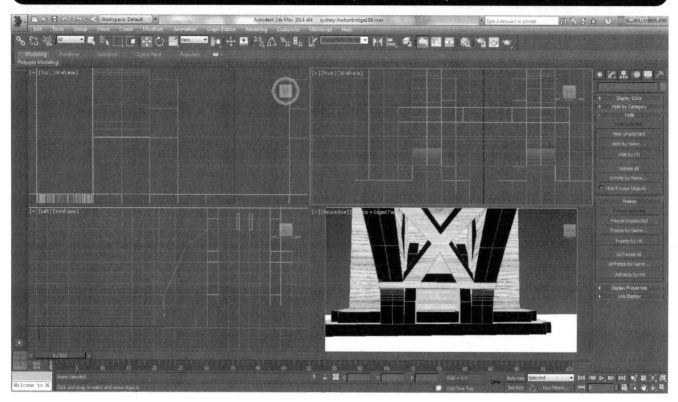

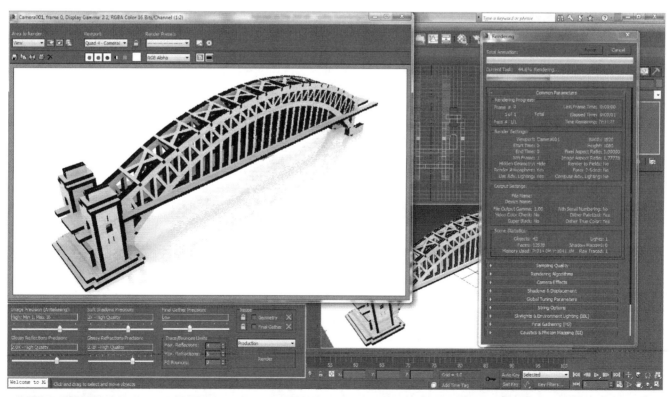

<u>Step 25: Image top of this page</u>
Now I need to go through a slightly convoluted workflow because I want to show dogbones in this model to produce a more accurate CNC table router model. This means I need to export all these pieces into 2D line drawings, apply dog bones etc.. and then bring them back into 3DS Max to rebuild the model.

This is why it's sometimes easier to just design a new fresh model instead of trying to modify an old one.

<u>Step 26: Image next page top</u>
As you can see in the above picture, there aren't too many parts in this model once everything is layed flat. That's for two reasons: I want to be able to build this easily with as many intuitive parts as possible and people will focus on the spans. The other parts just play a supportive role without the need for lots of detail.

These are still extruded, so I need turn them into 2D vector files.

<u>Step 27: Image next page bottom</u>
I got rid of the depth and added a small square that represents material thickness. This is vital because otherwise, I don't have a way to easily scale a drawing up or down correctly as I no longer have 3D parts. I now export this file as an Adobe Illustrator vector file format.

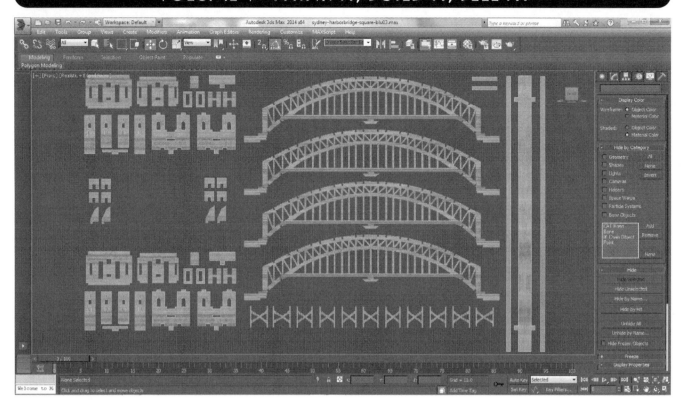

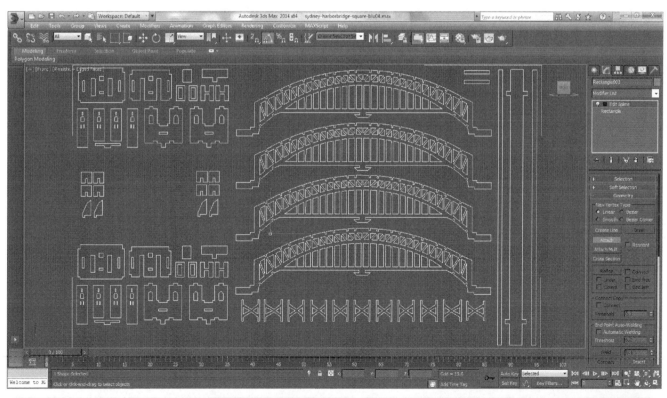

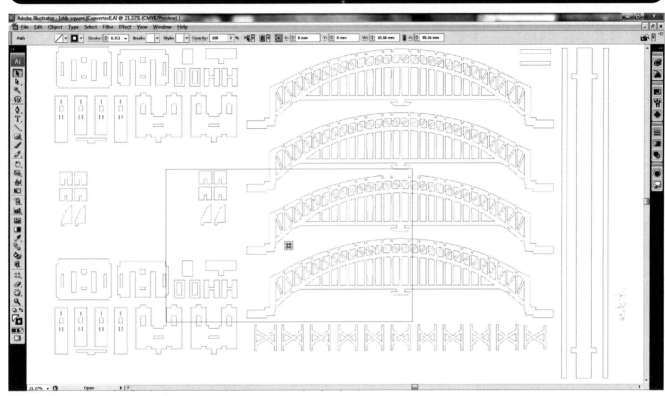

Step 28: Image top of this page

Now that I have the 2D vector file open in Adobe Illustrator, you see why it's so important to make that little square in the previous step. Notice how my 4 mm square has now magically scaled to 10.16 mm? There would be no way of knowing this unless I made the square in the first place.

What I want to do is cut this project out of 6 mm thick material, so I need to scale it down accordingly.

10.16 x ??? = 6 mm thus 6 / 10.16 = 0.59 so 10.16 x 0.59 = 6 mm I want

Step 29: Image next page top

Now the square is exactly 6 mm square which means that the whole drawing is now scaled perfectly to use 6 mm thick material. Because I made everything fit a grid that was 6 units cube, I can easily scale drawings up and down, which wouldn't be possible otherwise.

Step 30: Image next page bottom

Before I proceed though to PartWorks to create the tool pathing and dog bones necessary to CNC router this Sydney Harbor Bridge, I still need to get all these parts onto the same sheet size that I'll be using, which is 6 mm thick, 500 x 400 mm.

As you can see, everything will fit within these parameters except for the spans, an issue I'll have to deal with later.

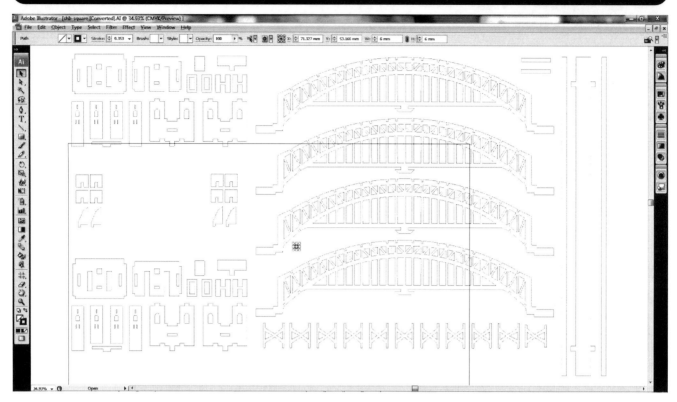

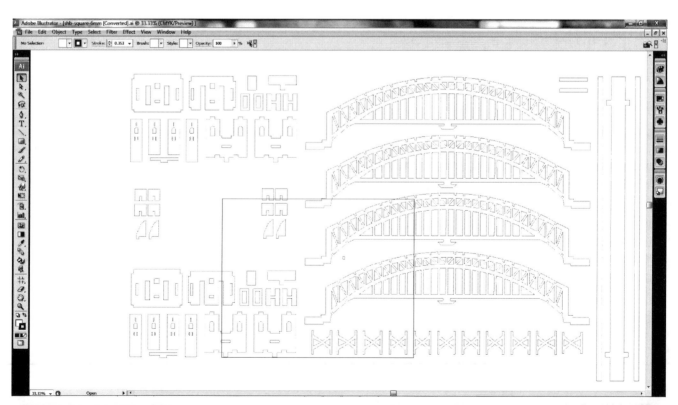

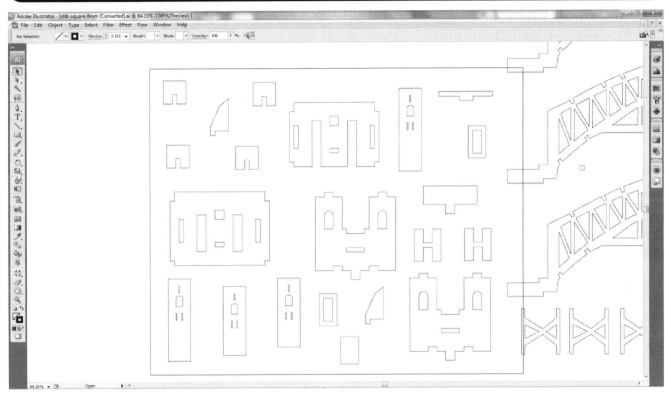

Step 31: Image top of this page

Although I could technically do this process within PartWorks (ShopBot's tool pathing software), I prefer to do it in Illustrator as I seem to have more control and I'm more comfortable with the tools it has than PartWorks.

Each software application has it's strengths and weaknesses, just like CNC machines, so I try to use each for optimal efficiency.

Before moving too many parts around, I group the vectors together that form one part. So the program knows not to separate them, otherwise inside parts are not linked to outside ones and, as soon as you move one, the other won't move with it, causing your design to no longer work.

Step 32: Image next page top

This may seem like a very chaotic layout (this is a major difference between lasers and routers is physical contact with the sheet). In this case, for a router, I want to give myself optimal placement for screws while at the same time, avoid any continuous lines going from one part to the other as each cut will weaken the board.

Think of it as brick wall, you don't just stack the bricks one onto the other but stagger them for greater overall wall strength, CNC routering parts is no different. I was able to place all the pieces that make-up the tower on one sheet which means I'll be able to cut that sheet twice to make-up all those parts.

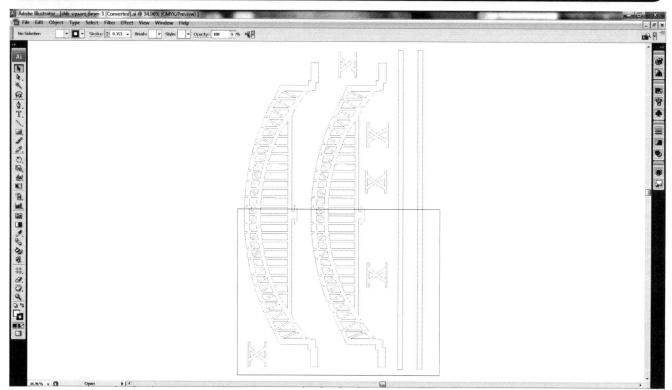

If I were to stop right now, I'd have an amazing laser cutting model with a lot more tolerances and give than my original model. When pieces are larger, it makes for an easier to assemble project but with lasers, where your primary concern is minimizing the rate most companies charge to cut with them, I've greatly increased the costs involved with this model. By how much?

Let's take a look at Trotec's JobControlX to give us an accurate representation of cutting costs using a Trotec Speedy 400. This excludes materials and labor.

Original Optimized Cutting Costs: Image next page top
This was the very first model of my Sydney Harbor Bridge, optimized with double lines removed and parts grouped together. Time = 15 minutes

Original Unoptimized Cutting Costs: Image next page bottom
For a more accurate representation, here are the cutting costs of the same model without any optimization, so that the other quotes are more accurate. Time = 18 minutes

Notice that by simply grouping and optimizing a file, I manage to save 20 percent off the cutting costs but, more importantly, a few minutes spent optimizing the file actually saves me 20% off laser time use! Of course, you still charge the customer the same amount as your time doing this extra work is still worth something. You've drastically improved your laser ROI over the lifetime of your laser while optimizing your files: remove double lines and squish all the parts together for shared cutting lines.

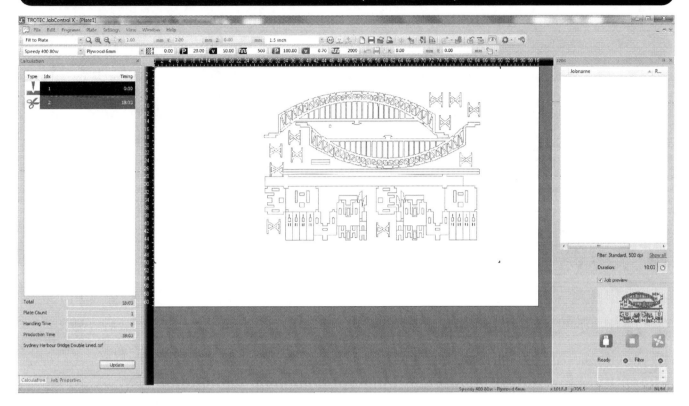

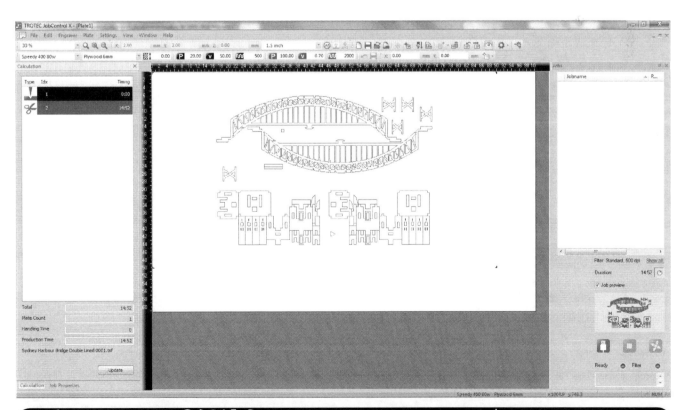

The above shows what the model would look like laser cut with dog bones - at the full size I've managed to create so far (6 mm double spanned). Let's now compare the cutting costs, with a laser, of this model cut at my new size both with and without dog bones to get a comparison of produciton costs.

In order to save time optimizing the file as I'd need multiple sheets at this size, I've just gotten a quote for one span for quick comparison.

New Full Sized No Dog Bones Cutting Costs: Image next page top
Time = 6 minutes

New Full Sized with Dog Bones Cutting Costs: Image next page top
Dog bones are rounded inner edges that are needed because of a round bit in a CNC table router but you can just as easily cut a model with a laser to replicate the same effect. Time = 5 minutes

In this case, the results are basically the same. You have a minute of time saved but it's more due to the way I modeled the span but generally, I'd expect dog bones to use slightly less laser time simply due to the fact that it makes the total line use across a highly segmented model decrease.

A 90 degree angle is rounded in the spans to use less line length, but for the tabs on the top and bottom, you are actually adding line length. So, I can't really say dog bones save or cost more laser time for this model.

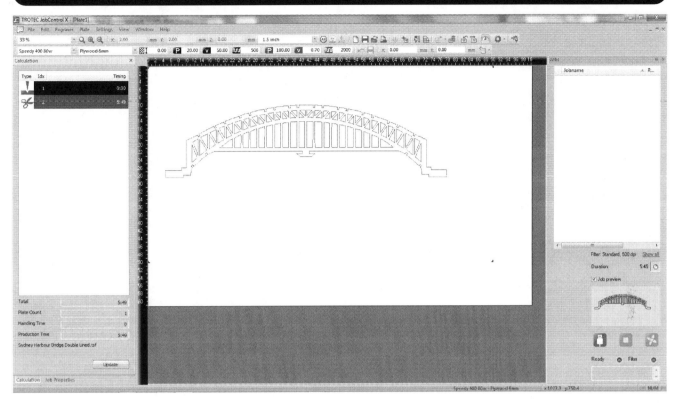

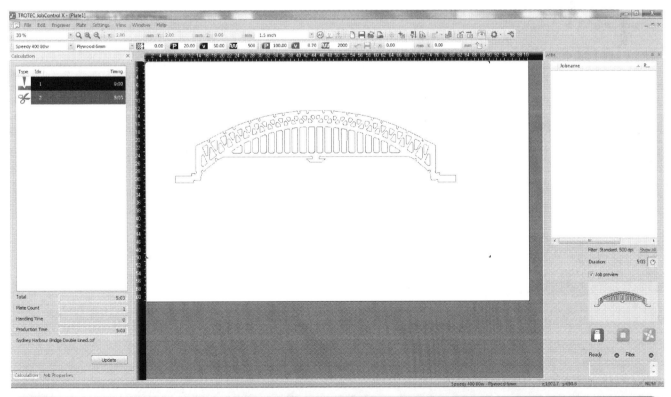

I want to make a CNC table router version of this model, so let's continue to transform the above render into physical form.

Step 33: Image next page top
Partworks is a great program for getting files ready for CNC table routing. Unlike a laser, the table router needs to know what parts are inside and outside and the deliverative movement and sequence of cuts must be outlined ahead of time as the physical contact of the spinning bit will affect the output quality you produce.

Step 34: Image next page bottom
You'll notice some pieces don't have a dog bone, the reason for this is that sometimes my vectors aren't closed properly from their originals within Autodesk's 3DS Max. This happens every once in a while and isn't a big deal because even if I have a square inside corner to these pieces, the bit will make it rounded by default anyhow.

Sometimes though, you end-up with a piece looking like the above picture. It prevents you from adding dog bones which means if you cut the piece as is, it will have rounded inner corners which don't work very well for interlocking parts because it prevents the piece from going all the way down onto the bottom of a part.

The solution in this case is to select a node from the left menu and hover over the line. Once you see a small squiggly line, you press "1" on your keyboard and it fixes the issues.

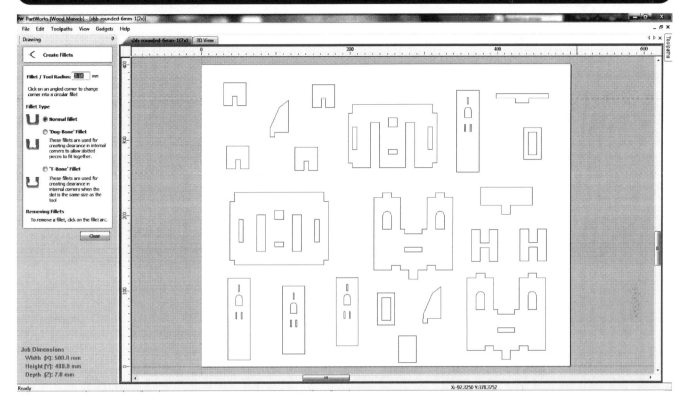

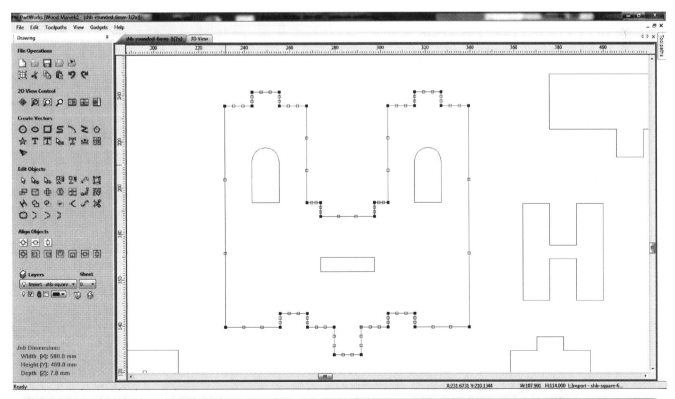

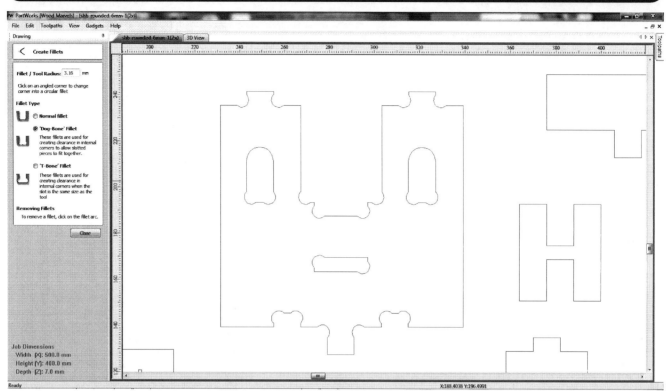

Step 35: Image top of this page

As you can see, the result in this case was a piece that looks like it has been chewed-up to look like dog bones - hence the name. I really should have made this bridge even bigger but in this case, it's the first time I indexed a project and wanted it to go in halves and not thirds - as there is a smaller likelyhood of something going wrong in my measurements.

The great part about having your own CNC table router and lots of material is that you can always go back and scale a drawing up further to make it bigger using this workflow. I'd just change the grids to "2" instead of "4" I used in this project and go through all the steps again.

Step 36: Image next page top

This model is now optimized to be cut - I need to duplicate this board twice (one for each side of the Sydney Harbour Bridge). There are a few pieces that are of concern, such as the "H" shape because the material is thin. So what I'll do is add a few more to the board in case they are cut. Also, the little windows in the towers might be too small. I did forget to optimize a few shapes; do you see them?

Step 37: Image next page bottom

The next step after the pieces are optimized is adding screw holes - this prevents my CNC table router from going over screws (if I put them randomly on the board) because there is no way to see the paths on an empty board. Add more screws than not enough.

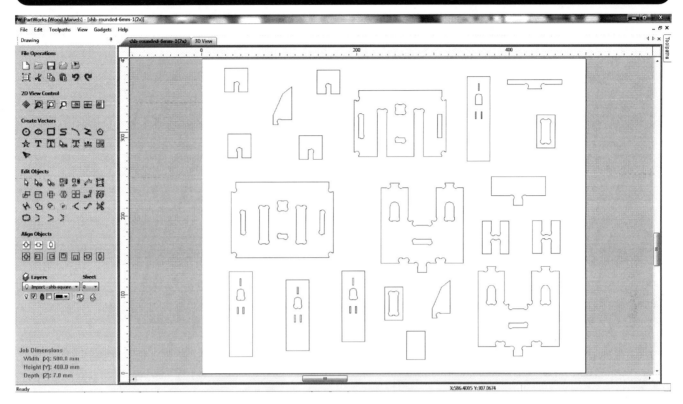

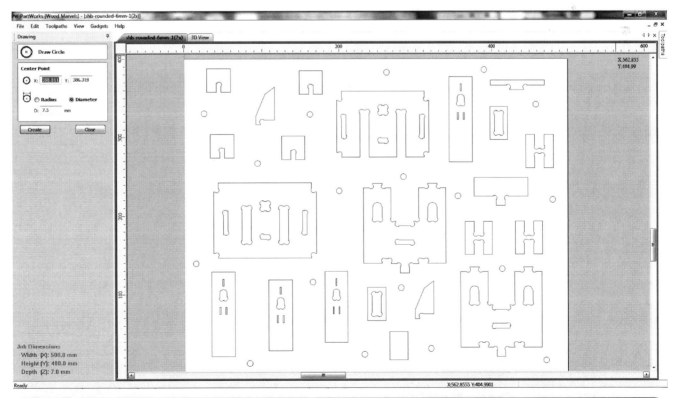

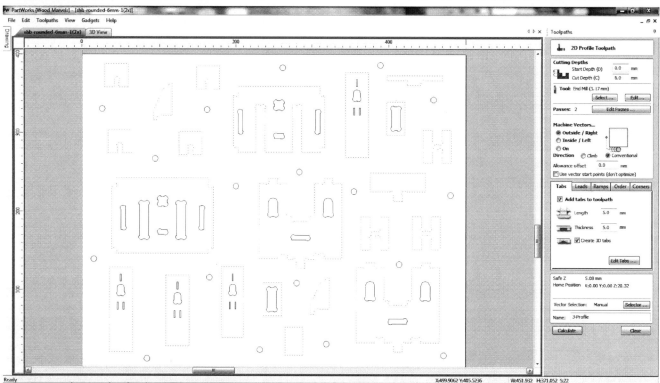

Step 38: Image top of this page

Partworks is a great program and it allows me to do a "virtual CNC table router test" which will help me isolate further issues, but before we do that, we need to create tool paths to tell the router which parts are inside and outside, and which are pockets.

We can also define the order and position of the initial plunges, but the default settings are so good for my application, I don't worry about it. What I did here was select the outside parts and chose a bit so the ShopBot will know this critical information to generate the G-Code from.

Step 39: Image next page top

I've now selected the inside toolpaths. As you can see, the calculations for the outside toolpaths is already done (you can see the arrows going along the outside edges of all the shapes). Here I filled the information to tell the ShopBot to cut on the inside (as opposed to the outside) of the pieces.

Step 40: Image next page bottom

Now that the inside and outside parts are figured-out by the software, I'm left defining the screw holes. I don't want these to go all the way through, only 1 mm into the board and I'll see the position (my board is 6 mm remember).

The purpose of screw holes is to define where I put the screw and nothing else. I don't want to weaken the board by going too deep.

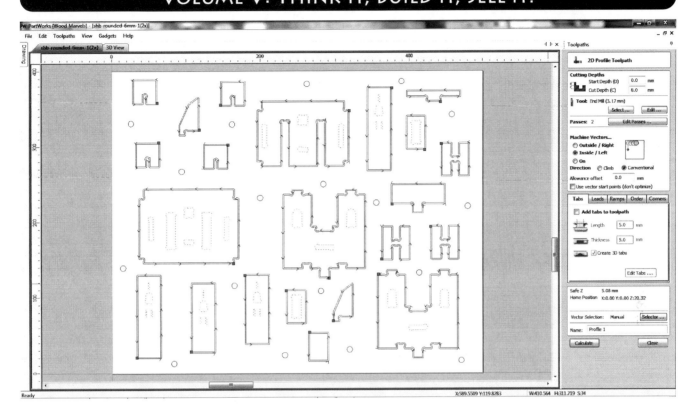

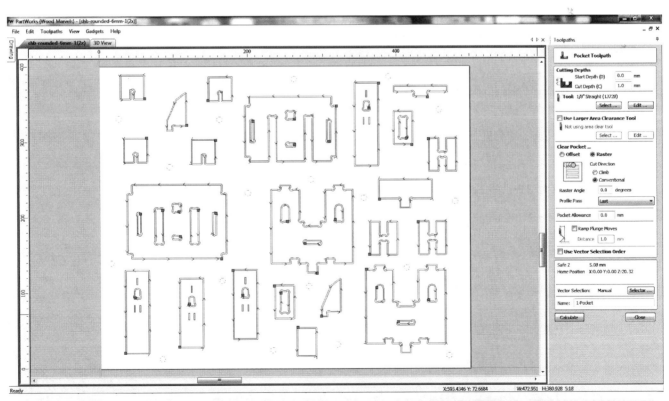

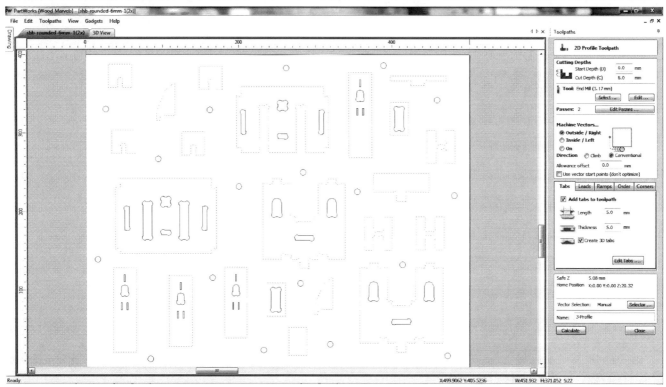

Step 41: Image top of this page

The preview of the cutting looks good but there is one major problem: I'll be cutting out the drill holes first, followed by the inside parts, but what about the outside parts? How will they stay on the board and not fly all over the place? I need to add tabs to all for them.

Step 42: Image next page top

I could automatically add tabs to save time, but I prefer to place my along edges, sometimes an automatic tab is at the wrong spot and makes it hard to get the piece out of the board.

I find putting tabs on corners the easiest to remove or along straight lines, but not on inside corners because the extra material can affect how pieces interlock.

Step 43: Image next page bottom

Everything now looks perfect except for the small windows. I've decided to leave them out in this case as somebody could still cut them out using a smaller bit after they buy my files, but my focus here is to test the model; these small details don't affect my build process nor the resultant model for sales.

I could make them wider of course, but again, not a big deal to me as they will show-up in the 3D assembly animation I make and I doubt most people will even notice them missing.

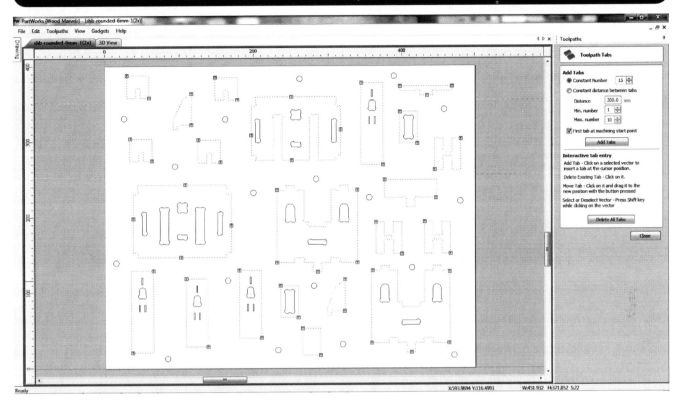

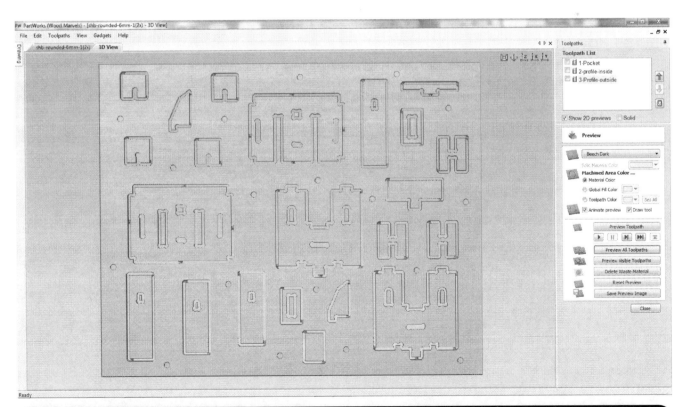

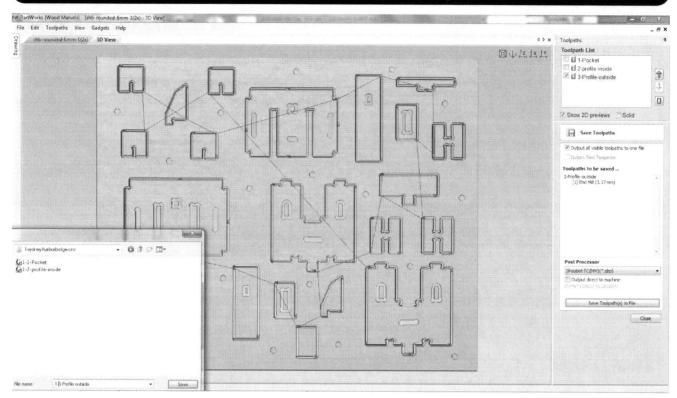

Step 44: Image top of this page
Now I save the individual toolpaths. You can see the path the table router will take and the outlines of the parts that will be done in that process (in this case, outside tool paths).

Step 45: Image next page top
As previously mentioned, I need to make two tower sections (one at each end of the bridge spans), but if I cut the same board 2x, my screw holes will be in exactly the same place which means that my hold down will be less than optimal.

I could move screw holes individually to new places on the board, but that takes too much time. A quick workaround to this is to simply rotate the entire drawing 180 degrees. This way the parts are in a new location and screwholes are also in a unique locations for optimal support and hold down.

Step 46: Image next page bottom
I had to recalculate the toolpaths, but using this "spin 180 degrees" method, the process was very simple. All the tabs are in the same place and in less than a minute a whole new board was created that is strong, well supported and won't move around.

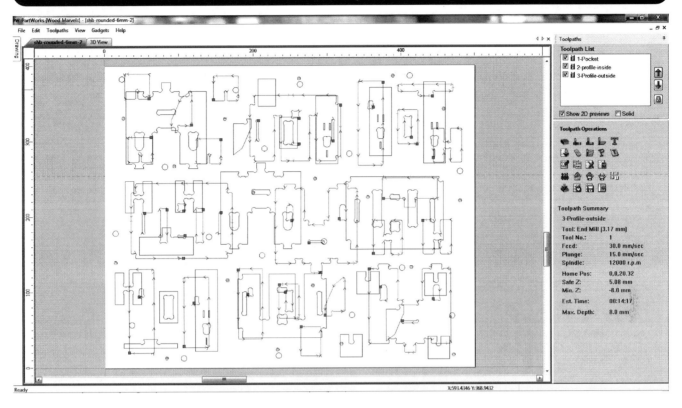

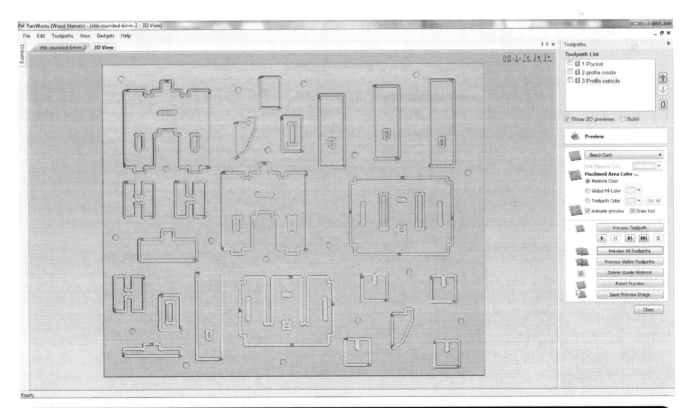

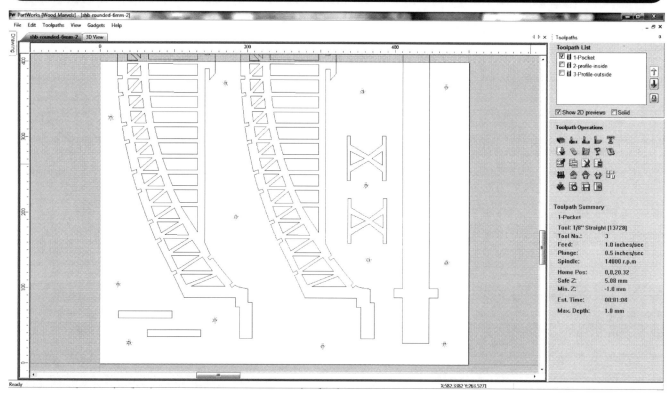

Step 47: Image top of this page

I've never done this before, but it seems straight forward to have the board cut dead center in the bridge span. What I'll have to do is cut the board then move it down (it's one long piece), re-set the home position to be 0 on the Y axis exactly where the board cutting was stopped (dead center in the middle of the span) and then cut the second half of the board. This is a theory at least so we'll find out if it works!

There are two challenges here: the first is making sure I'm dead-on as per the Y axis but also on the X axis. If the board moves only 2-3 mm to the left or right (X axis), then my spans will not be symetrical because one half will be taller or shorter than the other.

I've been racking my mind as to how to reduce the error on this happening and I've come to the conclusion that the only way to do so is to re-set the home position on my ShopBot Desktop between these cuts and make a long, perfectly straight board that the entire length of the board can rest on. I double-check with my table router to be dead straight on the Y axis (top and bottom X axis are the same position).

Step 48: Image next page top

This will take a while but there isn't any fast way to remove the brezier splines and replacing them with dog bones. Like I did for the towers on both sides of the spans, within PartWorks, I select the node editing tool and hover over the area I want to modify. When a squigly line appears, I press "l" on my keyboard to make it a straight line.

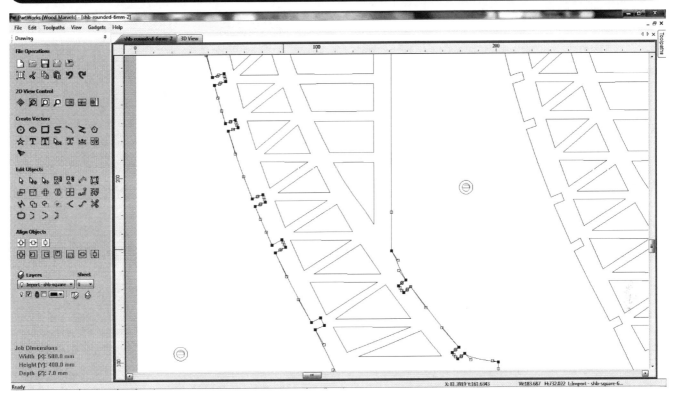

Step 49: Image next page top

Although I don't need to make the inside sharp corners in the spans rounded as the router will do this by default, I'm going through the process of optimizing it simply to provide a more accurate render and associated 3D animaiton for this project.

I've made a lot of models and showing sharp inner corners when you design a project for a CNC table rouer isn't a proper portrayal of what the consumer is buying although my old way of thinking was to leave them sharp because I use a 1/8th straight double-flute bit while somebody else would use a 1/64th straight double flute bit so the she differences would be far less apparent.

I do provide the straight files as well as the rounded ones, so if somebody wants to use a different bit or scale, they can easily adjust the drawing to suit their CNC's capabilities.

Step 50: Image next page bottom

On the left is the CNC table router version of this Sydney Harbor Bridge while on the right would be the CNC laser cutter version; it's a great comparison between the capabilities of each technology.

Notice the dog bones on the bottom segments that will go into the towers and the rounded inner holes within the bridge span itself.

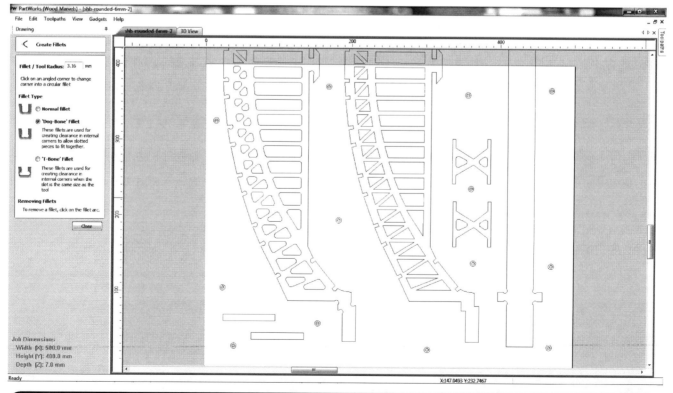

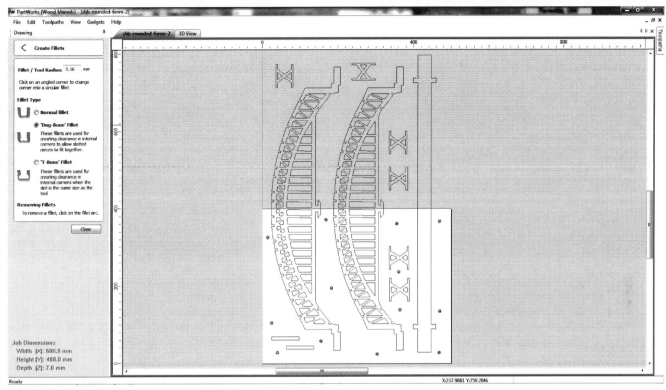

Step 51: Image top of this page

Now that I've rounded everything on the bottom span, I just have to optimize the top. After it's finished, I'll duplicate it. Since I have four spans, it takes about 10 minutes to optimize each one but only a few seconds to duplicate it. Be efficient with your time!

Step 52: Image next page top

The shapes are now finished being optimized, time to create the toolpaths!

Step 53: Image next page bottom

The toolpaths are looking good. I added some tabs long the top of the edge to make sure that when I move this piece down to be cut with the CNC table router, those large spans do not move. I can now export the toolpaths for pockets (screws) and profiles (inside and outside).

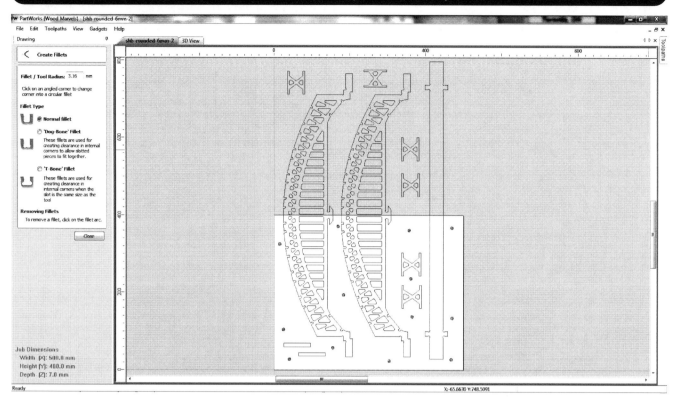

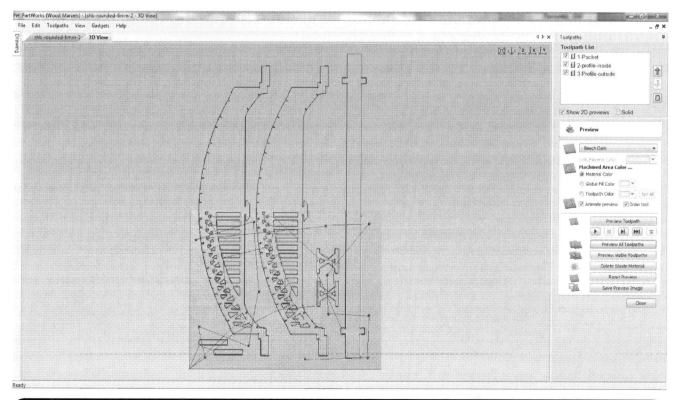

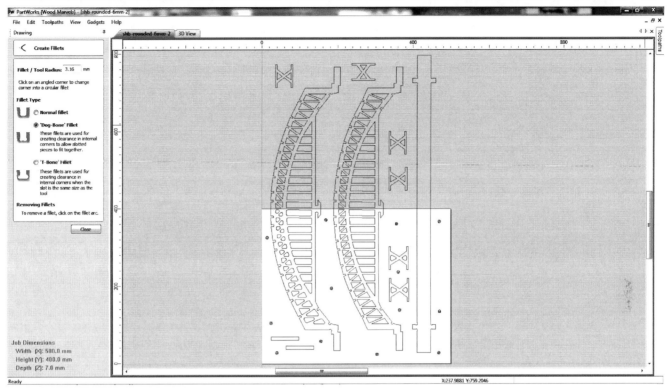

Step 54: Image top of this page
The top part of the first set of double spans is now toolpaths using the same steps I used to generate the bottom part of this sheet. I can now export the toolpaths for pockets (screws) and profiles (inside and outside)!

Step 55: Image next page top
I noticed one of my triangles was still square in the span which I fixed in this file and went back into the previous sheet to fix as well. This is why it's nice to have several different cross-checking systems established in your workflow.

In this case, it wouldn't have made a different anyhow because even a square inside shape will be made round by the router but it would have affected the 3D render and resulting 3D animtion I use to promote this product with. Overall, this project will take six sheets.

Well, everything was going smooth until what seems totally logical didn't work with my ShopBot Desktop. The ShopBot tried to keep going along the cutting path eventhough it wasn't part of my patworks board.

Luckily, these slight changes to enable tiled cutting were mostly done in the above steps. Let me give this another try. I've left my previous steps because not all software supports tiling and hey, learn from my mistakes!

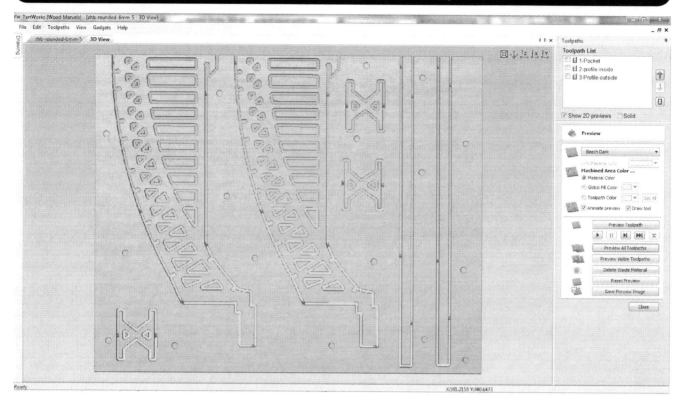

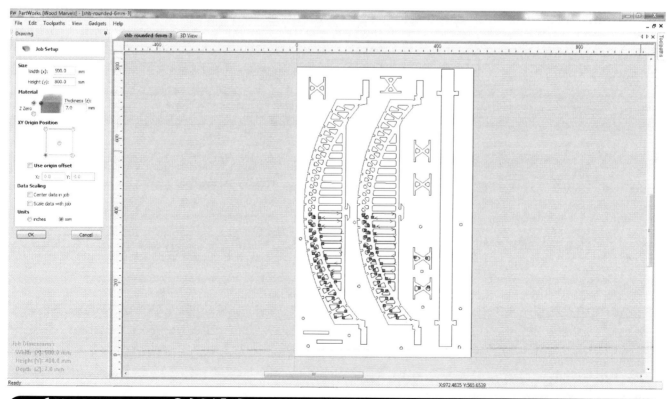

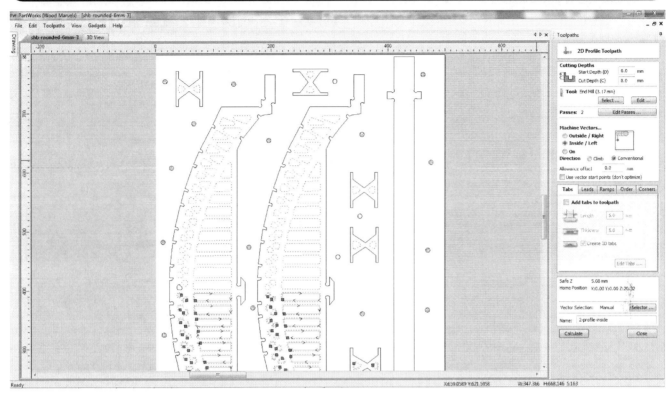

Step 56: Image previous page bottom

First step to tiling a design is changing my board size within PartWorks; I changed the height from 400 mm to 800 mm on my first sheet containing two (of four) spans.

Step 57: Image this page top

Now that we treat the entire board as one cut, I added additional screw holes in the top portion and had to create toolpaths for the entire project to be cut, as if it was going to be done in one shot.

Step 58: Image next page top

I've now divided my project into two where height (y) is 400 mm which means I have to pass the board up one more itme to get 800 mm. All I need to do now is export all the cutting paths.

As you can see, the two, tiles are made at the same time but I have to remember to cut tile 2 before I cut tile 1 because for me, working closer going outside is easier on my ShopBot than the other way around because I'll be doing my positioning by eye (hence no overlap).

When I make even larger projects, I'll take the time, to make tabs and use round dowels for more precise positioning, but because this is the first time I do this, I want to LEARN all that could go wrong instead of doing everything 100 percent to the book first time around.

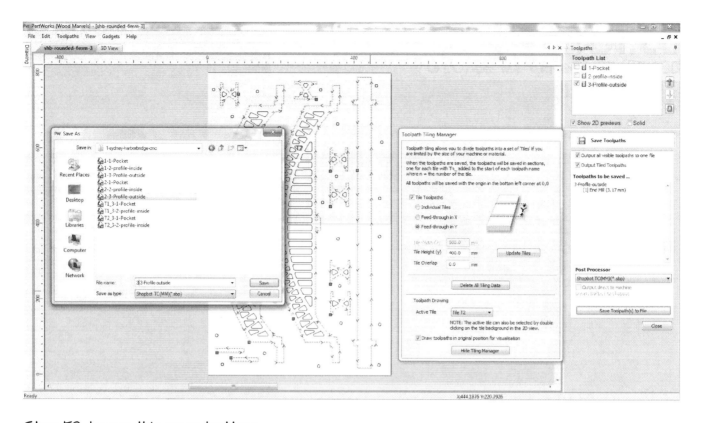

Step 59: Image this page bottom

I now have all my cutting paths established for my second board of spans. I numbered everything in order regarding file name so the cutting process should be very straight forward. Next step is cutting!

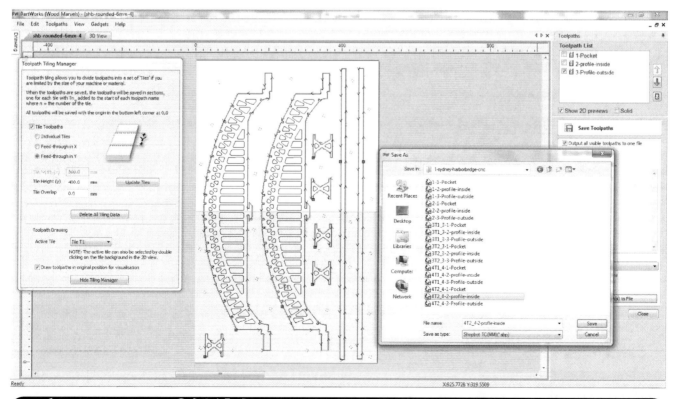

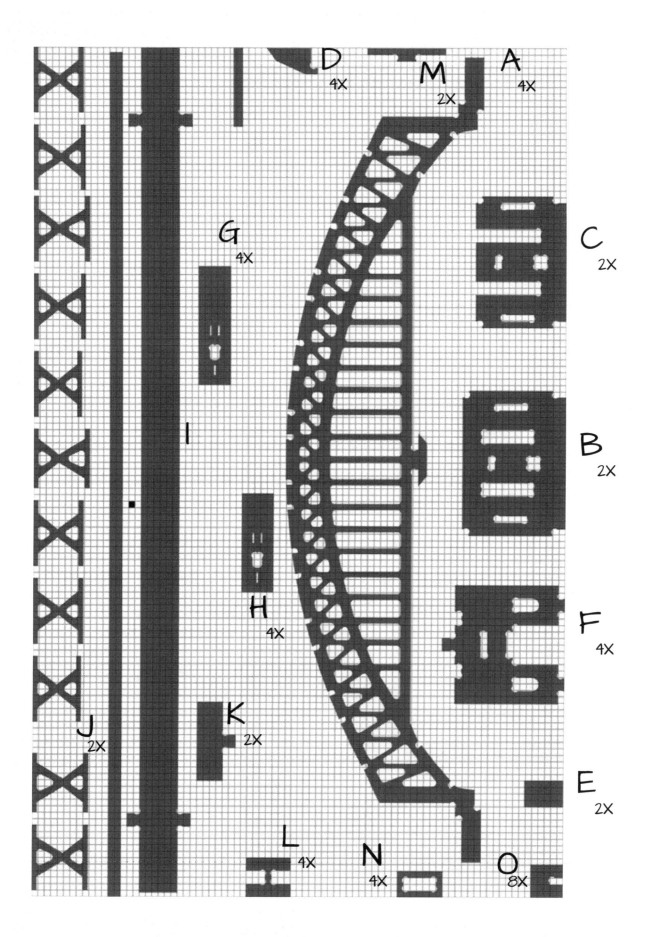

Step-by-Step Assembly Instructions

Step 1: Label and check inventory
Once you have all the pieces in front of you, the process of putting them together is no different from assembling pieces of Lego.

Label, using a pencil, the various parts and double-check your inventory. Take your time and enjoy the building process! Before jumping to the glue, be sure to do a dry run.

Step 2: Start the base
Using glue, double-up parts A (spans) and then slide into a parts B (larger tower base) and C (smaller tower base) on both sides applying glue where all the parts intersect.

Step 3: Add under-bridge blocks
On both sides of the bridge, add two parts D and a part E to add a little ornamental detail on the underside of the bridge. You will find it difficult to add it later in the building process which is why it's best to do it now.

Step 4: Start the towers
Add a part F (wide wall) into the single hole closest to the span within the platform followed by a part G (long wall) on the outside and a part H (short wall) on the inside. Apply glue where all the various parts intersect.

Step-by-Step Assembly Instructions

Step 5: Add roads
Slide and glue into place parts I (wide road) and J (narrow road).

Place another part F to cap the tower. Afterwards, glue and slide into place part K (ornamental wall lock) in the base of the tower and parts L (look like H) on the top. Do the same on the opposing tower.

Step 6: Complete the tower
Onto part K, slide with glue a part M (top cap) followed by a parts N (looks like O) and O (chimney stacks).

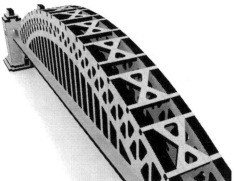

Step 7: Add cross members
Slide and glue into place the cross members across the top of the doubled-up spans.

Step 8: Perform some fishing touches
There is no need to apply any preservatives or paint; feel free to sand any sharp edges down. ENJOY!

Physical Results

If you look closely at this model, you'll notice a few aspects of the design that don't make sense. The most obvious is part F; I should really have two versions of that part, one with a hole in the middle right below the road and another without because I don't have any part going into the hole on the side facing the spans. I left it there to keep my "unique part count" down and to simplify the build process; it's under a road and behind a cross-member, nobody would really notice it anyways.

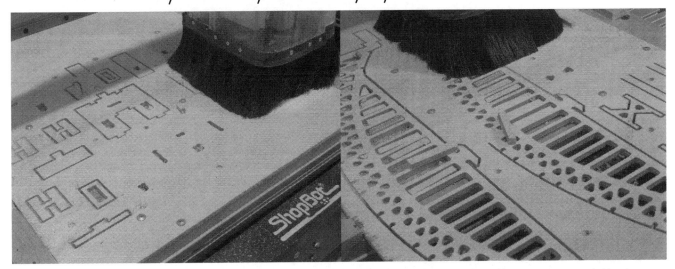

Another aspect of part F you'll notice is that I have a step under the main road that doesn't seem to serve any purpose. I realize that a lot of people will build these models out of MDF or cardboard, so I wanted to provide a way for extra support and strength in an area of the model nobody would notice because two ledges don't provide much support for such a long piece as a long flat surface would.

The build process went very well, I'm very happy with the result.

Assembled 255 piece model dimensions:
L: 296 W: 292 H: 296 (mm)
L: 11-21/32 W: 11-1/2 H: 11-21/32 (in)

Material Thickness: 6 mm (1/4 inch)

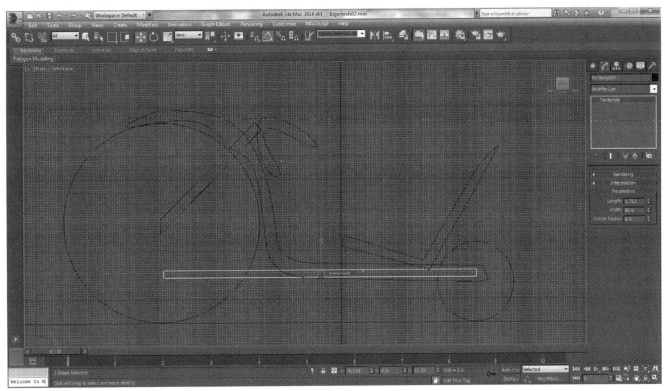

Step 1: Image top of this page

As this project is relatively big AND I plan on driving it, I sat on the floor to get the rough measurements of where I want things to be: distance of my bent knees in the "driving position" and where I'd be sitting next to a tape measure. I then figured-out my widths at this time as well.

I then put the rough measurements into my 3D modeling program so that I have a guide to follow when I'm building this model out.

The central distance between the front and back wheels is 80 cm which means the wheel in the front is going to be 50 cm in diameter with the back ones being 20 cm. I'd like a slight incline on the seat with the option to reposition it (like the original plastic version) beause it makes for a more comfortable drive.

What I will most likely end-up doing is making the seat move widely front and back to suit riders of all sizes which is easier than having the front handle bars move around because they will be pivoting as well. I will be using more plywood for this project than I used for my Kangaroo shelf which was the equivalent of 21 400 x 500 mm sheets!

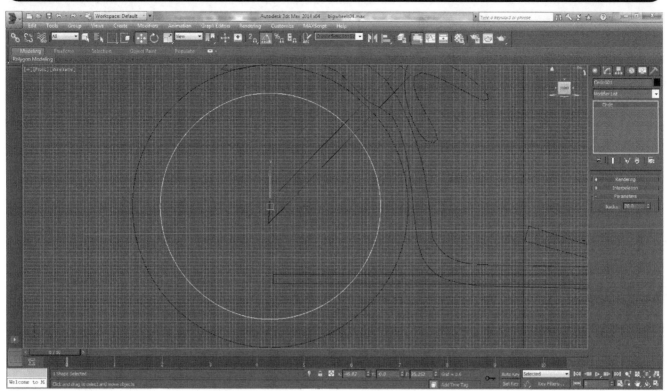

Step 2: Image top of this page

There are so many options as to where to start first, but I think the biggest challenge will be in building the wheel assemblies, what goes in-between them will fall in place easily afterwards. Because I don't have a full-sheet router, the front wheel will be the biggest challenge to work-out. I REALLY do not want to cut it in two tiles, so my limiting comfortable diameter is 40 cm, but this isn't big enough for this project. Although it complicates things, I might have to break it up in smaller pieces that are then glued together, but that would cause structural and design issues of their own and greatly increase piece count. ARG! Let's deal with this first! The first circle represents my "maximum one-tile" size while the outer wheel represents what I want to have.

Step 3: Image next page top

I'm really screwed whatever I do, so if I'm going to fail, let's fail big! I'll make the wheel 55cm in diameter! I'll make sure that the wheel is symmetrical so I can rotate the errors around the entire circumferance which would mean that any error isn't noticeable after a little driving on some hard asphalt. This is a Big Wheel, so let's make it massive! I want the wheel to be thin relative to the back ones, so I'll give it a width of 60 mm which means I need to cut roughly ten of these wheels... of course, it will have spokes!

Step 4: Image next page bottom

I believe I'll have more than enough strength in the front wheel because most of the weight will be on the back wooden tires which is why it was so easy to pop-a-wheely on these things. I'm making a lot of assumptions though, so just to be on the safe side, I'll keep the spokes at a minimum.

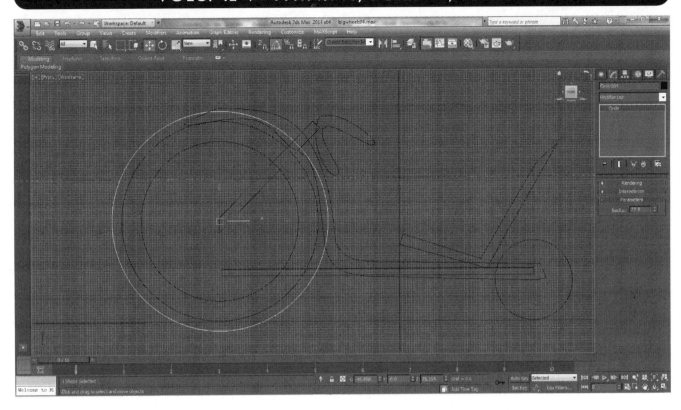

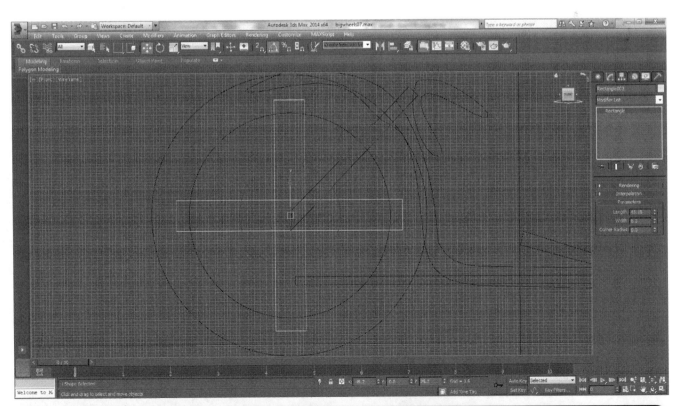

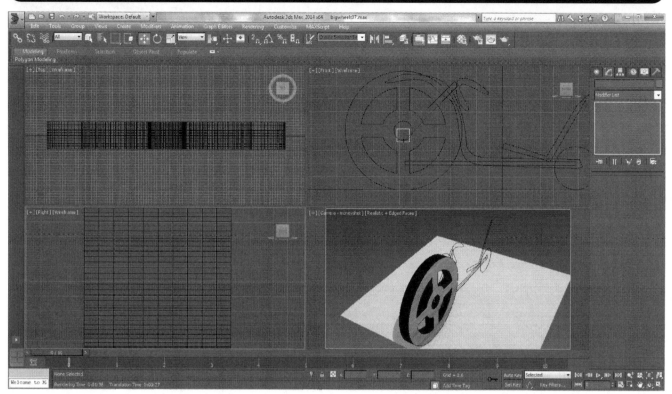

Step 5: Image top of this page
The front wheel is looking big and strong now, it has to freely rotate hence the hole in the middle of the spokes where I'll have 10 layers of plywood glued together to form the axle. There will be a lot of "spinning action" going on inside of here on the edge of the plywood but I think I've figured-out a way to smooth that out a bit in my mind.

Step 6: Image next page top
The back wheel will be extra thick and strong as most of the weight will be on these but that doesn't mean you can't add small details to make them more interesting than just a solid wheel. Here you see the mess of 2D splines that I had to create in order to create the spokes, they are thick but I wanted something that you could still see all the way through to add a bit more novelty to this Big Wheels.

Step 7: Image next page bottom
I added two guides to this wheel, it adds more strength and also makes the build process easier. I'll also be adding this to the front wheel later for the same reasons. The front wheels were multipled 10x so the back ones will be 20x.

This model will use a fair amount of plywood but I prefer to be safe than sorry when it comes to building models that will have forces at all angles on them.

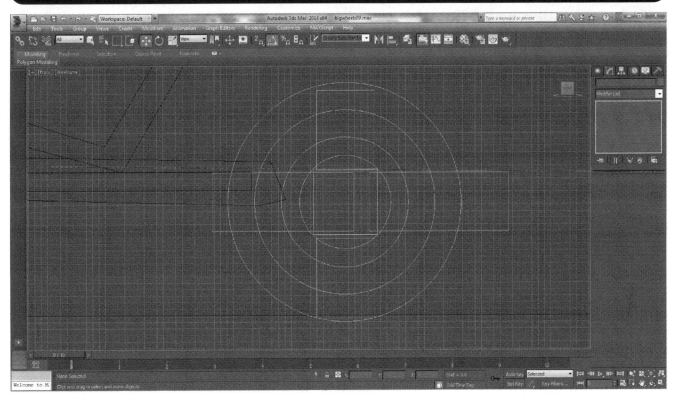

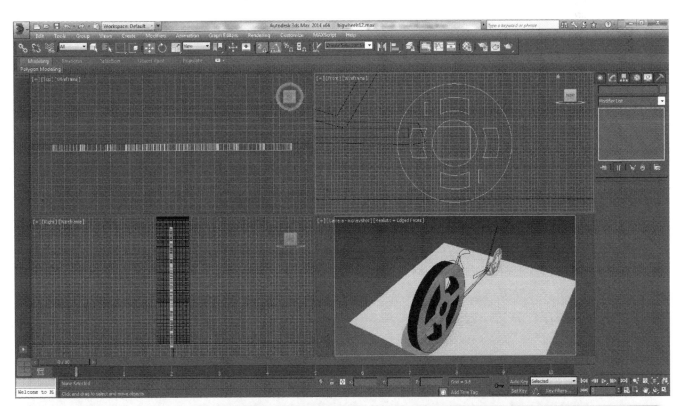

Step 8: Image top of this page

The basic shape is coming together well and I have 50 cm between the wheels though I may extend this further as I build this laser and router model out. Why did I make my back wheels with circles for the axle instead of one solid one? If you have a solid axle in the back, then both wheels need to turn at the same speed which is fine if you are going straight but if you turn, this cannot be the case - which is why cars and trucks have independent back wheels to not break the axle and have good traction in turns.

Step 9: Image next page top

I added slots into the axle to help create a bit more strength and to help make sure that these axles will be as square as possible. The wheels in the back need to be held in place by locking them from going outwards and moving inwards too much.

Step 10: Image next page bottom

The rectangle I've highlighted is the maximum one-tile-sheet that I have to play with and as you can see, I'll need to make it much longer to get these parts made. The challenge here is that, because I have to use more than one tile, it will be angled upwards meaning I'm severely limited as to how many I can fit on a tile. I think I'll be lucky if I can fit more than two of these long pieces going from the back all the way to the top of the front wheel. If I had a full-sheet router, this wouldn't be an issue, but as my maximum piece width is 60 cm at most, my tiles will be quite a bit messy as I try to fill the gaps. I think I'll need about 6 of these full-length parts on both sides of the steering wheel, meaning the necessity of 12 of them since they will hold my weight. I will add cross members to increase their strength but even so, I'm using lots of plywood for this project that would actually be far less if I didn't have to resort to tiling in the first place.

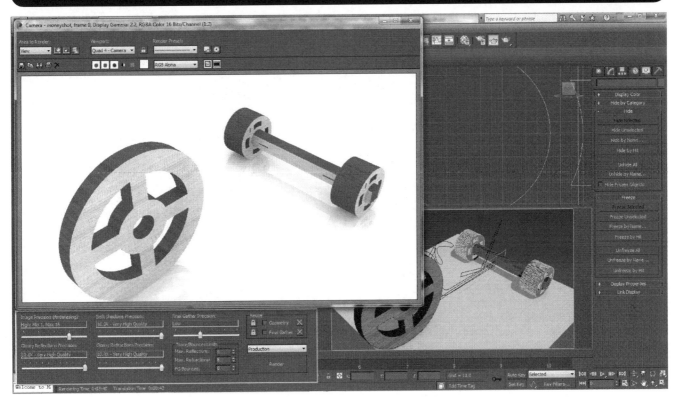

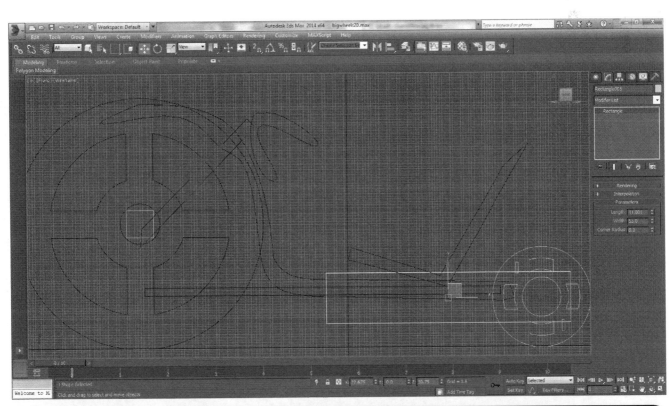

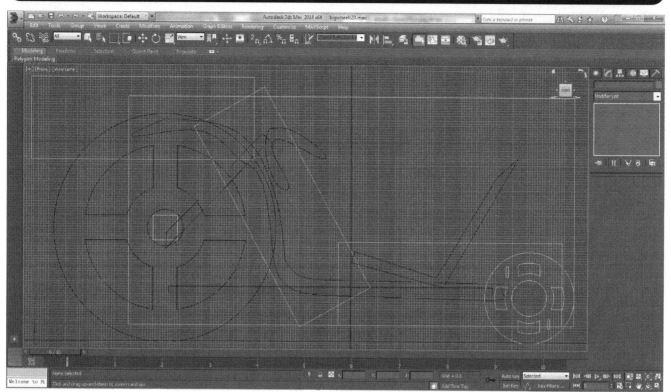

Step 11: Image top of this page

I think I'll have to split these parts into 3, so a front end locked in with a back end using guides mid-way through, even if this will weaken the structure. 12 sheets being used alone for only these parts 60 x 120 cm along with other large pieces isn't something that is a very efficient use of time or materials though this will greatly increase the piece count. The boards right above the wheel won't support any weight, so they will be far smaller pieces and more ornamental than supportive.

Step 12: Image next page top

I've worked-out some preliminary brackets that will allow two plywood floorboards to slide into them (making everything very solid and strong) that also lock the axle in place; I only want the rotation to occur on the wheels themselves, I don't want the axle to be spinning. Once I work-out a good locking mechanism for the front and back brackets (back wheels through to the big front one), I have a feeling that I'll be heavily modifying these brackets to look and function better with the seat that will go above them since I could have part of the seat created at the same time as the bracket though that would take one full 400 x 500 mm tile alone; ten of those would help make that entire assembly very easy to assemble.

Step 13: Image next page bottom

Here you can see the guides I make to help me build pieces that will intersect across several parts across multiple axis. What I will do to create a solid platform is have the same two pieces that make-up the floor of this project, will just slide into place through the sides and into the back axle.

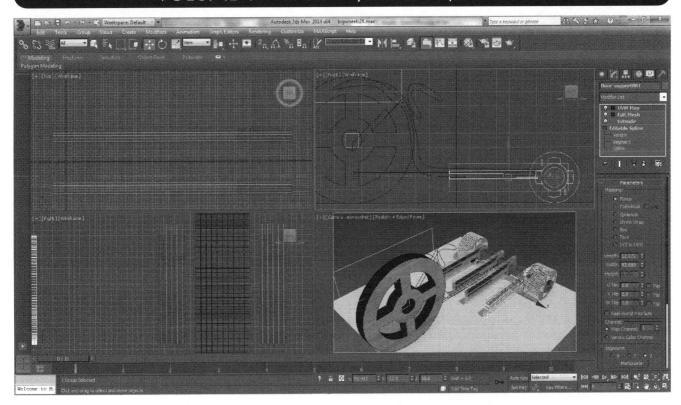

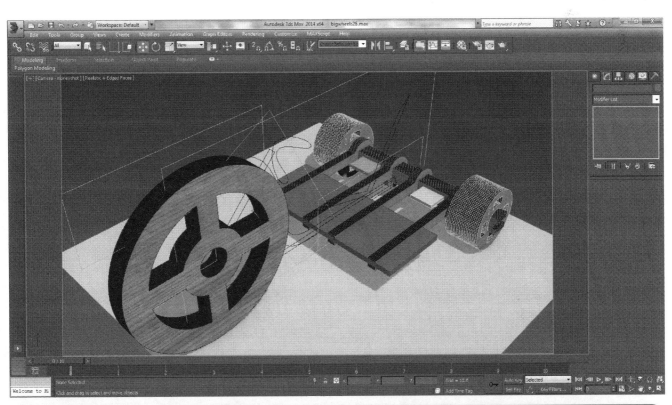

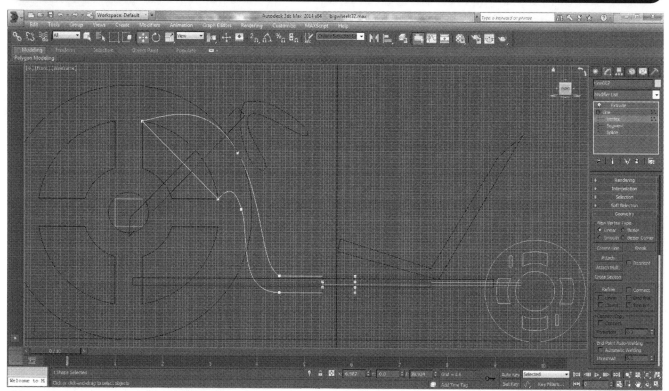

Step 14: Image top of this page

The challenge I have here is making the second piece strong enough to hold the wheel assembly in place. If I just wanted the wheel to go straight, it would be easy but I want to be able to steer this project easily, which means having the steering column lock into place. Easy if you have steel tubes and exterior hardware, tough when you only have glue and plywood.

Another option I'm thinking of doing is having the middle supports that are found on the floor actually extend the length of the model somehow.

Step 15: Image next page top

I know that the design I have now won't work since the steering column has to work from the center of the wheels to work properly, so I'll have to develop something that goes on both sides and locks it into place. Doing all these calculations in my head is a good workout because I only plan on building one of these and having everything work perfectly on the first try.

Step 16: Image next page bottom

After a lot of going back and forth, I decided to make the central column all one part front to back; it adds so much strength to this model and also greatly simplifies the build process. There is also a lot of room to add character to the model. I want this to be strong, functional AND COOL! I have enough now to start work on the steering column. The seating will have to be able to go back and forth to accommodate the driver, but that works great when you have two levels of flooring to go through.

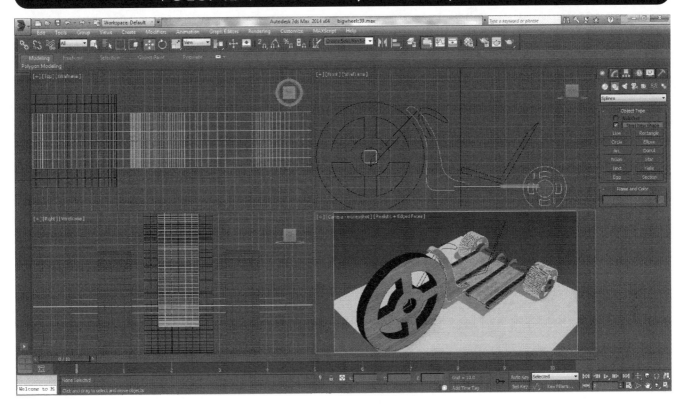

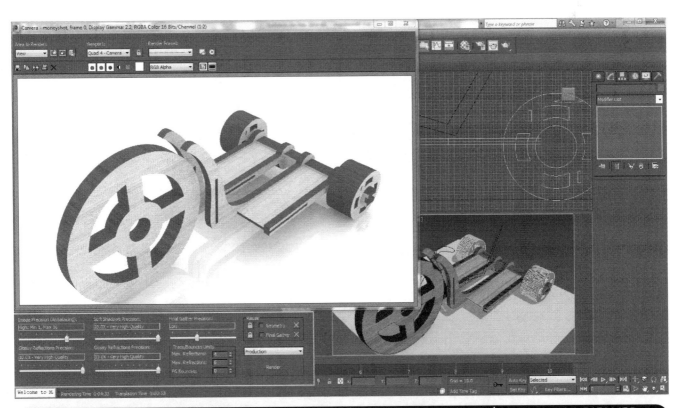

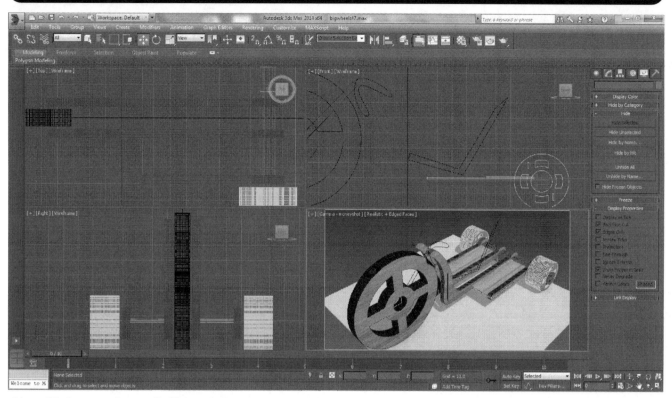

Step 17: Image top of this page

I extended the back further which means bigger kids than me would be able to drive this, but it also allows me to add some storage in the back, like a basket to carry things along. I also thickened-up the full-length supports to give them more strength while keeping the ones on the side the same to begin adding more layers to the model.

Step 18: Image next page top

Time to build the seat! I've made a 30 cm square box and gave it a slight rotation so that driving is a little more comfortable, though I'll probably make this seat into something that's compounded so that it looks a little cooler than just a regular seat. At this position, the middle of the seat to the middle of the front wheel is 68 cm.

Step 19: Image next page bottom

The seat will have a lot of strength onto it as the back is what you are pushing up against to get some torque so it must be extremely solid. It would be incredibly uncomfortable to sit on edge-on plywood with related splinters, so I'll be using full sheet faces for the seat and backrest.

This also greatly reduced the piece count that I'd otherwise need to cover a distance of 30 cm, 6 mm at a time. You can see that I've already created the tabs.

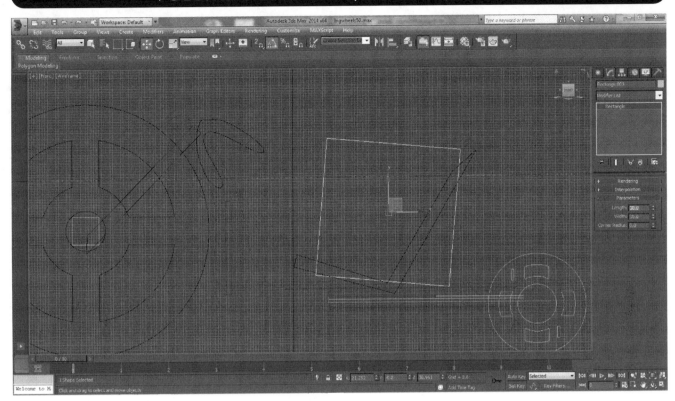

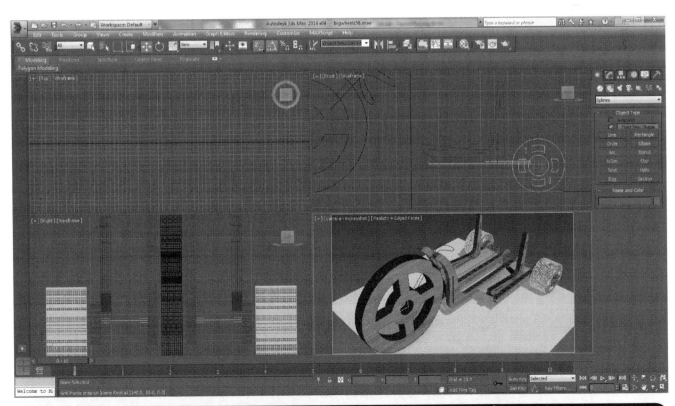

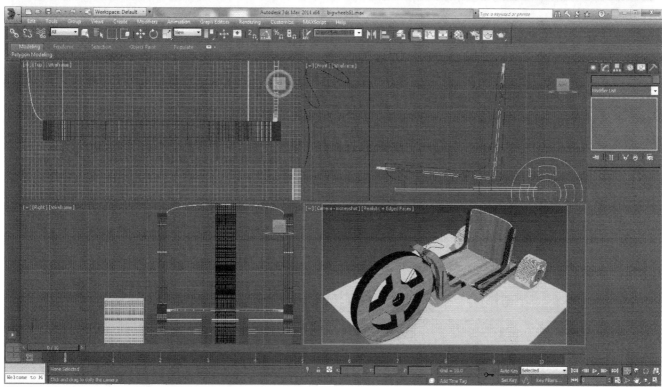

Step 20: Image top of this page

For ease at the moment, I made the seat and the back the same piece which can each only go one way and both set-back 5 degrees. I think I'll double-up the seats panels just for some extra strength; one sheet of plywood might bend to increase comfort but I also want people heavier than me to be able to sit on this without it breaking.

Step 21: Image next page top

Fixed-up a few parameters with the seat to make it stronger, should be fine to support some pretty heavy kids now. Next-up is getting the steering column worked-out.

Step 22: Image next page bottom

It's now time to fix the front wheel as if I have a round hole inside of it with a square axle. I will have absolutely no torque because the pedealing will just spin the inside axle and not the wheel. The wheel needs to be locked into the pedals for maximum torque.

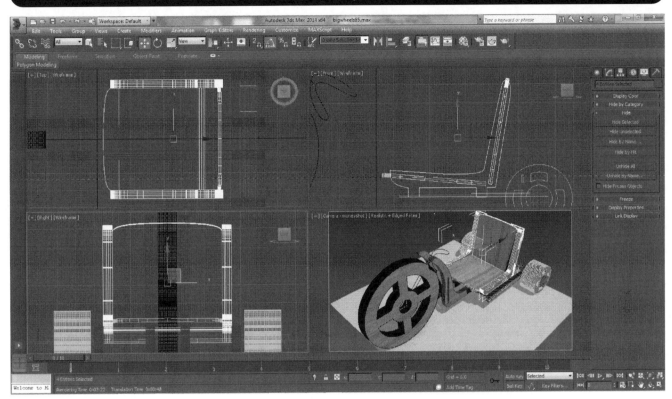

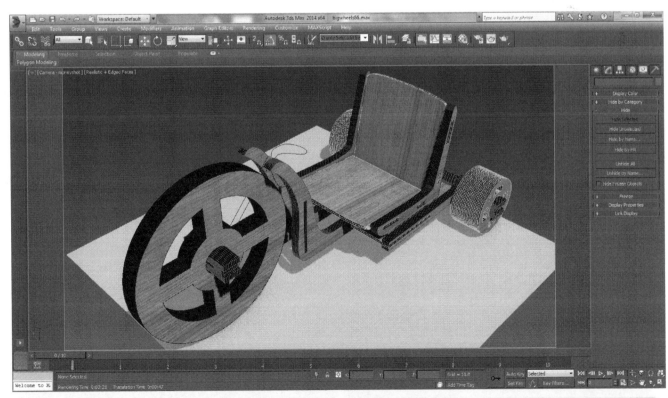

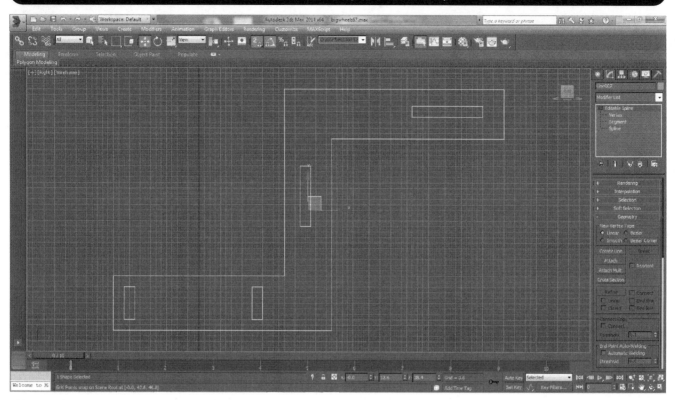

Step 23: Image top of this page

The pedal has to be extremely strong; I'll make them symmetrical so one side is just a mirror of the other on both sides of the main big wheel. There will be a lot of pressure on this both pushing and pulling (reverse pedaling to stop faster). Plywood is a strong material but it does have limits especially when you have pieces out afar without any supportive guides to keep them in place.

They will each be 5 x 0.6 mm in thickness. I also have to lock both pedals together within the axle, hence the two guides in the axle area.

Step 24: Image next page top

My pedals are a little too large here, but this gave me an idea. I can actually alternate the vertical pedals with horizontal guides, creating the strength I need while also making them more functional since they'll be completely symmetrical on both sides.

Step 25: Image next page bottom

This is looking far better, the pedals seem a little too thick because I need to make pedals that spin along with the wheel otherwise you will have to constantly move your feet.

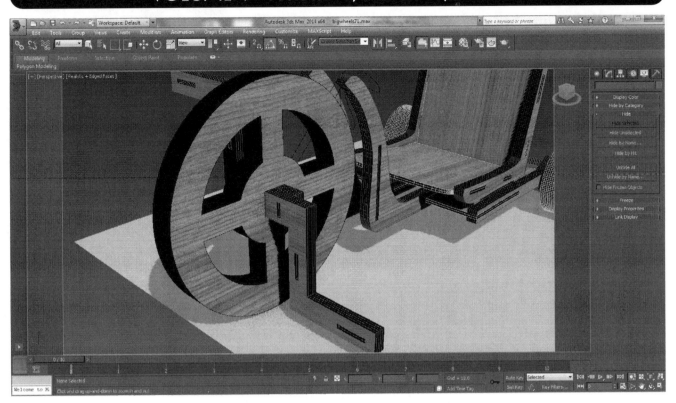

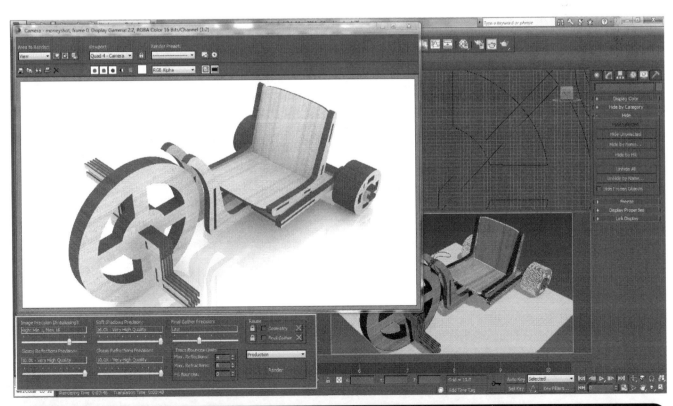

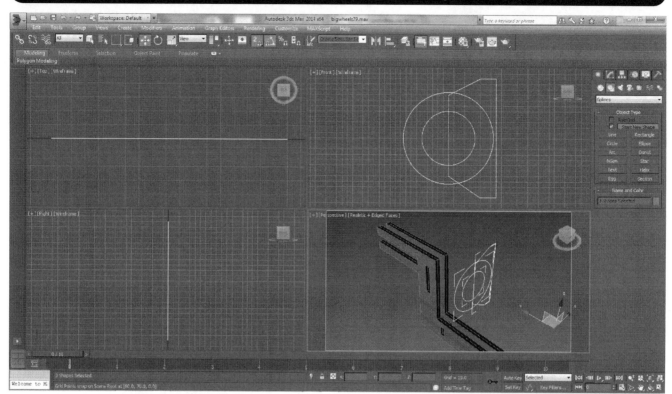

Step 26: Image top of this page
I need to make the pedals very strong since they rotate around the pedal. This is where it would be fantastic to use exterior hardware to introduce strength and to make things smooth, but in this case, the more you use the Big Wheels, the smoother everything will be because it will naturally wear out.

Step 27: Image next page top
The pedals are looking good, I just need to fill-out the axles and pedals with cross members and a lock so that the rotating pedals don't come off the pedals.

The same process will be done in the back wheels as well to keep them from spinning off the axle having internal cross-members dramatically increases the strength and doubling them up further will assure that moderate pressure won't make the pedals break.

Step 28: Image next page bottom
I've completed the pedal; they should be plenty strong and be able to swivel without too much friction. I added a hole inside of the foot pad just for fun. Throughout the model thus far, I'm still very much roughing out ideas and concepts.

I will focus on making things "nice" once I have the fundamentals sorted otherwise it's just too much work to constantly go back and forth between structure and esthetics.

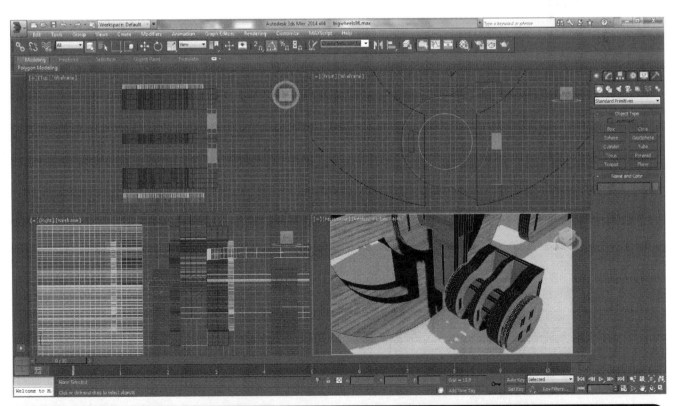

Step 29: Image top of this page

This is looking messy! What I need to do is create a steering column in-between the two arms for the big wheel that doesn't hit into the side support frames. The column doesn't have much pressure on it but it is holding the entire front of the Big Wheel up and, on hard turns, it will have a lot of strength on it. This is becoming quite a challenge - so much easier if I was making this out of metal where one 6 mm sheet of stainless steel would be stronger than 10x 6 mm plywood.

Step 30: Image next page top

I figured-out how to make the streering column strong enough; I split-up the wheel into two parts so that there is a very strong central column with two side arms. They will be locked into place in the upper parts of the steering column while the wheels and pedals will keep them in place at the bottom around the wheel. This is by far the best solution I've been able to come-up with and although it makes the Big Wheels look a little weird, it also makes it look kinda cool as well.

The wheels are solid disks with cross-members inside of them, so they won't be going anywhere and will have quite a bit of momentum built-up into them. The pedals now have a 30 cm circular diameter in movement, so plenty of leverage to move the whole thing.

Step 31: Image next page bottom

The steering wheel is half way into the column and half way out to give it strength. Once the entire assembly is glued together, it should be plenty strong especially after I add some internal guides supporting everything together.

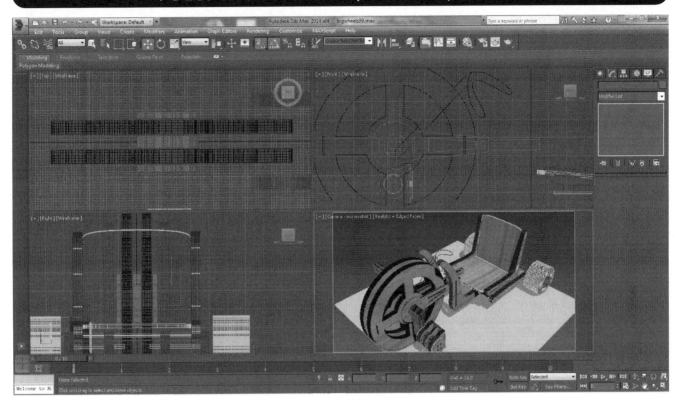

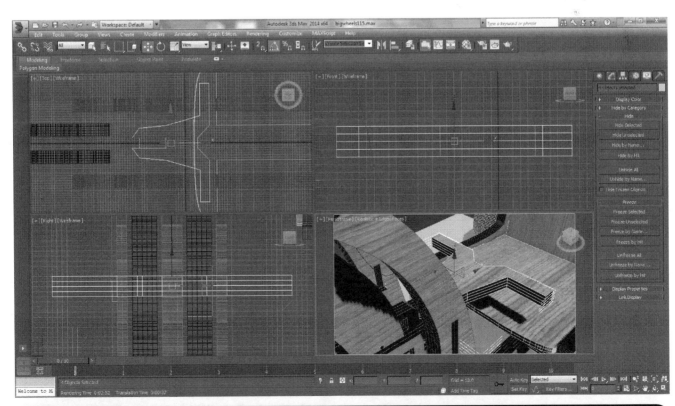

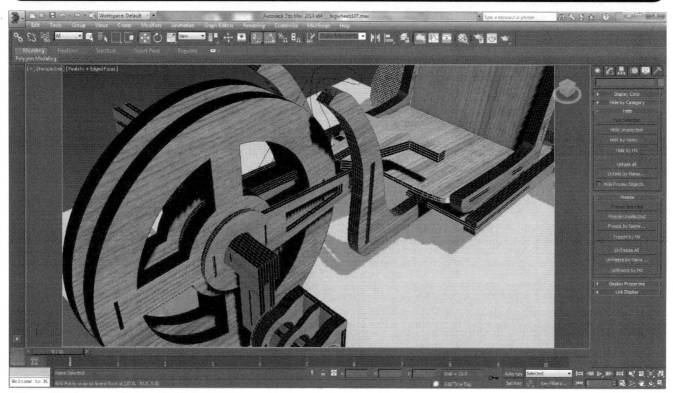

Step 32: Image top of this page

I'm now going to finalize the pedals, add internal supports across the front since that won't change then get the frame working.

Step 33: Image next page top

The front wheel is looking good and solid now with all the internal supports; next-up is getting the frame up to spec. I'm thinking of having the steering column slide into place, then have it locked into place using guides that go on either sides which will require some extensive frame modifications.

Step 34: Image next page bottom

The arm in the front is now solid. It should pivot easily and be plenty strong; the bottom where the axle is will be held in place by the wheels and pedals. Lots of intersecting parts to add more strength to the entire steering column.

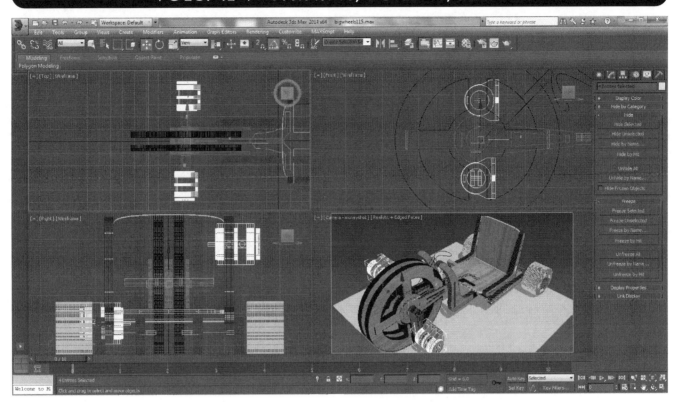

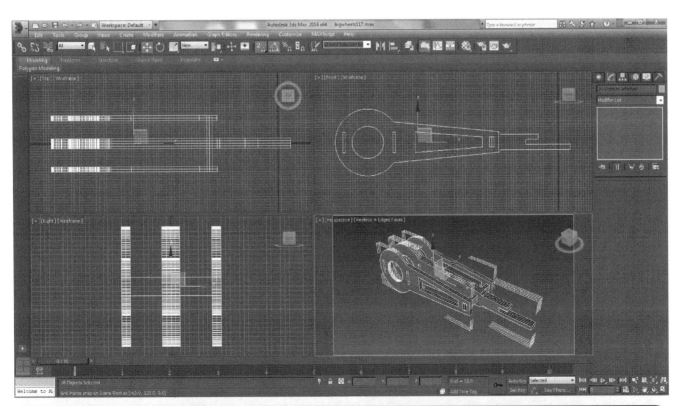

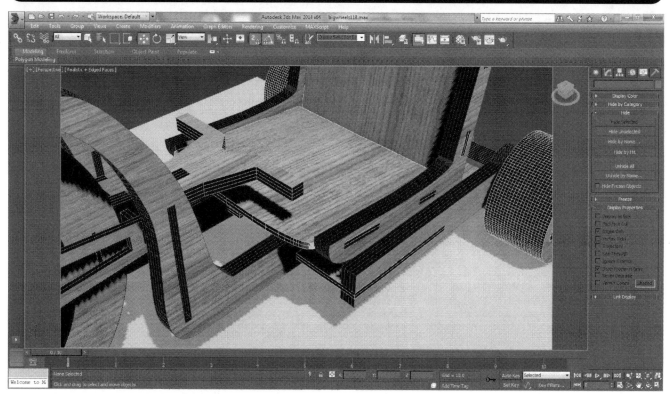

Step 35: Image top of this page
I've almost doubled the thickness of the frame that goes under the seat to make absolutely sure it will not bend or break under pressure. This included thickening-up the back axle supports. Next step is getting the platform done that will hold the seat in one of two positions, one forward, one further back, to accomodate people of different sizes.

Step 36: Image next page top
I'm going to have two levels of doubled-up board for the seating. This should introduce plenty of strength when interlocked with the frames and more importantly, prevent the seat from moving around as it will be inserted across two levels of board so it won't be moving without needing any clue to keep it in place.

As you can see, the old board positioning no longer works right but this hallowing-out of the center area is on purpose. I have a cool idea I want to try and it needs the room under the platform. While building this, I realized that having a hand brake on the back wheels isn't the most efficient placement for it; maybe stick it in the front instead to stop the big wheel up front instead.

Step 37: Image next page bottom
I now have my two levels of doubled-up board figured-out. Now I need to make the holes for the seating, by making six holes in the board, but a seat, with only two pegs, it would give me three different positions for the seat if done right.

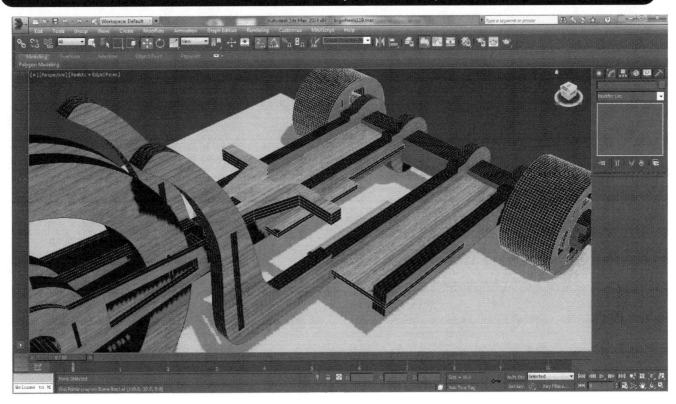

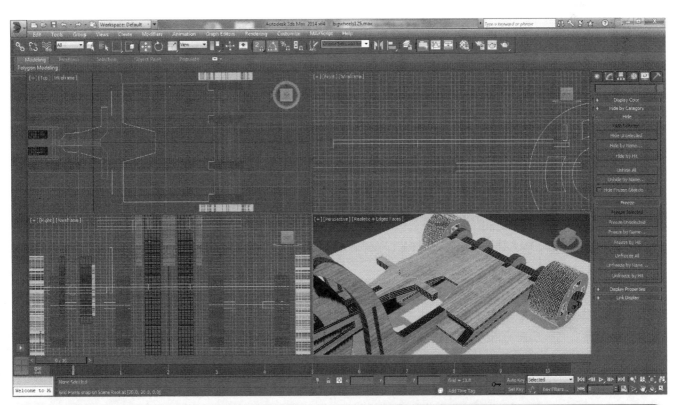

Step 38: Image top of this page

I now have the platform that will support the seating sorted out. I want to add a board slightly lower for storage and a basket in the back for additional storage options. I don't expect this to be driven to work but it is nice to empty your pockets onto some trays on the Big Wheels instead of the road all around you while driving this.

Step 39: Image next page top

Now that the storage is over and I've refined the front block to prevent rocks from jumping-up from the wheels and heading right for your face. I really have to get the seating modified to fit within the new parameters I built into the floor's holes which will lock it in place.

Step 40: Image next page bottom

I've now modified the seat, so it fits perfectly within the new parameters I've established and got rid of the raised sides so that even larger people can easily sit in it. Now I need to get the steering column resolved.

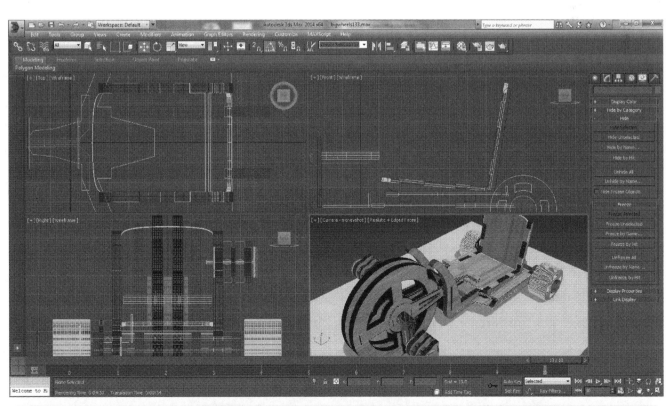

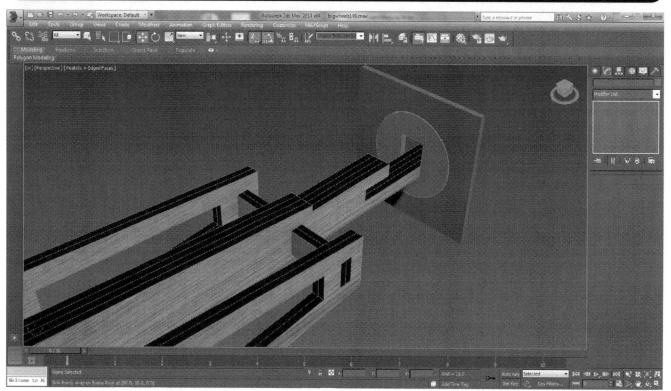

Step 41: Image top of this page

After a lot of thought, I've come to the conclusion that the easiest way to build the steering column into the frame is to use a two stage process similar to what I used for the back wheels. Basically, you have one round disk that turns inside of another part with a round hole in it. This will make sure that there is just enough movement to allow the swivel to be easy, yet strong enough not to break from the forces involved. The part you see in the picture will slide down the shaft.

Step 42: Image next page top

I never built a vehilcle that I could ride with a CNC machine, much less a steering column, but this picture looks fine except it isn't possible to assemble. These happen regularly and I generally catch all of them. Basically the steering column would slide into place with plates keeping it in place. It can't be pushed up because the steering arms block it in place but can slide down. So I thought of just putting guides through the column on the other side but if you look carefully, how can I possibly slide these blocks in place if I have a solid frame on both sides? It simply isn't possible, so my initial idea doesn't work.

They can rotate fine but I just can't slide them through the frame. The solution is either make holes in the frame to allow this (weaking the structure in the process) or thinking of another way to stick locks in place. After half an hour of trying to think of an easy way around this, I realized that the steering column can swivel 90 degrees, at which point, sliding the blocks in place wouldln't pose a problem at all!

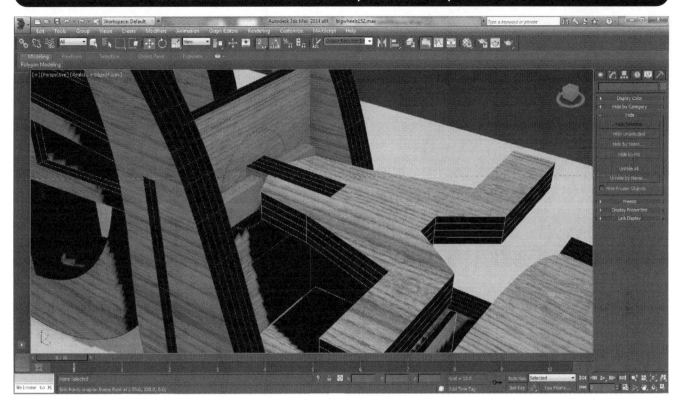

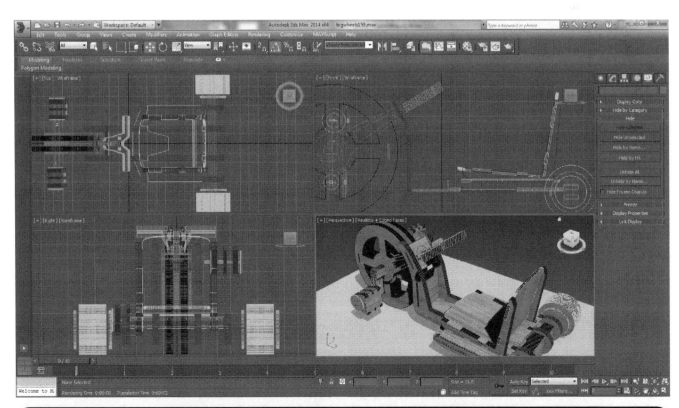

Step 43: Image previous page bottom and this page top
I moved the entire arm up 30 degrees after a few additional modifications to the frame and after doing a final review of every part, I'll call this model finished. I was thinking of adding a basket in the back but it's not really needed because the storage in the front is pretty large to hold a wallet and anything else you may have in your pockets.

This model is roughly a meter and a half long, a meter wide and half a meter high, and is made-up of 237 pieces. My wood is 6.7 mm instead of 6 mm as this model is designed for. So I'll scale everything up to fit accordingly except I have one issue, the largest wheel in this model would come to 61 cm from 55 cm from this upscaling which is just the limit of my ShopBot Desktop which may pose some problems.

However the next sized wheel comes to 58 cm which is fine, so if I have any issue, I'll just double-up the next size up instead of trying to cut the larger one to right size.

Step 44: Image next page top
Having every component based will make sorting the cutting files easier and more importantly, allow me to make more sense of all these pieces.

Step 45: Image next page bottom
I then broke the components down into their individual pieces to all be facing me. As you can visually see, the back wheel is by far the most complex part of this project with about a third of the total piece count.

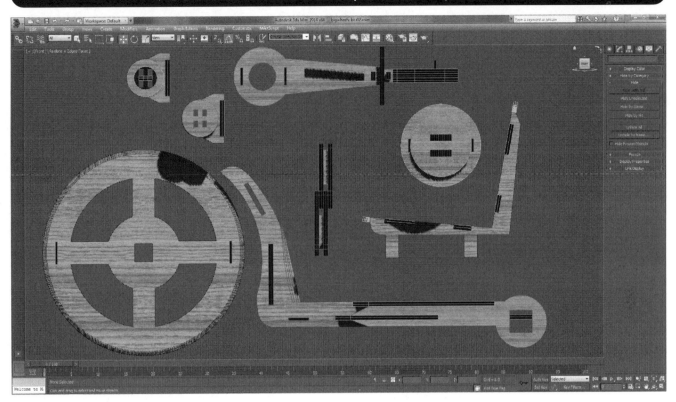

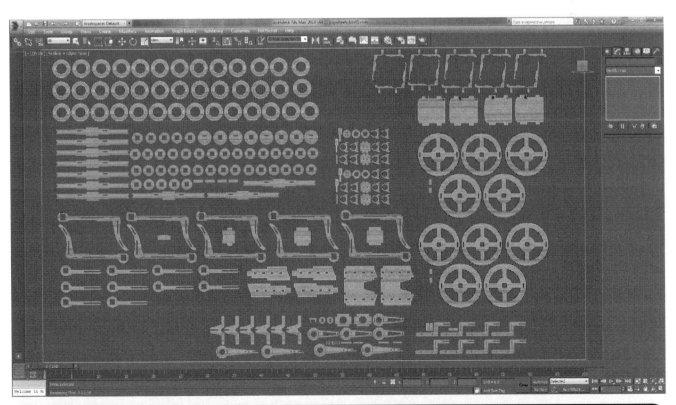

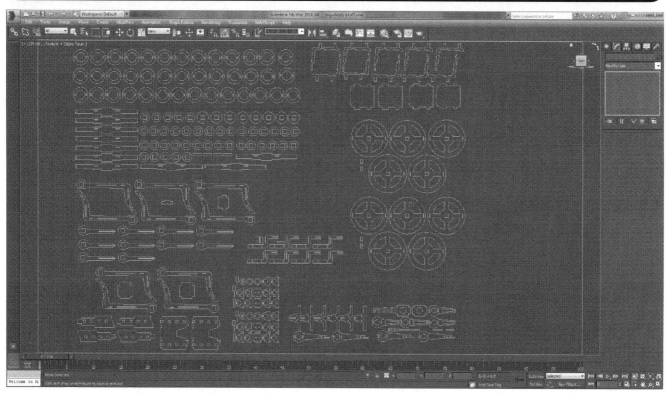

Step 46: Image top of this page

After getting rid of the extrusions on all these parts, I convert these 3D parts into 2D outlines which can then be used for toolpathing.

Step 47: Image next page top

The square in the middle of the page represents my board size of 600 x 1200 mm. As you can see, I'll be using quite a few of them and I need to optimize all my parts to fit onto this board. Just looking at the wheels, it seems I have a full sheet there alone (4 x 600 x 1200 mm).

Step 48: Image next page bottom

There was one "mistake" in my design, the front arms tended to be too loose along with the wheels. I should have doubled the up further but it was a quick fix using blocks on the axle to keep everything aligned and where it should be.

My wood is 6.5 mm and not 6 mm. I'll scale the entire drawing up by 10% to make sure that everything fits properly. This model will be even bigger than I envisioned!

After exporting the file from Adobe Illustrator and importing it into PartWorks, I then begin the tedious job of adding dog bones to all the inner pieces.

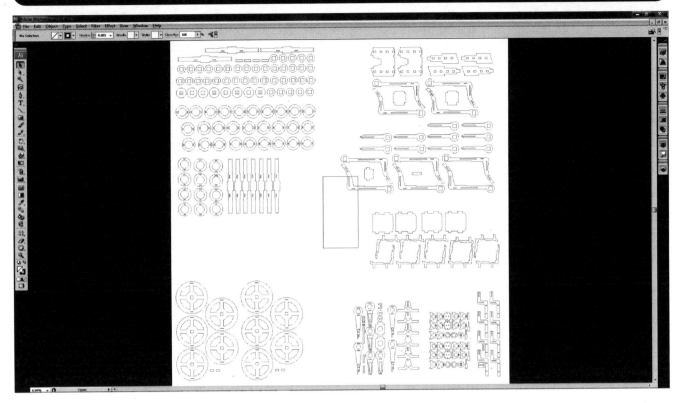

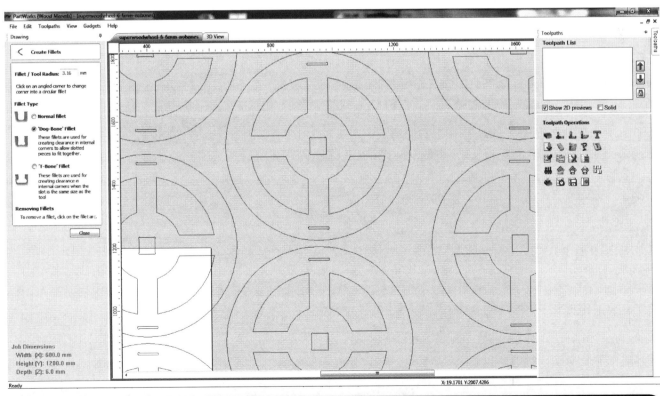

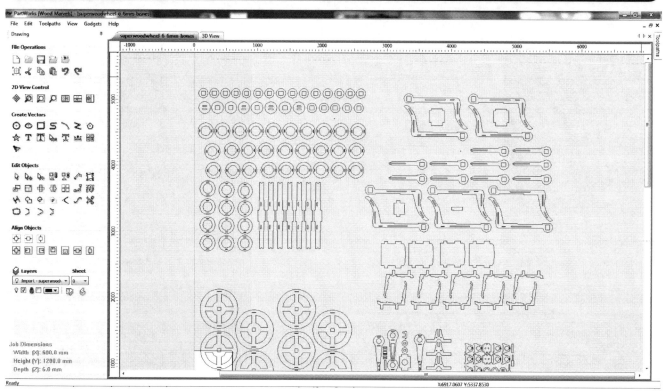

Step 49: Image top of this page
It took a little over an hour, but I've now finished dog bonning all the parts that needed it. Next step up is sorting them all out by board, but first I need to group all of the individual components in each piece to make sure nothing gets lost (inside parts) while I move them around and rotate things to fit.

Step 50: Image next page top
I watched a youtube video where somebody was table routing a project and I noticed he used automatic nesting... I didn't even know this existed! I just about fell off my chair as I've been manually optimizing my sheets for two years! I set-up the parameters and 5 minutes later, the sheets are better optimized than I ever could have done in a fraction of the time! Wow... never too late to learn new tricks!!!

Step 51: Image next page bottom
The only issue I have with the automatic tiling is that I need to further optimize the placement of the parts as I want to cut them as whole as possible so it means repositioning smaller segments to fit onto one tile instead of across two.

This has still saved me a tremendous amount of time, just doesn't replace manually fixing and tool pathing that needed to be done anyways.

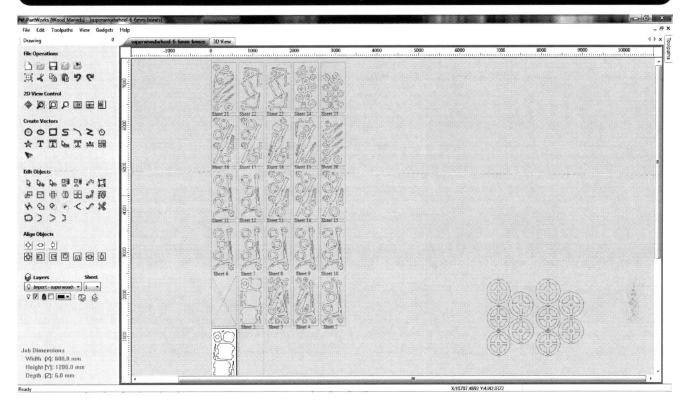

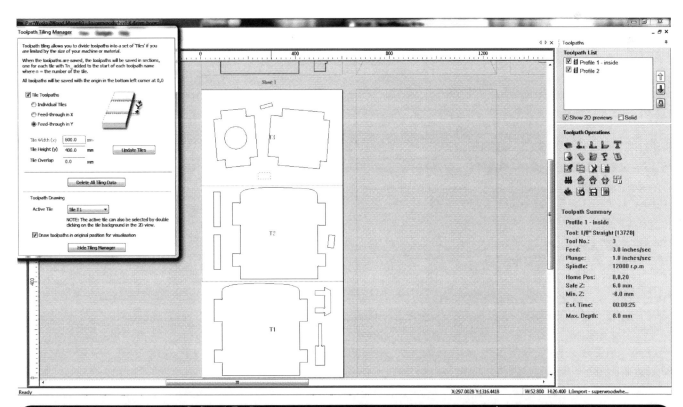

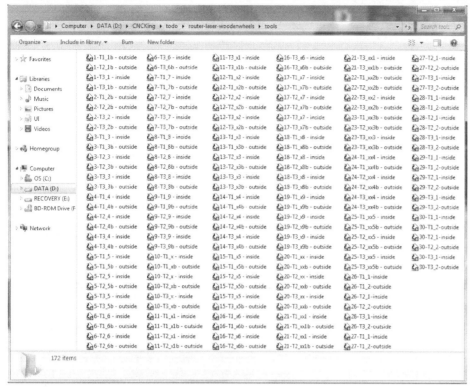

Step 52: Image top of this page

As you can imagine, it took a few hours to clean-up the toolpathing and the result is 172 individual cut files for this entire project since I have to do each 60 x 120 cm sheet in thirds to fit through my machine.

This is easily a full day of just cutting... then it's the fun task of organizing all these parts into assemblies and into the final model. If the scope of this isn't big enough to warrant a full-sheet router, then I don't know what will convince people. I know for me, full-sheet router is a must if I have to cut this again!

Step 53: Image next page top

Half way through the cutting process, I realized I was missing some parts. For some reason when I brought in files from Adobe Illustrator into PartWorks, it skipped the outer parts, so what I did was create another cutting file containing those missing parts. This worked out for the best because I actually found a mistake in my model in the process: the lower floor for the seating wouldn't be able to be made in the real world because you can't enter tabs in two corners at the same time. This project just got even bigger!

Step 54: Image next page bottom

Now that I have a bit more experience with nesting and setting-up my parts, I realize that I could actually reduce orientation to 1 degree and fit a lot more parts per board as a result. In hindsight, I should have checked through to make sure all the pieces were in my original import rather than assuming and using 1 degree instead of 5 as I probably would have ended-up with the same board count overall with a lot less wastage.

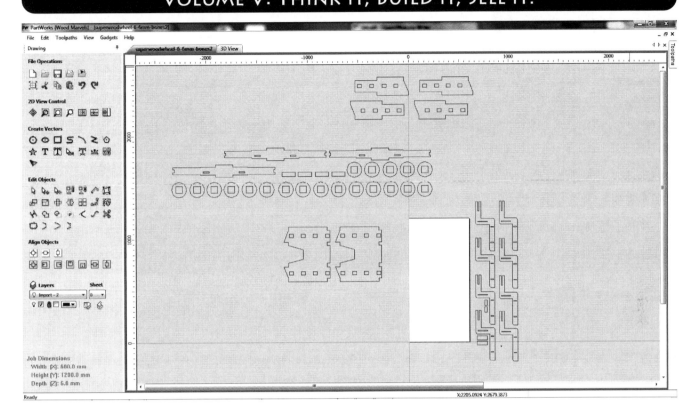

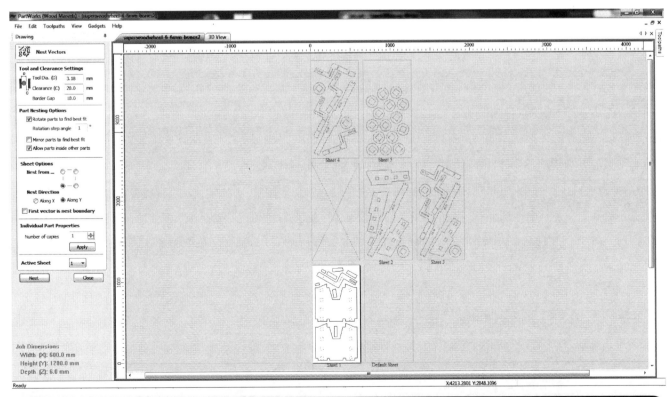

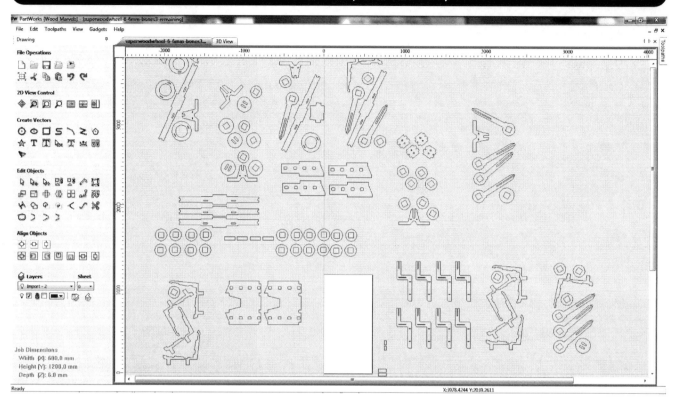

Step 55: Image top of this page

What I'll do is bring-in all the remaining boards (I was up to #17 which I marked all with a pencil for easy reference) and mix them up with what I missed here into a third document which should optimize things further.

It take a bit more time on the computer since I'll have to re do all the toolpathing, but I save material and money as well as quite a few hours in the process.

Step 56: Image next page top

As the part density is far higher now, I will have to put screw holes in all these boards, while in most of the previous boards, I was able to skip this step and figure it out by eye which saved a lot of time. Win some hours and lose some hours!

The total sheet count left to be done is 12 sheets, originally I would have had 5 (new) + 9 (remaining to be cut); so this exercise saved me three 60 x 120 cm sheets in total which is about an hour and a half of saved time which I will now spend remaking the toolpathing I made a while back on the original nesting.

My boards are now fuller as well, which means less wastage! I saved almost a full sheet at the end of the day which is 44 $AU/sheet!

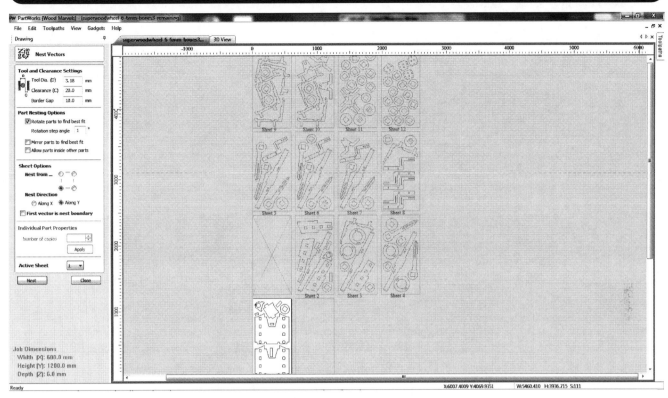

Step 57: Image next page top

While I built this model, I realized that my steering column was simply too weak to support my weight. It actually broke the moment I sat on the completed model. As a result, I decided to go back and redesign this aspect of this Wooden Big Wheels so that this part was dramatically stronger.

Step 58: Image next page bottom

I had a lot of trouble modifying the column to support my weight on the tricycle, so after lots of tinkering, I decided to just rebuild the front part while trying to salvage the large wheels and the pedals as those parts were fine.

Sometimes it's easier, though a big pain, to just throw away and restart; this delays the project by another two days. In this case, the column will have another two layers, be much beefier and it will mean re-building the steering to suit the new design. This is a major weak point that I need to wickedly overbuild for any hope of success.

At the same time, I'll also get rid of some disks I added inside the wheel since they won't be needed with this design update.

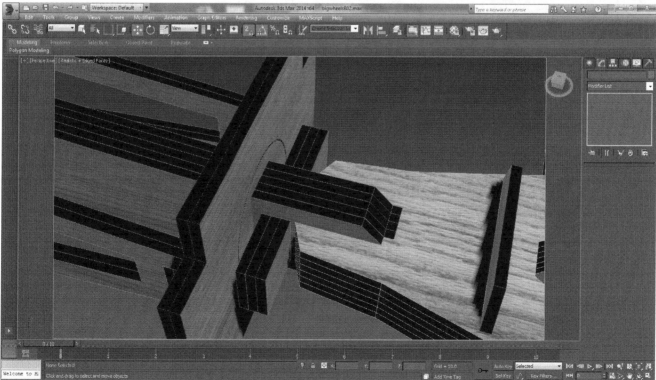

Step 59: Image top of this page

After playing with the real steering column, I came to the decision that, due to the weigh, there is no way a driver is going to be turning at any great angle, there is just too much mass in front and in the back, so that means I can add a few more layers to the steering assembly arms on the outside, the turning radius will be compromized but it's compromized regardless.

Now I'm starting to get something a lot more hefty! My original design has 4 layers on the inside, this new design has 8 layers inside. I have no plans on going through this AGAIN so I'm overdoing it.

Step 60: Image next page top

The disk I have holding the steering column is alarmingly thin on the edges and will be prone to break. This would be an easy solution (give it a wider diameter), but now that my second part is all glued-up, it would mean breaking that all apart which isn't something I wish to do. What I'll do instead is modify the pegs, so instead of being rectangular, they are semi-round disks that interlock on both sides, wider than the hole. It's the only solution I can think of.

Step 61: Image next page bottom

These disks interlocking on both sides will be a pain to stick into place, but there is a lot more support building it this way rather than straight pegs.

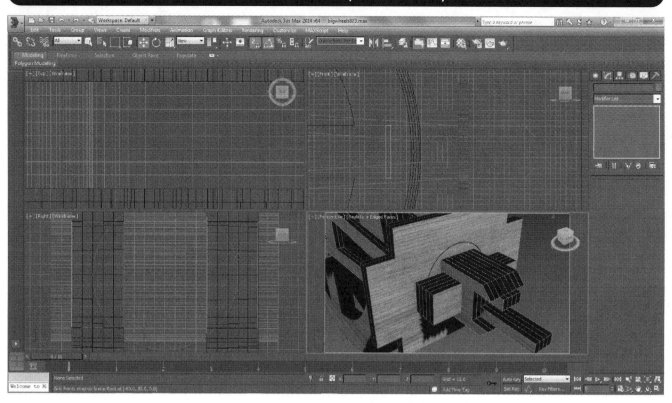

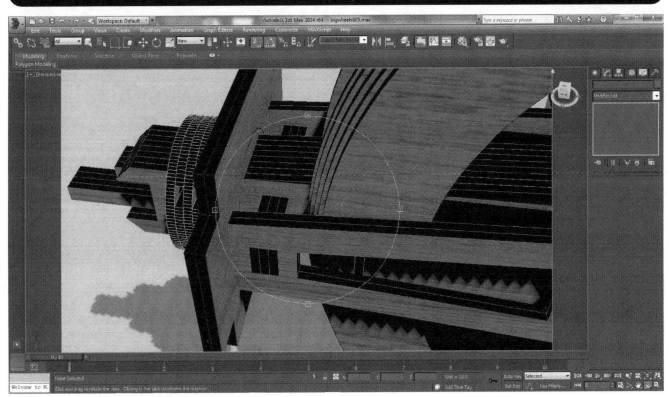

Step 62: Image top of this page
The pegs on the other side are now stepped, something I wished I did earlier during assembly so that my spacing is more accurate. I do see a new problem though, the wheels will be too tight against the sides, still trying to figure-out a solution to this.

Step 63: Image next page top
This is already far stronger than the frankenstein version I made earlier to strengthen the steering wheel assembly.

Step 64: Image next page bottom
Along with a few other modifications to make my life assembling this project easier, I've also made the steering wheel all the same parts as well instead of 2-3 different ones.

The interlock, as you can see in the picture, will be plenty solid and directly connected to the steering column going all the way down to the wheel.

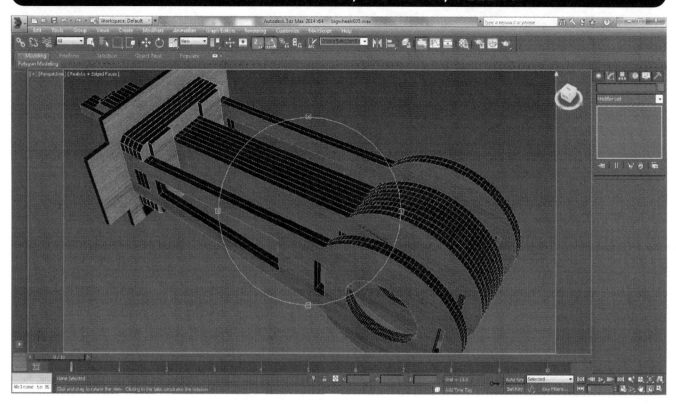

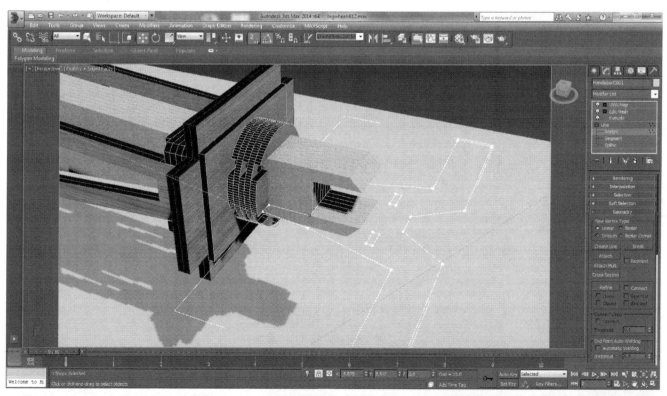

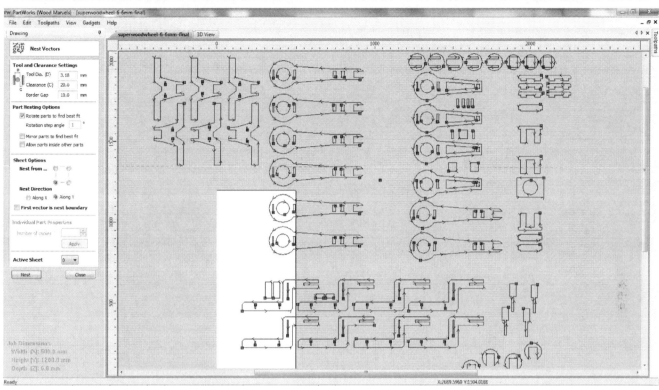

Step 65: Image top of this page

I now have all my new parts sorted, it's basically the whole front area minus the wheels and the pedals. Let's see what the automatic nesting does in this case.

Step 66: Image next page top

Automatic nesting manages to fit everything onto 6 sheets measuring 1200 x 500 mm which is pretty good, but from past experience, as I'm indexing by eye, there would be too many problems using these highly optimized sheets since I'd be a few mm off and, although I'd love to cut only 6 sheets, what this shows me is a lot of headaches in real life. Let's run another simulation.

Step 67: Image next page bottom

Surprisingly, changing the maximum angle of movement of each piece from 1 degree to 90 degrees actually uses less sheets and everything seems to fit far better because I'll be dividing these sheets in 3.

This makes far more sense, at least my few mm off will only slightly modify things, along 90 degree interval instead of 1 degree. Let's optimize these sheets, create tool paths and then cut them out!

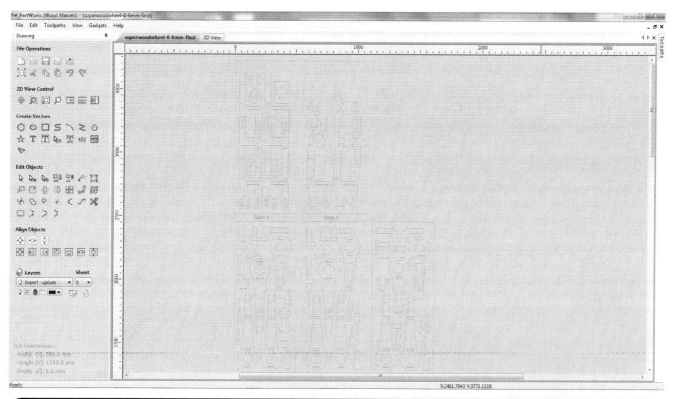

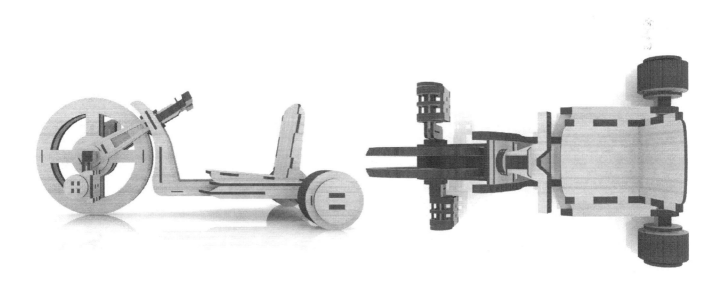

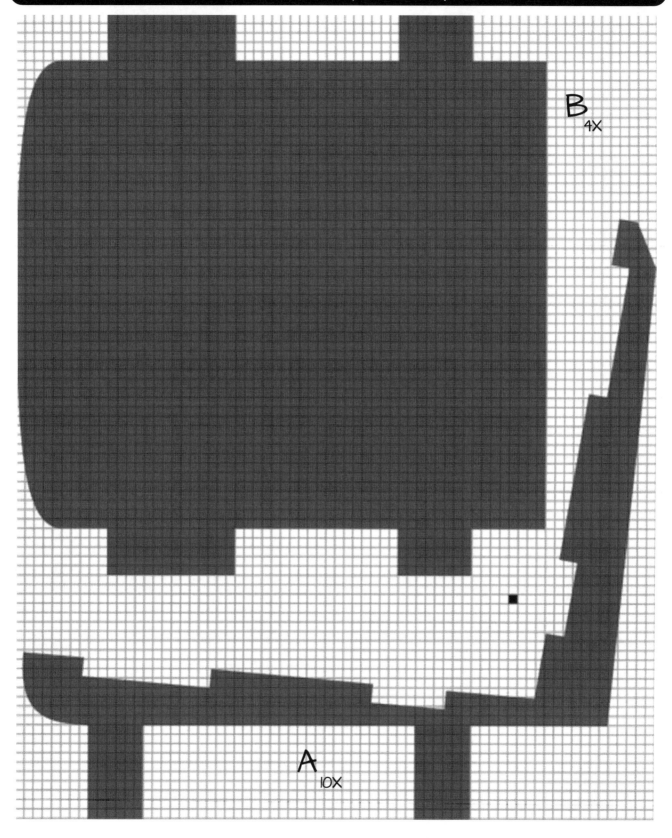

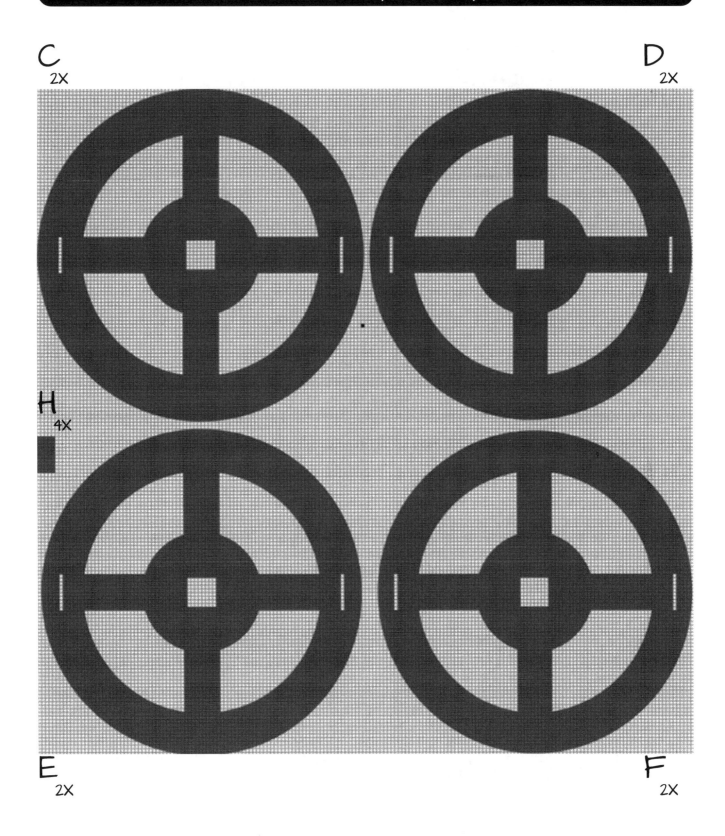

Step-by-Step Assembly Instructions

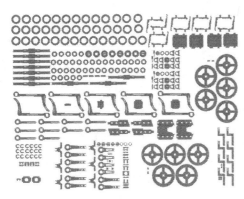

Step 1: Label and check inventory

Once you have all the pieces in front of you, the process of putting them together is no different from assembling pieces of Lego.

Label, using a pencil, the various parts and double-check your inventory. Take your time and enjoy the building process! Before jumping to the glue, be sure to do a dry run.

Step 2: Build the seat

We will build things out, component by component, then at the end put everything together.

Start by glueing together two groups of 5 parts A (seat side) followed by doubling-up two sets of parts B using clamps to keep everything together until it dries.

Afterwards, you can put these assemblies together to form a chair, applying glue where all the parts intersect.

Step 3: Build the wheels

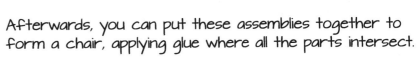

Glue together using part Hs, a staggered level of wheels from parts C to G. Use part AA (internal guides) to make alighment perfect for the wheels.

Use clamps to keep everything tight and allow it to dry overnight.

Step 4: Create the pedal foundation

Glue together four sets of doubled-up parts I pedals but do not insert the tabs seen on the blueprint page, yet, they must be added once the final assembly is built.

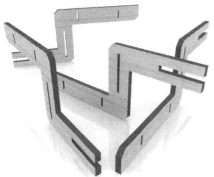

Allow to dry overnight.

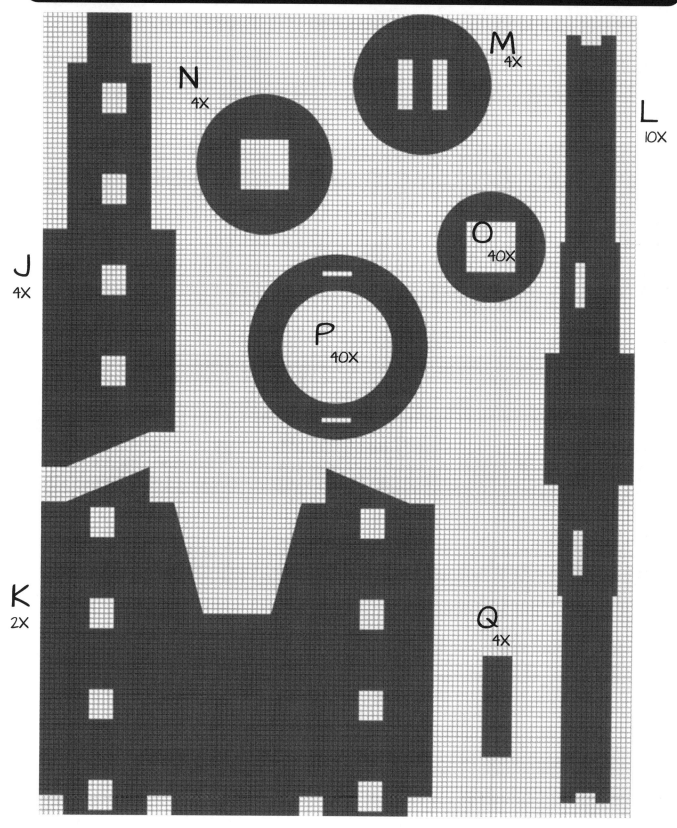

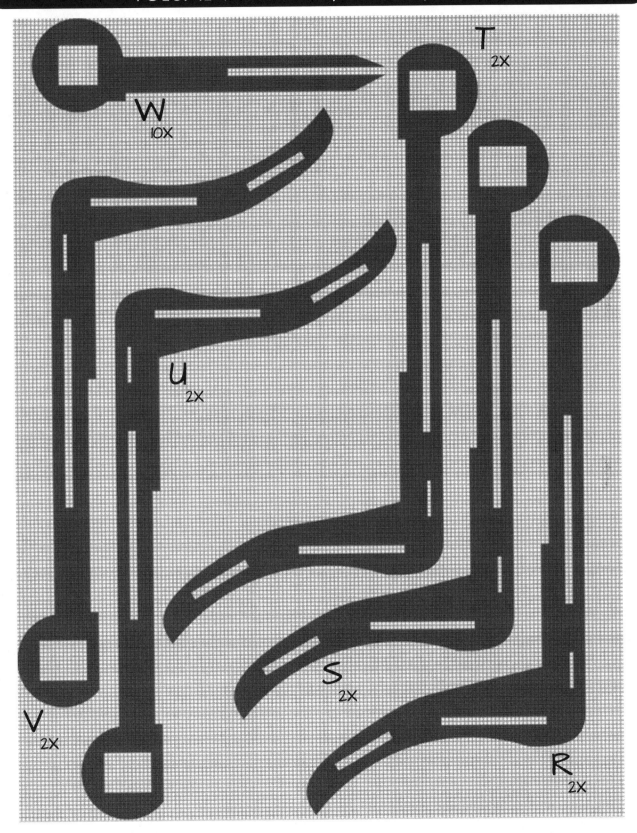

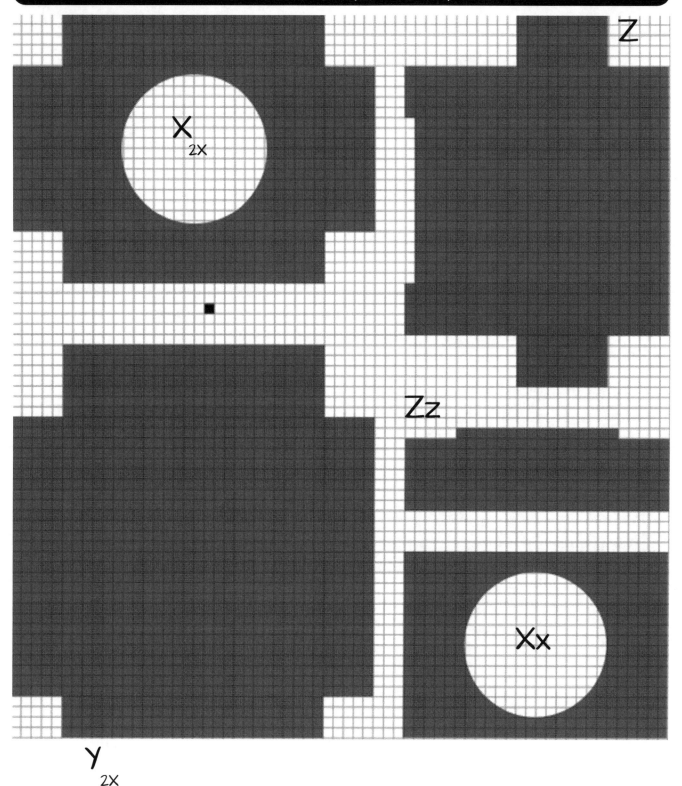

Step-by-Step Assembly Instructions

Step 5: Glue parts together

Double-up with glue parts J and K which will help secure the chair to the body, parts M and N which will help keep the back wheels in place followed by all 20 layers of parts O and P with part Q as the guide.

At this time, also glue together all parts L to form the axle using scraps as guides. Allow everything to glue overnight and you may need a rasp to smooth things over.

Step 6: Glue frame segments

Glue together parts R through V so that there is a mirrored stagger, the larger R to the smaller V on the outside.

Glue together all five parts W in two sets and allow everything to dry overnight.

Step 7: Start the frame

Slide into place using the other parts as guide, both large frame assemblies you built in the previous step with the axle assembly (glued together parts L). In between, starting from the floor upwards, a part Z horizontally, a doubled-up part Y and a doubled-up part X.

Once in position with all intersecting parts glued, put onto the part X assembly a part Xs.

Step 8: Add more width

Onto the frame you built in the previous step, slide and glue into place the doubled-up parts J (smaller frames) followed by the parts W you made in step six.

On the back of part Z facing the axle, slide and glue into place between the two large frames, a part Zz.

Use clamps to keep everything tight while it dries.

Step-by-Step Assembly Instructions

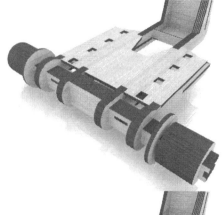

Step 9: Start the back wheels
Onto the top, slide and glue into place the doubled-up part K assembly and, on each side of the axle, the doubled-up part N followed by part O assemblies.

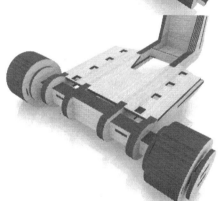

Step 10: Finish the back wheels
Slide onto the parts N, parts P (outer wheels) without any glue as you want it to slide both left and right and rotate easily with as little friction as possible. Once in place, slide and glue into place the doubled-up parts M (outer stops).

Keep in mind that the part O assemblies need to be "slippery" enough so that there isn't a lot of friction on them when you later slide into place (without glue), part P assemblies. Use a rasp at first on both the inside of the parts P and the outside of parts O then apply or place something slippery.

I've had suggestions of PVC piping, I myself thought of some thin gage metal and others have suggested simply using hardwood with grease for these two pieces instead of plywood because the friction would be far less. There are a number of things you can put in between but be sure to test it with your full weight.

I found that, for me, using 6.6 mm plywood on this model posed no friction problems when rolling it on the ground, but when I sat on the chair, that's when it was evident that something had to be done. Although I could overpower the friction using the front pedals, it puts a lot of strain on the frame that really shouldn't be needed as the front wheel rotates fine.

Your results will vary but it's important that you find and test this mechanism once all the parts are dry. Any stress will weaken the glue if it isn't fully given time to dry once you sit on this model. As always, apply more glue than you think you need.

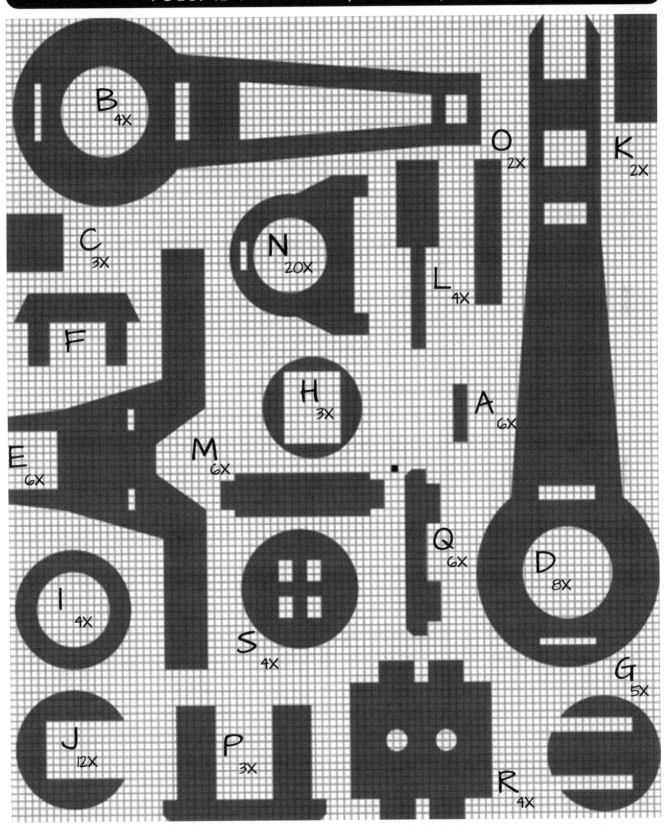

Step-by-Step Assembly Instructions

Step 11: Glue parts together

Slide and glue together, using parts A as guides, two doubled-up parts B. Using parts C as guides, glue together all parts D together.

As for the steering wheel, slide and glue together all parts E (handlebars) using part F as a guide and together all parts H. Also, glue together all parts G together.

Step 12: Start the front wheel assembly

Slide and place without glue in-between both large mirrored staggered wheels (inside with biggest wheel with smallest on the outside) with part D assembly in-between them with the part B assemblies.

You can then glue and slide into place staggered pedal assemblies you made in step 4 with the same parts AA you put into the large wheels going through the new pedal assembly to lock them in place.

Step 13: Lock the pedals in place

On both sides of the wheels, glue into place parts J onto the axle that's made-up of the pedals to help lock them into place while providing enough room for easy rotation.

On vertical slots, slide and glue into place parts K (rectangles) and then, at the end of each pedal, slide and glue into place a doubled-up part L to help lock their spacing in place. Through the ends of part B and D, glue and slide into place a tripled-up part M.

Step 14: Start the pedals

Onto pedals, slide into place without glue a part I followed by four-uped part N, a doubled-up part N and another four-uped part N. Use a part O to help guide the parts N in place. Repeat on the other side.

On the end where the steering column intersects with part B and D assemblies, glue and slide into place a part P under part M and two above it in the opposite orientation.

Step 15: Finish the pedals

Starting at the end of the steering column, slide and glue the part H assembly you built in step 11 after you slide and glued into place all six parts Q around the column in between the parts P and insert a few scraps to make this a solid mass.

On the pedals, glue into place a doubled-up part R (foot plate) followed by a loose part I and glued doubled-up part S.

Step 16: Allow everything to dry

Before you proceed with the unification of the wheel with the body of the Wooden Big Wheels, make sure everything is tight and well glued. Use clamps extensively and don't take them off until everything is allowed to dry for at least 24 hours.

A weak structure will break under the load unless everything is strong and well built, ESPECIALLY where the steering column meets the frame.

Step 17: Slide column in frame

Slide the steering column through the frame you finished building in step 10. The column should be snug and relatively easy to freely rotate.

Step 18: Perform some fishing touches

Slide into the steering column the part G assembly you built in step 11 followed by the steering wheel. You want a tight fit but not so tight that it makes turning the steering column difficult. If things snap or start to bend, your wood isn't strong enough and you need to further solidify the structure using glue and wood.

There is no need to apply any preservatives or paint; feel free to sand any sharp edges down. ENJOY!

Build Lessons - CNC Router Version

This was by far the biggest and most complex project I've ever made with my awesome ShopBot Desktop. It required a ton of wood, glue and time to put everything together. What's surprising to me in hindsight is how easy it was to complete the model!

Using "tiles" to cut out longer pieces was pretty accurate but still needed a jigsaw to refine guide holes because a few mm off did cause some issues that required a bit more work to get going straight. I think I filled-up two bins with my ShopVac with all the wood chips generated from this project.

Projects like this take a lot longer than it should have because I kept running out of clamps, this means gluing components together across several drying phases, building things up on a daily basis until I have them big enough to add to the final assembly to finish the model. Read about the press I got for this project further in this book.

Build Lessons - CNC Laser Version

It was quite a contrast building the same model at half scale using my Trotec Speedy 400 flexx. I had the same "not enough clamps" problem, even with 3x more here in Canada than I did in Perth, Australia where the other one was cut and built. I had to build this model in phases though it did go much quicker.

The "pain in the neck" part of assembling this model though was removing all the masking paper on the parts. I had a massive pile once I was done because both sides of my pieces were masked, something you don't need to do with a CNC router since there is no smoke.

The build actually went a bit smoother because I didn't use tiling this time around, so everything fit PERFECTLY together. Although I can't ride the CNC laser version of my Wooden Big Wheels, I could easily cut this at a larger scale and do just that because the finish is far cleaner. But I doubt I'd get any farther due to friction issues with the back wheels. I donated this model to Trotec Canada after it was done.

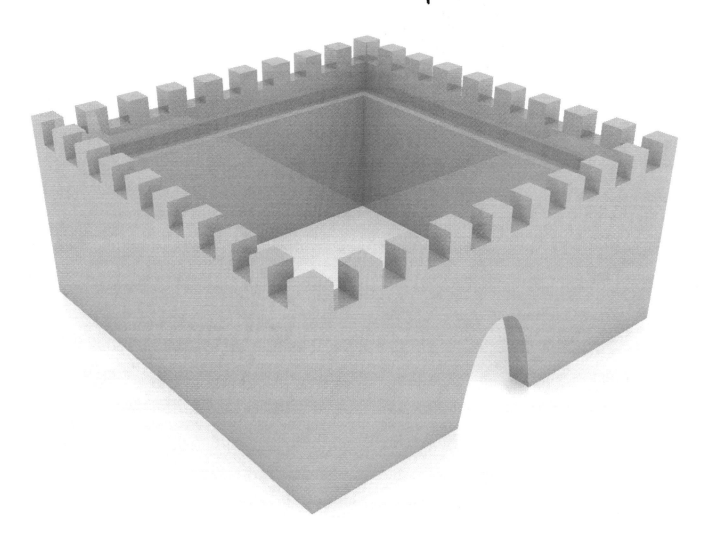

Detailed Design Notes

There are a few features of this design that warrant extra attention as they may not look obvious from the start but make a very important contribution to this 3D printed Castle Walls.

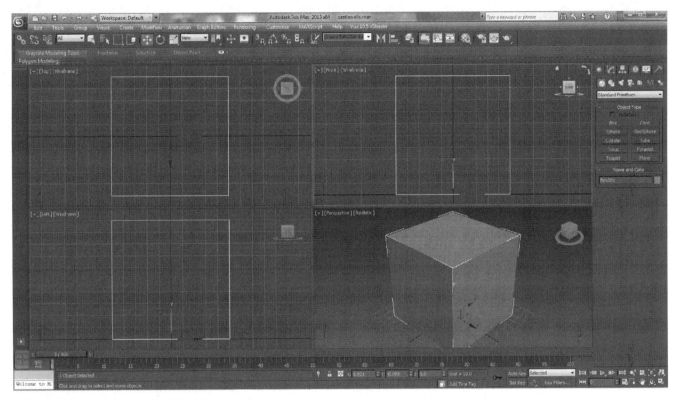

Step 1: Image top of this page
My build process always start with a cube so I know the maximum 3D printing volume I have to within.

Step 2: Image next page top
The most complex wall in tihs model is the entrance with an arch, I had to be careful with my angles here as an arch that's too wide would cause some material to fall as I need support material all the way up for my 3D extrusion printer and one that was too narrow would just look odd.

Step 3: Image next page bottom
Once I had a symmetrical wall, I then replicated it three additional times to form my other walls. These walls would NOT have an entrance so I saved myself a lot of modeling time by later removing an element rather than trying to add it to a mesh that might now work, asking me rebuilding all of the walls over again.

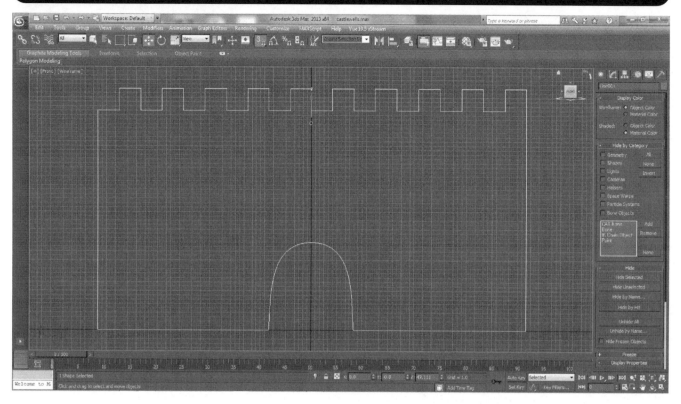

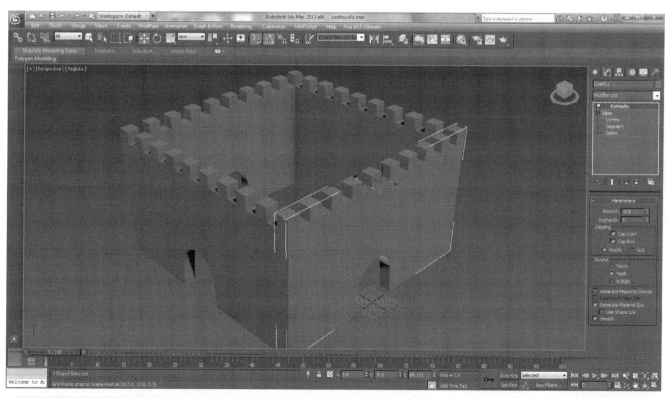

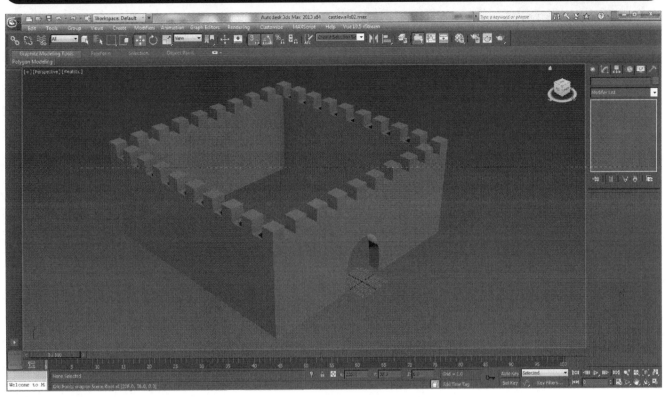

Step 4: Image top of this page

Once the additional arches were removed, I needed to do some fine tuning to the model to make sure that all the walls fell perfectly into one another at right angles.

I had to make sure the wall structure was "water tight" and as symmetrical as possible from all sides to make sure I wouldn't have any mesh errors caused by gaps in the wall structures or spacing of the individual peaks in the top of the wall.

Step 5: Image next page top

I now made the inner walkways by making a C-shape using my line tool and extruding it to the height I want. I also modified the arch in the front to be more rounded to make sure the extrusion process happens seamlessly there.

Before I exported this model as an STL, I grouped all the pieces together and ran an STL check that told me it was all clear to be 3D printed with my 3D Systems Cube.

Step 6: Image next page bottom

Importing the model into my Cubify software, I was then able to resize the model slightly and produce a build file that the cube uses to create a physical version of the virtual model. Just under five hours is more than fine!

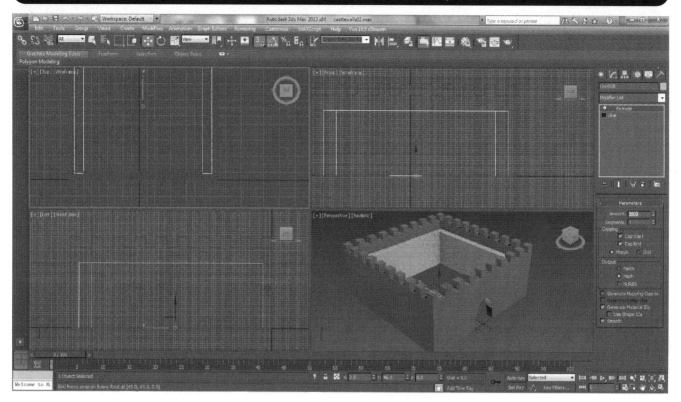

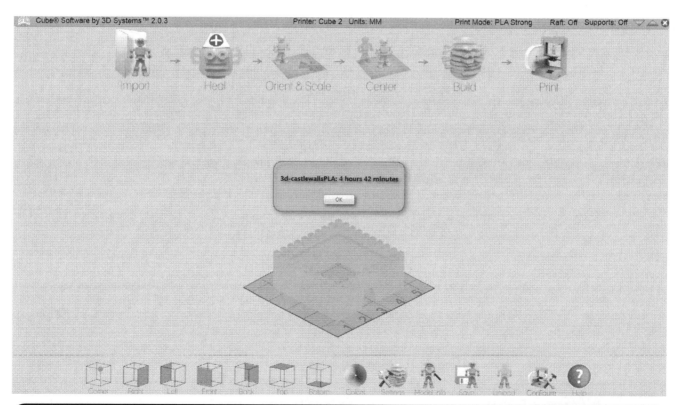

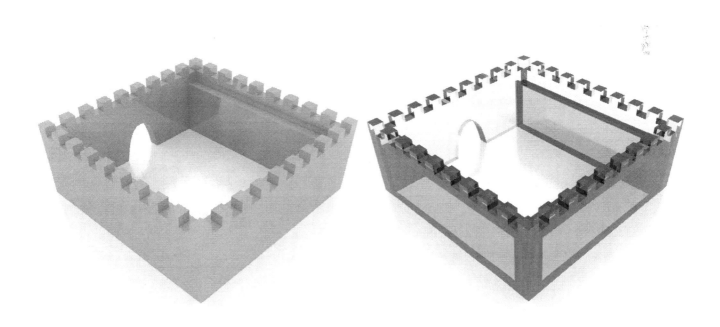

Physical Results

The 3D printing process went off without a hitch or error. The model is relatively simple and, looking at the arch, I estimated my tolerances almost perfectly - there was a little fuzzing around the top of the peaks though but that's easily removed and not a design flaw. Sometimes a little bit of plastic string doesn't get completely cut off in the 3D printing process.

Although my goal with this model was to make a very Simple Castle Walls model, now that I know this model works great, I can go back and add another layer of increased complexity to this model.

When I first got into 3D printing, I'd go all-out detail wise but then have a host of problems pop-up without any idea as to what went wrong. I wanted to test the arch and repeatability of the peaks, next step, stairs and elaborate ornamentation.

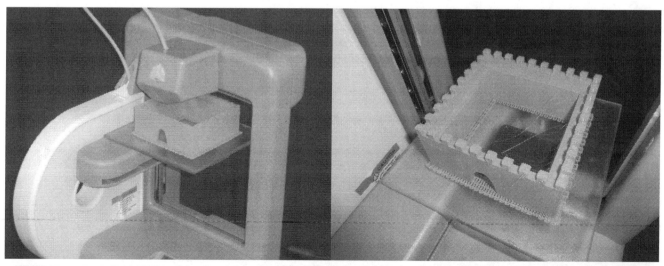

Detailed Design Notes

After the success I had making and 3D printing my Medieval Castle Walls, it's time to go all-out and build something even more complex with more detail! I want to have arched windows, 45 degree angled wall details and a few turrets! Unlike vases, using a grid for reference will come in very handy for this project to keep things symmetrical.

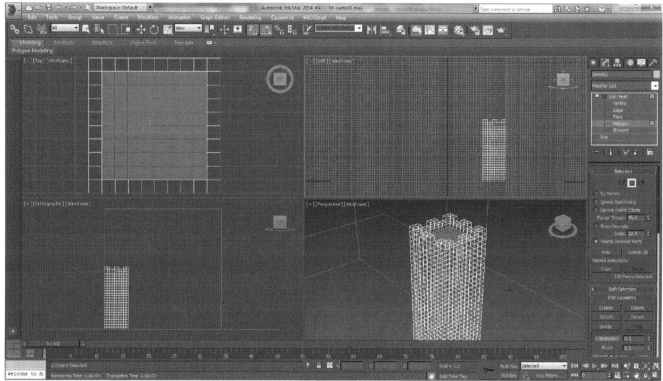

Step 1: Image top of this page
I want this castle to have a crazy amount of detail in the mesh, as such, all my meshes will have a lot of information in them to give me the resolution required to extrude directly onto it as much as possible without having to resort to bollean operations. Boolean operations are great but they have their limits.

Nothing beats the accuracy you can get from topological modifications straight on the mesh itself. In this case, I created a turrett and extruded the top square surfaces to form a wall and negatively extruded the floor to create some height.

Step 2: Image next page top
Once I had one turret roughed-out, I put them at all four corners of my build, the next logical step is adding a wall from one wall to the next and adding medieval details to them.

Step 3: Image next page bottom
Here the wall is made in much the same way as the turretts. I extruded my way towards making the details I wanted to make. I would like my model walkway to actually go through each turrett which will mean hallowing out the inside of the turrettes, but first let's take a look at how everything looks all together so far.

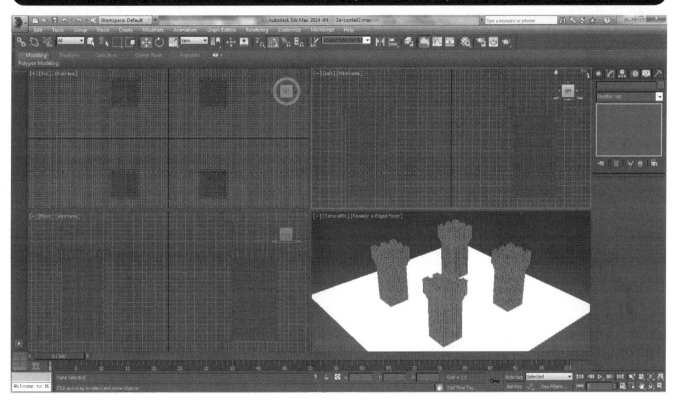

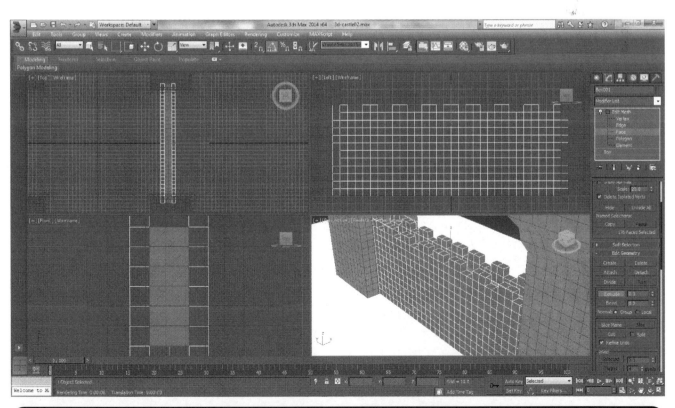

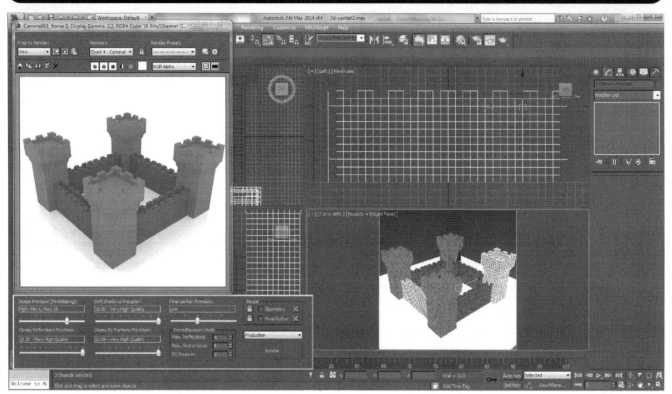

Step 4: Image top of this page

Looking good... I need to either make the walls higher or the towers shorter as they seem way out of proportion with one another. There is also some smoothing going on with the towers that I dislike. So I'm going to have to work a bit more to refine those.

Step 5: Image next page top

Modeling mesh is pretty easy so once you have a form and proportions figured-out, it's generally easier to just rebuild it from scratch instead of trying to endlessly modify elements in a model. Keep in mind that, although I may have a model made-up of 8 seperate elements so far, I really only have three that are unique - ON PURPOSE!

Here are the results of the turretts are split in half (lower part separated from top cap) and the walls are now beefed-up. I want to make this model big and stocky unlike the first version of this wall.

Step 6: Image next page bottom

What I did here was heavily modify one of the walls to create the entry gate in an efficient manner. I then created an archway mesh which I'll then boolean to delete from the wall.

This is for an extrusion 3D printer so I can't have any 90 degree overhangs, they have to either be a 45 degree slope or arch to be printable.

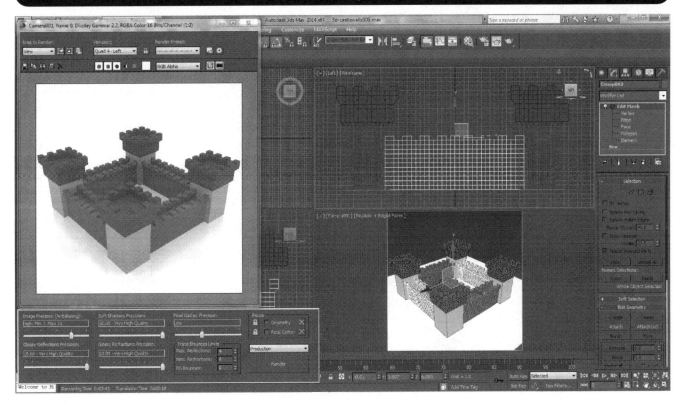

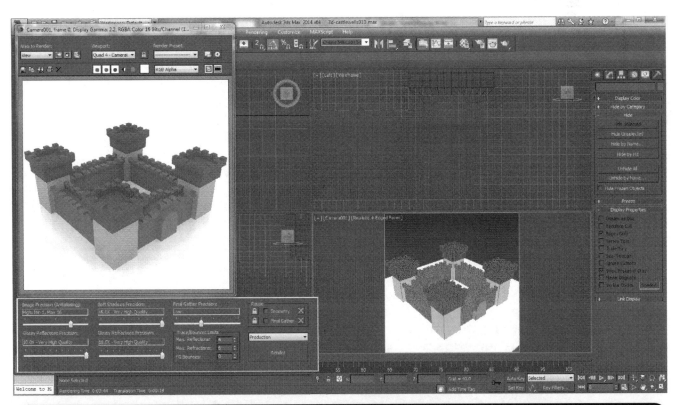

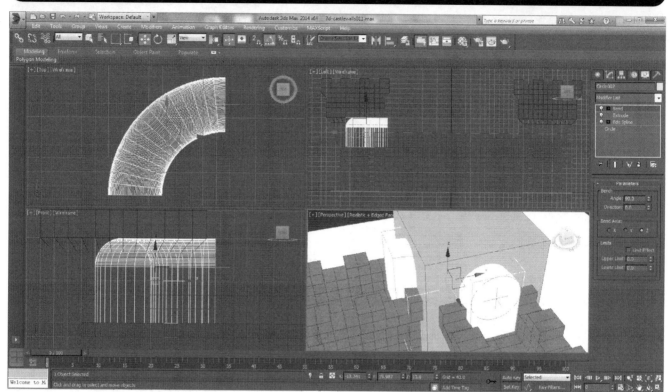

Step 7: Image top of this page

Although I'd like to create a gate that opens and closes for this model, it would have to be 3D printed vertically but my market for this project is for kids and this model is already going to be pretty small. It's just something that will get lost too easily, but what I can do is have the walkways go through each turrett.

They were built by extruding an arch then bending it 90 degrees until things lined-up walkway to walkway. As these turrettes are all instanced, modifying one modifies the others. To have a bit more room for the walkway archway, I made the turret slightly higher for extra tolerance.

Step 8: Image next page top

I find it easier to do all my boolean operations at the same time as adjustments are easier before the operation is performed rather than after. I'm also playing around with adding some ornamental details to the model. Again, focused on only one turret column which will automatically be applied to the others in this model.

Step 9: Image next page bottom

The medieval castle walls B are looking good - remember how the first version I tested to see if fine details would work along with arches - this time around, I've added a lot more of both elements and now inside of each turret, a walkway is shown along with some elements removed from it on both sides. I like this model, I think there are enough changes from the first version to see how it 3D prints. I could keep adding details but let's test what we have done so far before doing further with more details.

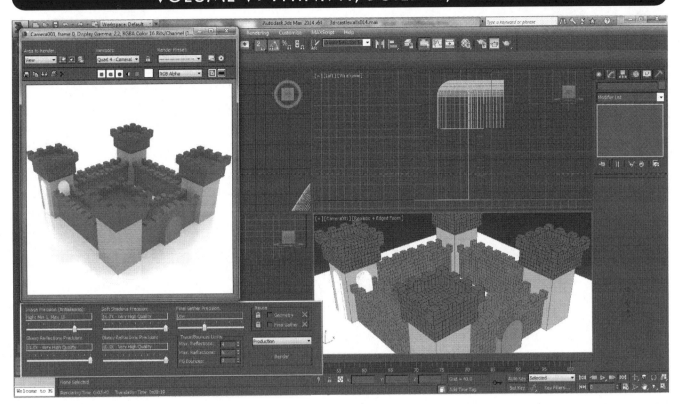

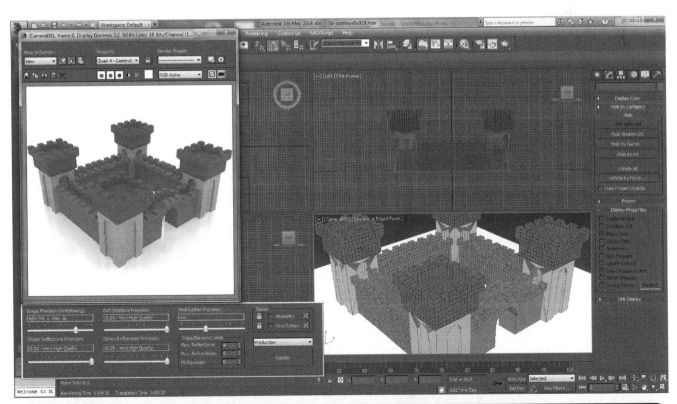

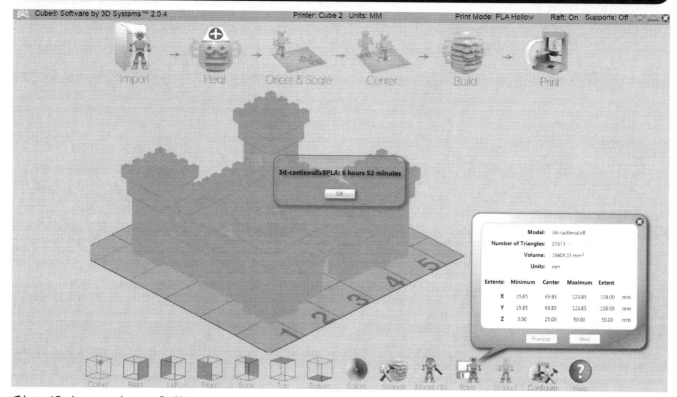

Step 10: Image top of this page

After doing an STL check and exporting the project as a STL file, I opened it in Cubify and the verdict is in, we are looking at a build time of 7 hours... not bad at all!

Physical Results

This is by far the best model I've ever made on my 3D Systems Cube. The mesh came out perfectly the first time around except for the fuzzies on the top (easily removed, like spider webs). The mesh was solid, the model was strong and I was really surprised at the detail I managed to achieve even inside the walkway going through all the towers.

I wasn't sure it would work but I was once again surprised by the quality of what this machine is making!

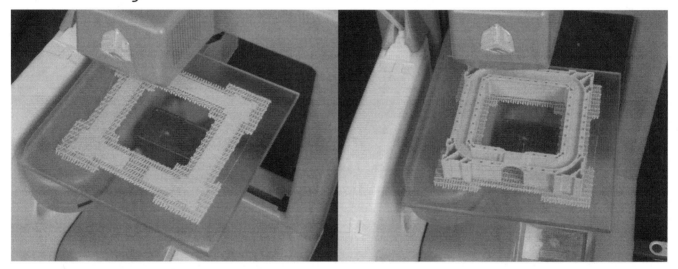

The total build took 8 hours and 46 minutes which is a very decent build time... something you can run overnight and wake-up in the morning to. I think the openess of the mesh means that the cooling rate once the filament is extruded from the printer creates a more solid and consistent mesh than something that's completely solid, which seems more prone to warping from experience. I do plan on making a third version of this model with even more details.

Detailed Design Notes

It's interesting after doing a complicated project like the Castle Walls B to jump into something simple again, in this case, a simple cog but lessons learned from this can be applied to a future castle walls like making extra detailed turrets.

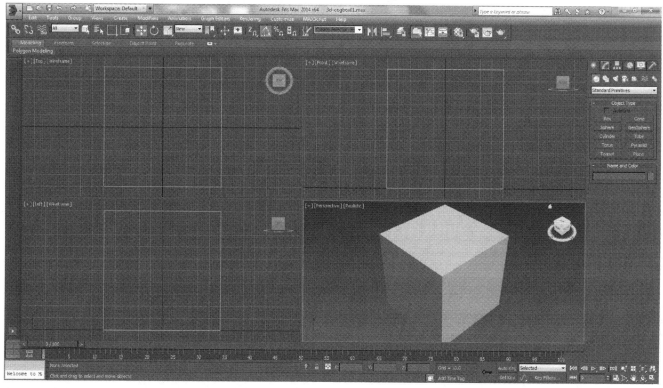

Step 1: Image top of this page
First step is deciding the cube that you'll be building into which represents your 3D printer's build volume.

Step 2: Image next page top
I now traced out a cog from another project I made (gear box) to fit into the square that I built.

Step 3: Image next page bottom
I've now extruded the cog to form the shape that I want, I gave myself some room.

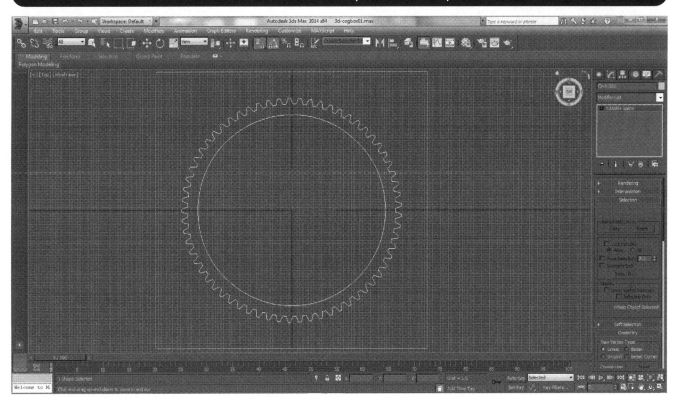

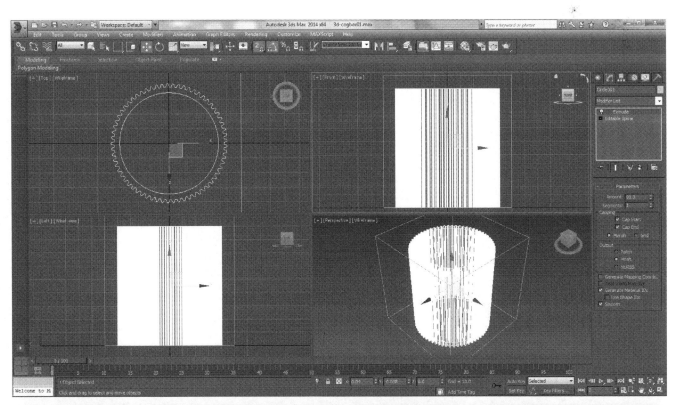

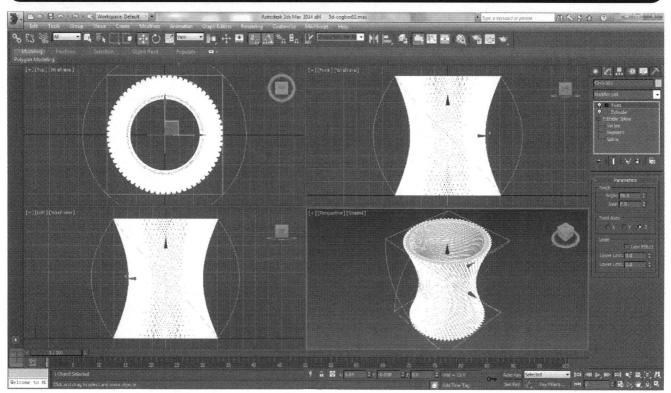

Step 4: Image top of this page

I've now added a slight 90 degree twist from bottom to top to add a little more visual appeal. I now have to make a solid platform for the cog box to sit on as otherwise, this is nothing but an empty roll.

Now you know why I gave myself a little bit of room around the model so that I had more build options that still fit within my cube volume.

Step 5: Image next page top

I decided to go with a simple cylinder to form the base but it seems to break-up the look I'm after, so what I'll do is stick it on the inside instead of having it on the outside so it becomes a hidden base.

Step 6: Image next page bottom

Hiding the mesh (extrusion and twist) allows me to see the original shape so it's easy for me to scale the cyclinder to fit perfectly into the mesh in the X, Y and Z axis.

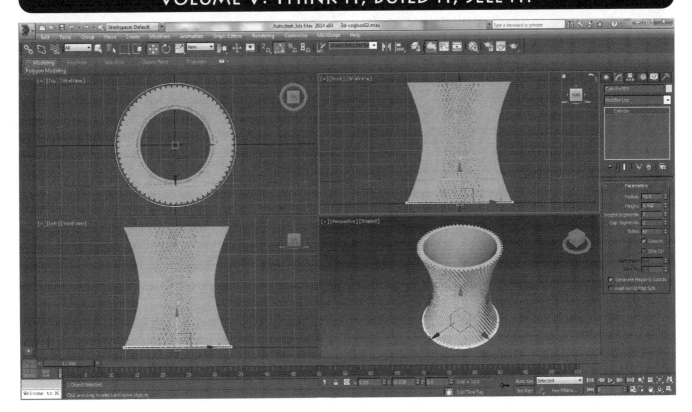

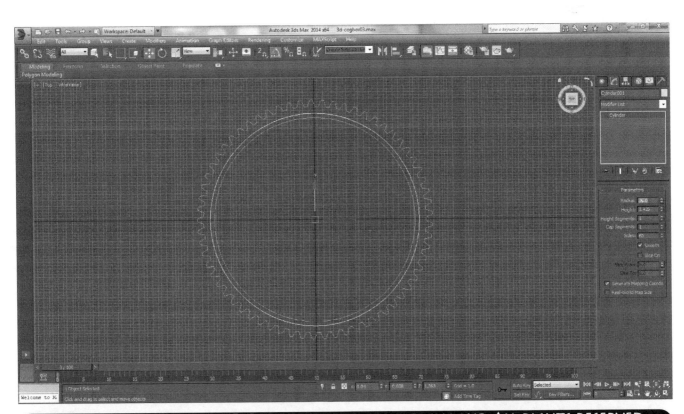

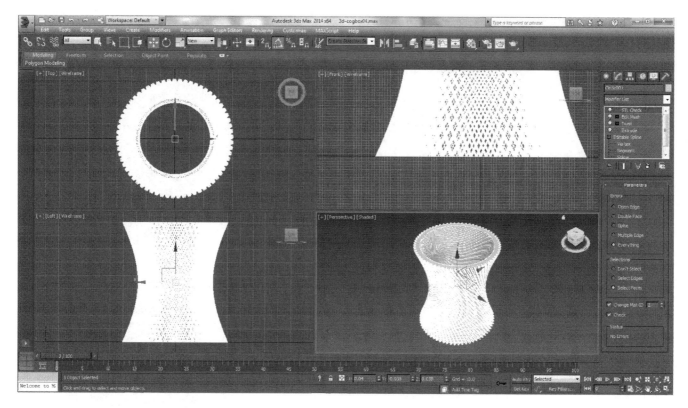

Step 7: Image top of this page
After I've unified the two shapes together, I ran an STL check and my mesh is perfect.
Ready to be 3D printed!

Step 8: Image bottom of this page
It will take about 11 hours to print this model using PLA. Now that we have the build file,
let's bring this model from the virtual world to the physical one!

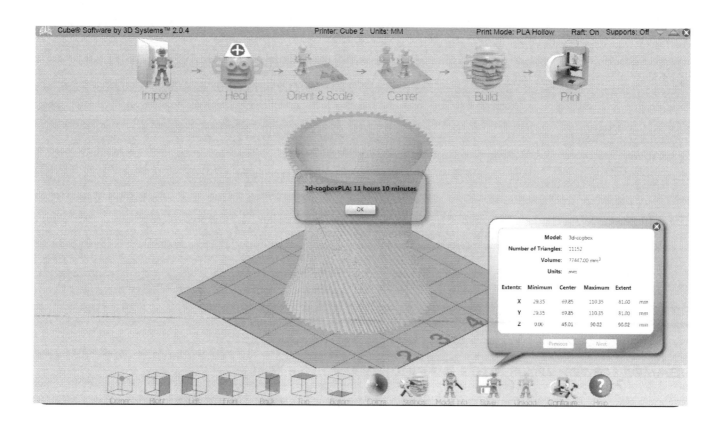

Physical Results

The print came out fantastic, as do most prints now that I know how to properly design for my 3D Systems Cube. The material strength was very surprising, I can't squeeze this model in the slightest. I'm guessing that's because of the twisted ridges going all the way around the model in a seamless way.

As with all my prototype 3D prints, I use rafting to make sure stuff doesn't get unstuck from the platform, though for this model with a flat bottom, it is not necessary at all.

A surprising aspect of this print was the final print time. Usually Cubify is within half an hour but if you look below, you'll see that I was able to print this 3D model in 8 hours instead of eleven which is rather surprising. I don't know what the cause of this is but I like it! If it were the other way around, I wouldn't be as pleased. In hindsight, I could have made the walls of this project about half the thickness that I used, the texture added more than enough strength to the overall model.

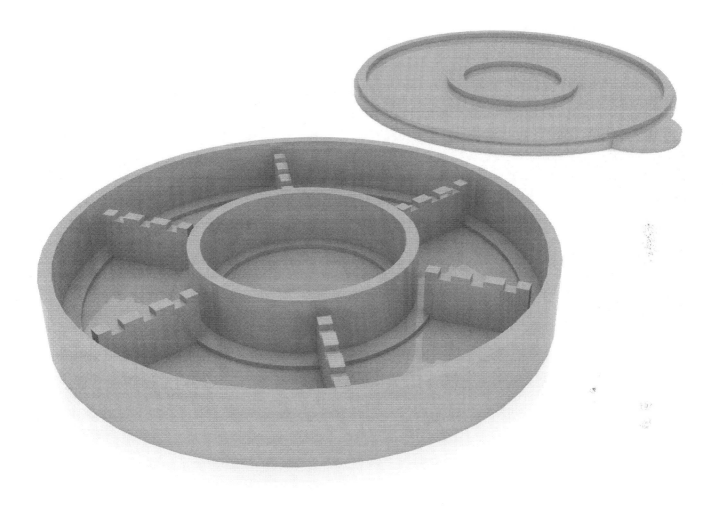

Detailed Design Notes

I wanted to make a weekly pill holder but couldn't find something I liked so I decided to design my own with my 3D Systems Cube. I want this pill holder to hold a weeks worth of pills (7 days) and within an optimally useable area.

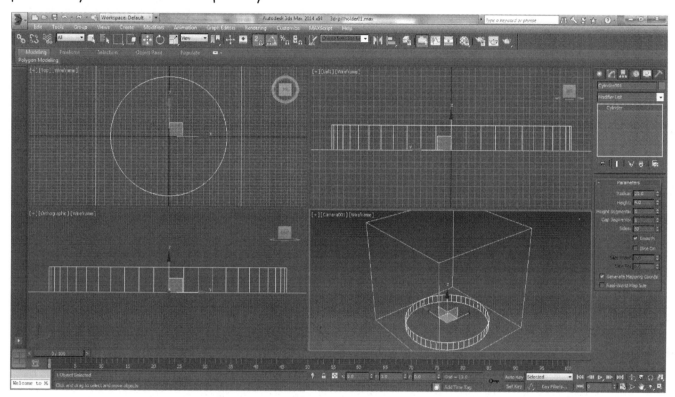

Step 1: Image top of this page
My goal is to make the largest circular base as I can as esthetically, something round looks better than something that's square. I've already set-up my square working area.

Step 2: Image next page top
My building method here (for variety) will be removing layers from this base cylinder, then adding an inner tube for the 7th day OR as a way to hold the rotation mechamism - I'm not sure at this point what the final design will look or function like, but I have a few ideas that we'll see how they end-up.

So, instead of using the lathe function, I'm just going to build this model using boolean unify and subtractive modifiers.

Step 3: Image next page bottom
My idea here is to have 6 outer modules followed by a 7th in the middle. This way, everything will look symetrical instead of trying to have 7 divisions in the circle with a useless (too narrow) inner pointy area.

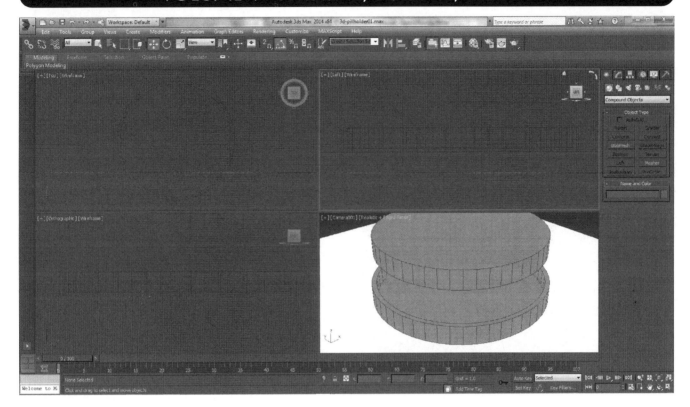

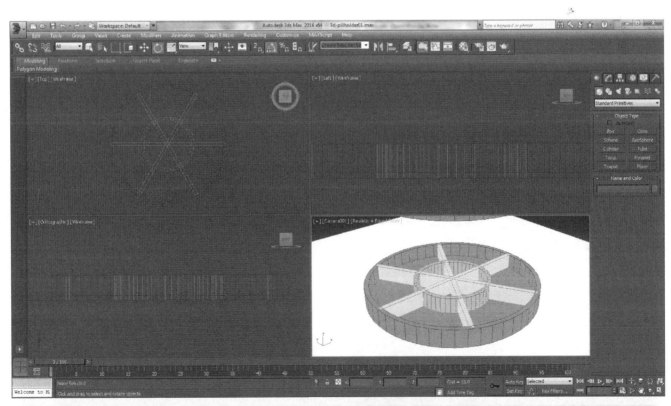

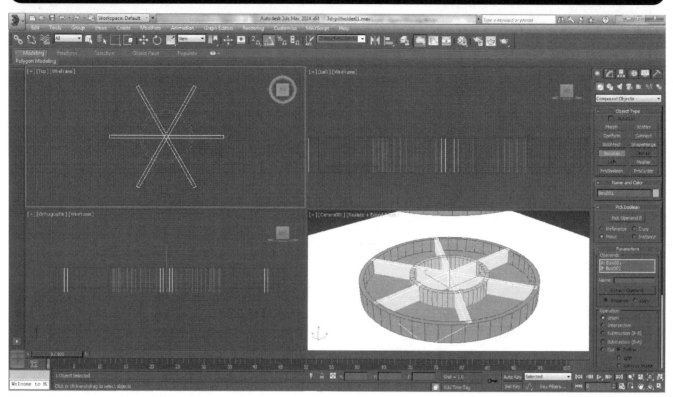

Step 4: Image top of this page

What I did here is unify the inner borders using a boolean modifyer and, as I already know my inner and outer boundaries, I'll then create an inner cylinder and outer tube to cut these bits out.

I'll leave a slight space at both ends as well as within the structure to reduce the amount of material (and printing time) for this model as a solid wall or a semi-solid one is just as strong to hold small pills.

Step 5: Image next page top

I now have the six dividers sorted but I want to add a little bit more detail to them... I really like the caps I made on my Simple Medievel Walls bulding so let's add that here using boleans. This will be very straight forward, just make a bunch of tubes in regular intervals.

Step 6: Image next page bottom

All I need to do now is subtract there three sets of inner rings from the inner dividers.

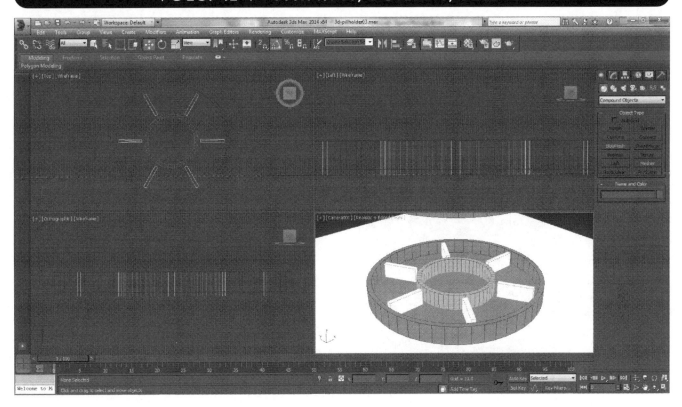

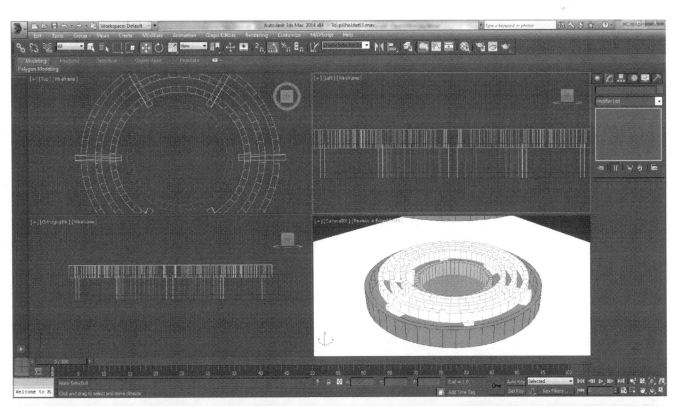

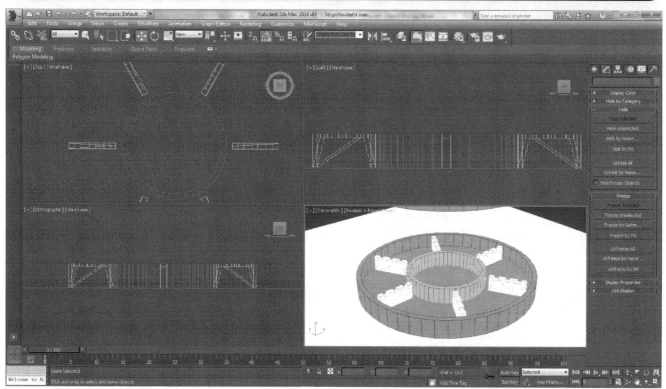

Step 7: Image top of this page

This look perfect. Although this will sit on a table, I will create a cap that fits inside of the inner ring for reference.

Step 8: Image next page top

I don't want a tight fit but something with just a little friction and just to make things all the easier I've added a tab. This means that I'll have to print this project in two steps. I do have a concern though about the pills being slightly too large to fit inside of this, so I'm going to remove a bit more material from the bottom of this pill box and, at the same time, create a small step design in the base of it just to add more visuals.

Step 9: Image next page bottom

As I haven't unified this model yet (each element is still separate, I can just bolean out the original cylinder with a wide tube which will remove an extra mm or two of material and still keep my dividers as they are not part of the model yet (they will be once I unify things).

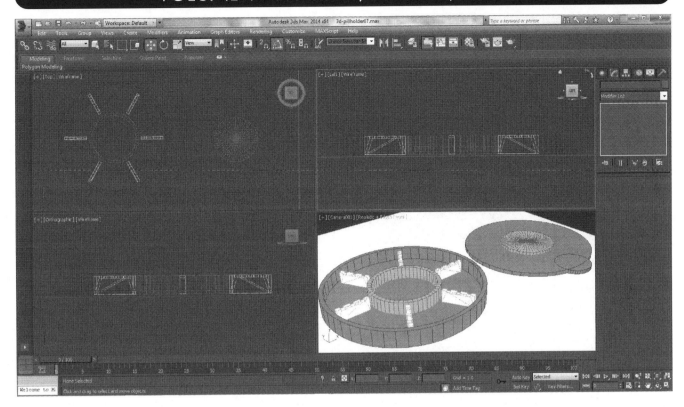

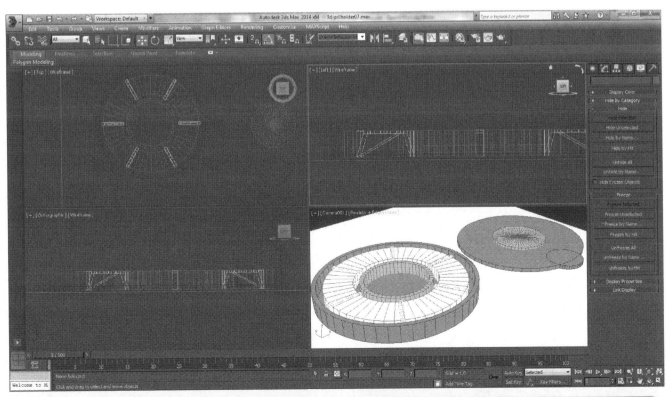

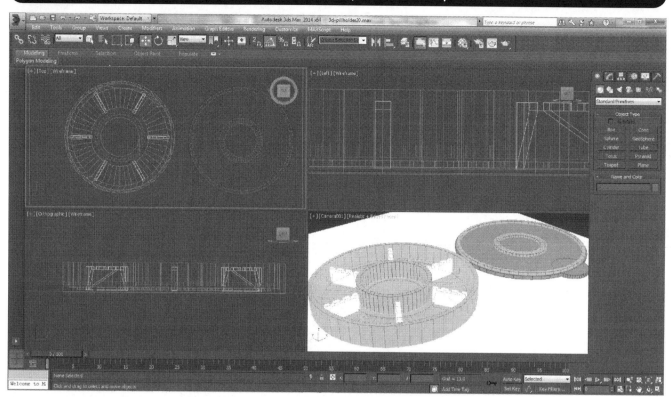

Step 10: Image top of this page
I did a few finishing touches: I added a little more height to the pill holder and also hallowed-out the lid so that it uses less material in the center where none is really needed while adding an outer rim to it that also fits inside of the outer rim of the pill box.

I now have everything looking the way I want - time to unify the structure, export it as an STL file (after a STL file check) and move onto the 3D printing process.

Step 11: Image next page top
Roughly 3 hours to print this model, next up, the lid!

Step 12: Image next page bottom
The lid takes roughly 2 hours so we are looking at a total of 5 hours for the entire build of this project!

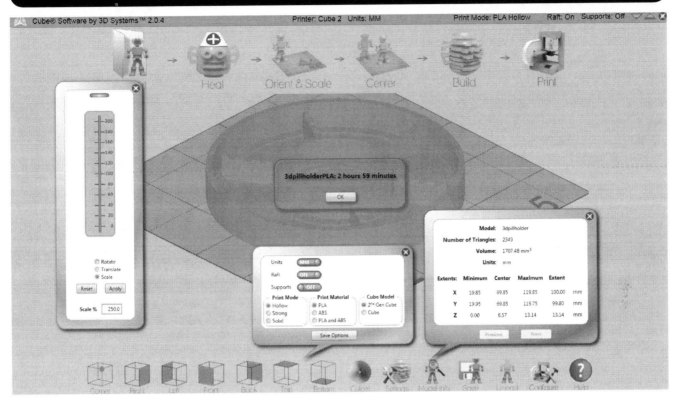

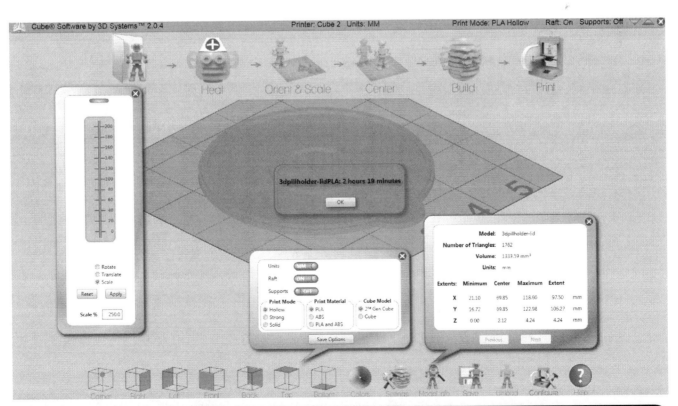

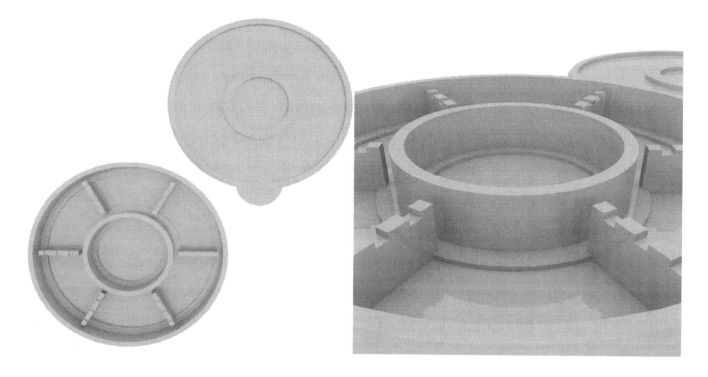

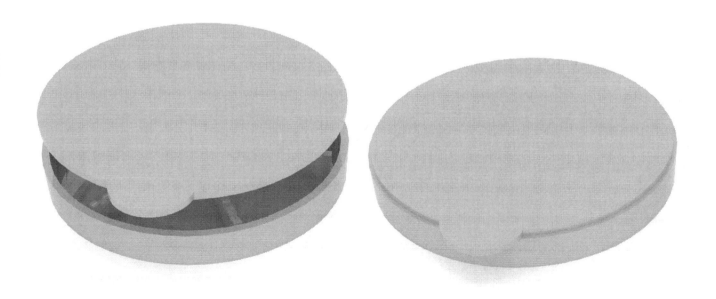

Physical Results

I don't know how many times I've seen my 3D Systems Cube make rafting for a piece that's about to print but it's always magical to me. It tells me that this model works and that, what will be finished in a few hours will be exactly as I envisioned it. It's just fun to see a CNC machine move so elegantly when you realize that it's a bunch of metal and screws holding various larger materials that are making it all possible.

The print went off without a hitch, the results are perfect. If I were to rebuild this model, I'd probably make the walls a little higher and increase the scale of the overall model to fit the entire bed just so I have a bit more room for the pills.

All that being said, I didn't print the lid for this model - I have the files for it of course but just don't see a need. The pills won't get that dirty over the course of 7 days and it helps to keep everything cool having things open like this. It's a quick visual as to how much is left to be taken and the week in general!

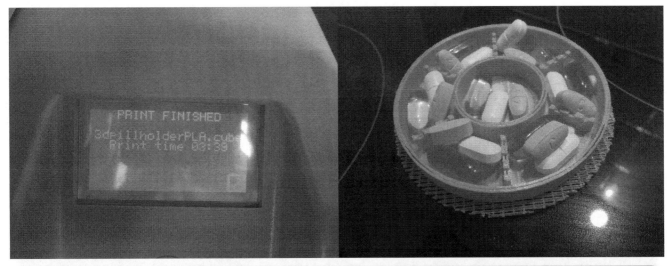

Vase

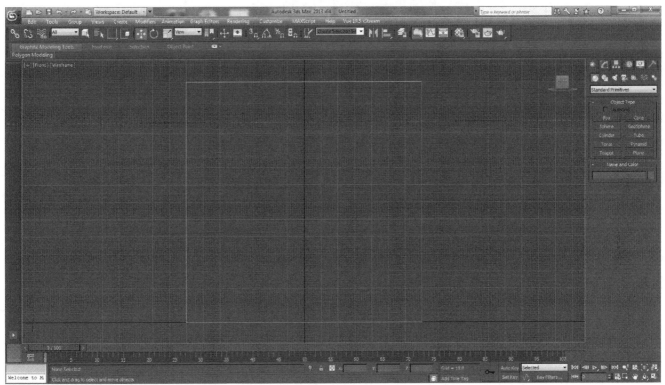

<u>Step 1: Image top of this page</u>
First step is to establish your volume parameters - dimensions are relative so it doesn't really matter what size the cube is as long as it's equal on all axis (X, Y, Z).

<u>Step 2: Image next page top</u>
As I'm going to lathe this object - all I need to do is create a 2D spline. It will then be spun around 360 degrees to create the vase. At this point I don't care too much about the details of the spline, as long as I have the general shape I'm after.

<u>Step 3: Image next page bottom</u>
Now that the vase is created, I can get rid of the cube as I know my object will fit within my platform's limits and start to smooth it out a bit. The more segments I have making-up the vase, the smoother "around" the vase will be. If I had only 4 segments spun around, it would form a square vase while 360 segments would be an extremely smooth surface as the reference spline would be created every 1 degree of rotation.

If you decided to make this vase out of 10 000 000 segments, it wouldn't be any smoother than one made out of 1 000 segments though - going over the capacity of the human body to feel/see or machine to produce doesn't produce better results, it just creates larger print files that take longer to print without any noticeable difference.

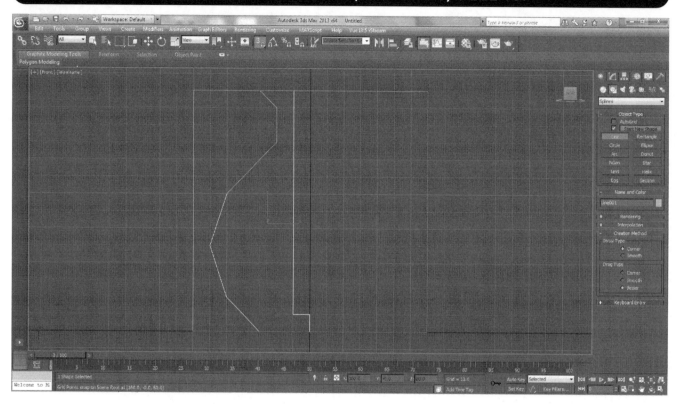

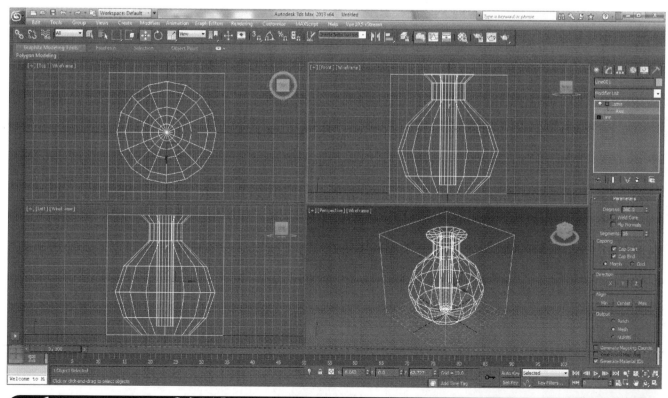

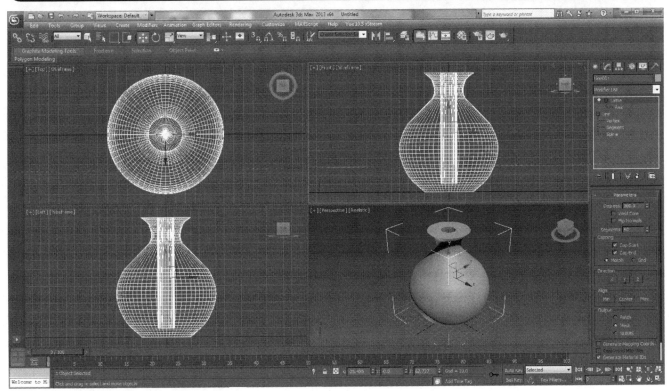

Step 4: Image top of this page

I now have a round vase; I changed the vertex to smooth and increased the segments around 360 degrees to 60. We now have a new issue to deal with, the inside. As you can see in the previous step, I have a vase but the inside of it is rather small - all that extra volume will be 3D printed - taking that much longer to print and costing more money in material.

The solution is to go back to the spline and make the inside edge follow the exterior surface closer.

Step 5: Image next page top

All that I have left to do now is make the inside as smooth as the outside and spin it around again to see the results. I hate using supports, so I build this model in such a way that no inside angle exceeds roughly 30-45 degrees and, as this object is round, it won't need any.

Step 6: Image next page bottom

I now have my vase, I've left the outside edge thicker for two reasons. First, I want it to be strong. The thinner the sides, the weaker the structure and, secondly, I want it to have some weight to it. This is for an extrusion 3D printer. It is best to give yourself some extra tolerance and clearance. If this were for an industrial SLA 3D printer, then I could make this just a few mm without too much concern.

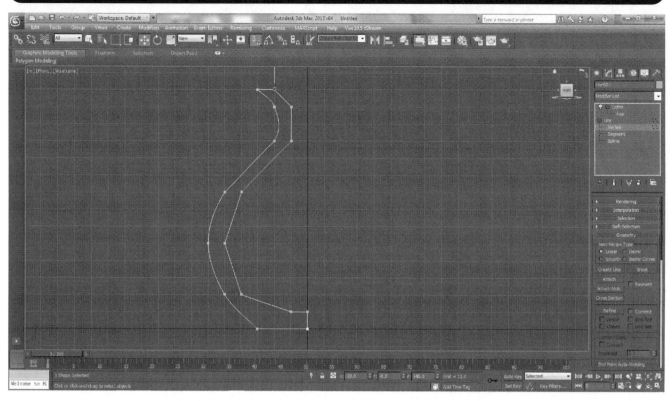

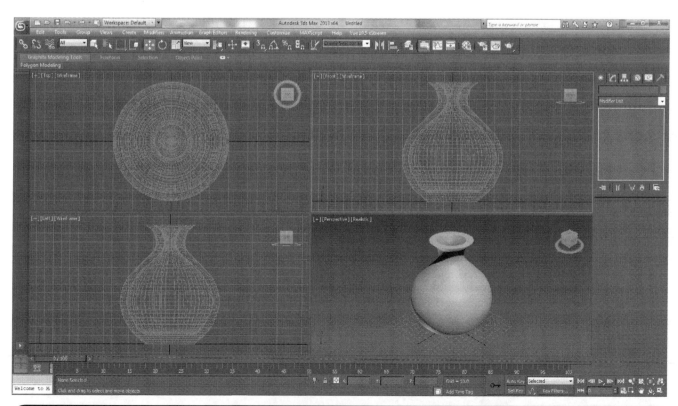

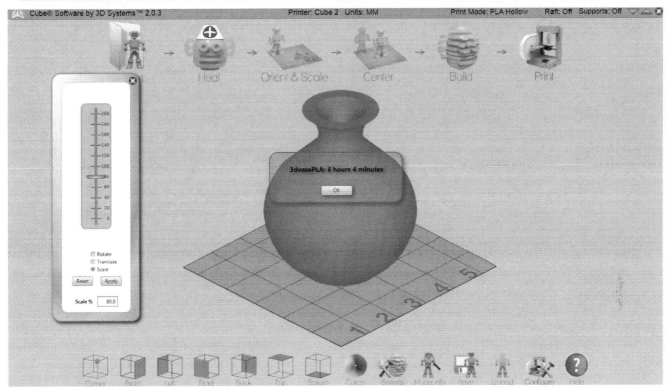

Step 7: Image top of this page

Before we print it, let's export the STL, scale it to for the platform and produce a build file in my Cubify software. 6 hours... not bad!

Physical Results

A vase is among the easiest shapes to build and print with a 3D printer; the lathe modifier is incredibly powerful and quickly builds a mesh that's attractive with minimum modifications.

The physical results from this model were spectacular; it was smooth where it needed to be and where I left one of my vertex "square". Even that aspect was 3D printed perfectly.

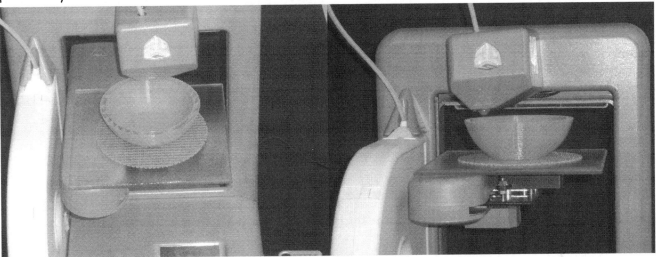

The options using this construction method are endless. You can make a vase that's square, rounded, square at the bottom but round at the top. Basically, one simple lathe tool offers a host of design possibilities that can be quickly generated with even the most rudimentary knowledge of 3D modeling.

For this vase, my best came-out fantastic. Next step is to add some complexity to the model by adding holes and adding some random noise modifyers.

Detailed Design Notes

I've been wanting to make projects that people currently build using support materials without having to use them at all, thanks to a design that is optimized. Sometimes you absolutely must use support material. It has it's purpose and necessity but you can certainly tweek a design to use less if not any of it. My goal by making an "open basket" is to accomplish without using support material, what would generally be required.

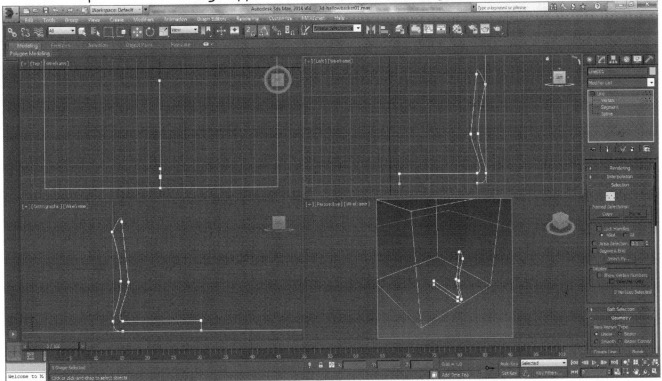

Step 1: Image top of this page
After creating my reference cube, I made a very rough outline of the shape I want my open basket to have. I'll be creating clones of this shape so that I can easily modify the shape later in the process.

Step 2: Image next page top
I've extruded my 2D line to give it some depth and then set-up a new pivot point in the center of the reference cube. I left an extra empty space between the end of the 2D line and the middle on purpose as I want to give myself more design options down the line using tubes to pull everything together.

Step 3: Image next page bottom
I used an aray modifyer which allows me to quickly build-out my cloned 2D profiles to form a circular shape. Looking at the results, they look alright but with all the mesh, it's a little hard to visualize so I'll switch my perspective from wireframe to realistic.

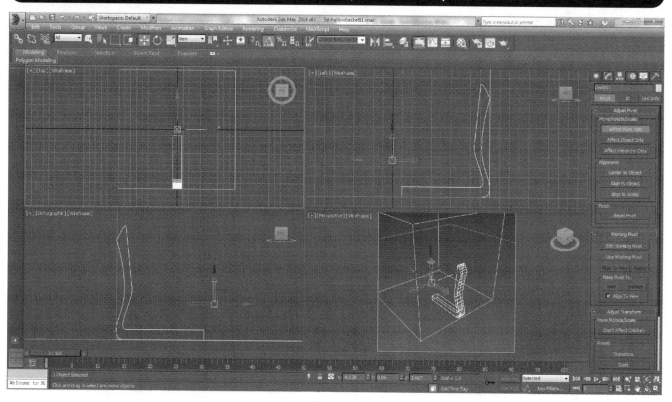

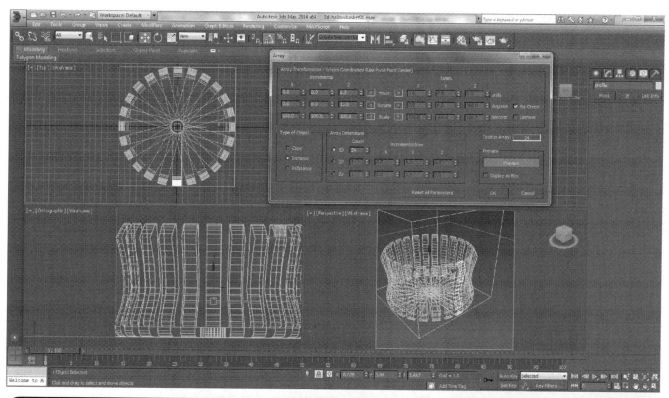

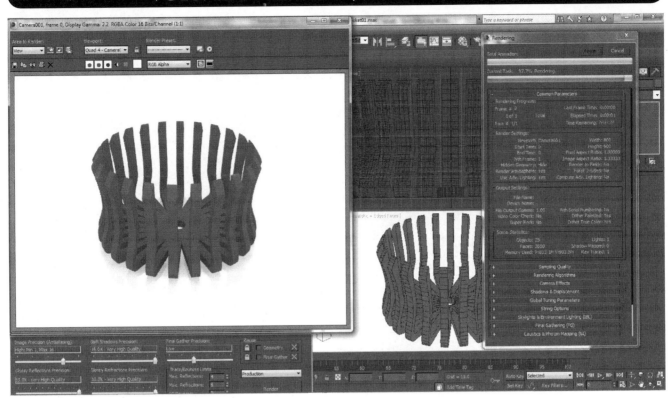

Step 4: Image top of this page

A quick render shows me what the model would look like if I 3D printed it right now. What you see there would be easily 3D printed as is and I'm confident I would have no issues printing it, but I want to add a few more details to it going across the basket.

Step 5: Image next page top

This is looking far better now but there is one major problem: I have a 3D extrusion printer, not a high-end industrial machine, so what I have here is something that isn't possible with my 3D Systems Cube unless I use support material, which is exactly what I want to avoid.

If I 3D printed this, all the cross sections would just fall straight down. I have better things to do with my time than remove the support material between each hole with pliers over the course of an hour.

Let's fix it but first, I'm going to fix the mesh of this model a bit so that everything is symmetrical as when I changed the width of the 2D line drawing, an offset was created and that complicates mesh modifications.

Step 6: Image next page bottom

Although the mesh may look identical to what you saw in the previous step, compare the screenshots from this step and the previous one. The model is now perfectly symmetrical.

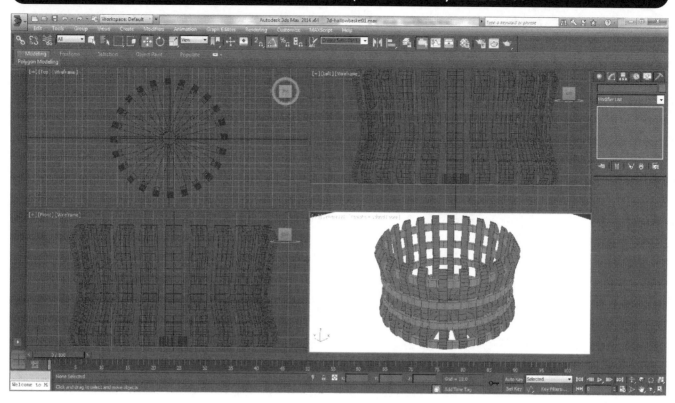

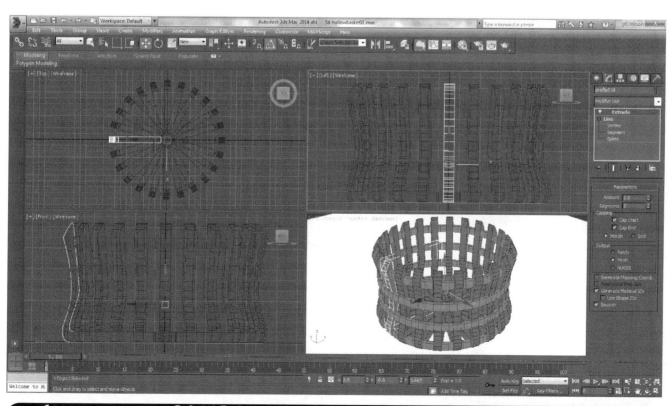

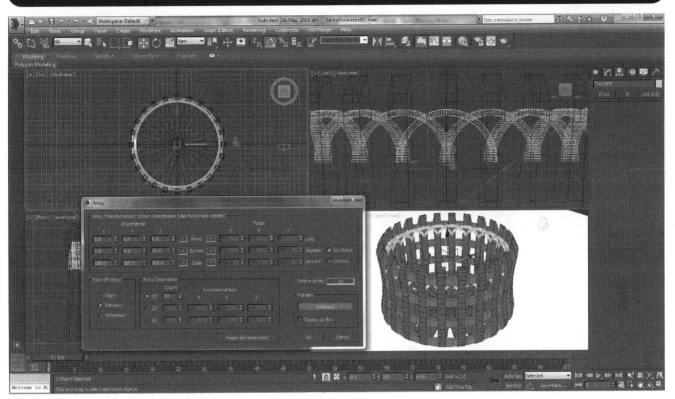

Step 7: Image top of this page

Like my original 2D profiles, I've made arches which are easily 3D printed with my Cube and set them up in an instanced array all the way around the basket. This is the easiest method for me to accomplish my goal.

Step 8: Image next page top

That looks interesting but rather ugly. The reason why things don't seem to make sense is due to the different thicknesses I have in this model. Having thick parts intersected with angled smaller parts is very hard to get right. Let me play with this model a bit to get something more pleasing, yet Cube friendly.

Step 9: Image next page bottom

What I really like about 3D modeling is that you can jump from idea to "virtuality" within minutes and dramatically take a design in another direction. In this case, I cut down the 2D profiles and made my sliced tubes "whole", and I really like the results!

As I've radically altered from my original design path - not a bad thing - I need to now fix the base of this hallow basket as circular sides with straight lined base just look weird. Let's keep going on this concept and make the base out of round tubes as well!

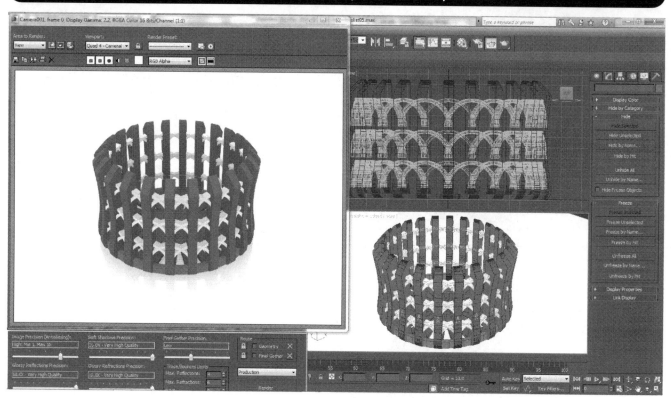

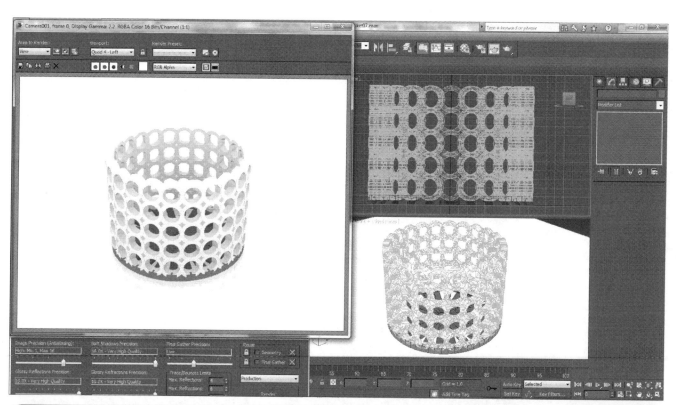

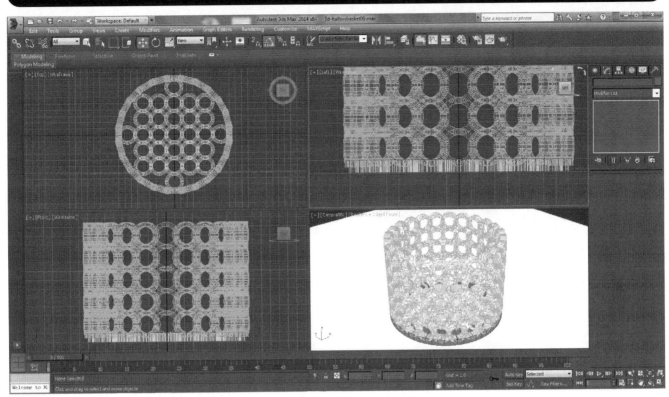

Step 10: Image top of this page

I created the mesh on the bottom manually by aligning their center points and made the outer rim a little thicker to make sure that I had plenty of strength as the ring going around the entire basket is what unifies the vertical and horizontal tubes and thus, the weakest area of this whole project. I know I've done overkill in this area but I can't help it. I tend to do this regardless of which CNC machine I design projects for.

Step 11: Image next page top

I rounded the edges of the rings in order to smooth the model out a bit and create more surface area for the 3D extruded material to stick to. I made the inside radius a little smaller for the rings so that the outer rings didn't come through the radius inside the inner rings of neighboring rings. All of these changes added a bit of texture to the front for a bit of added detail that should look good in the final 3D print.

You'll notice I rotated every second row by 7.5 degrees so that each layer fits more nicely into the one around it - removing that possible small diamond problem I outlined earlier.

Step 12: Image next page bottom

Roughly seven hours is highly respectible. My only concerns at this point are the upper parts of the tubes that make-up the vertical body of this model. I've done lots of arches with great success but these are far more tighter tolerance wise. Let's see how it goes!

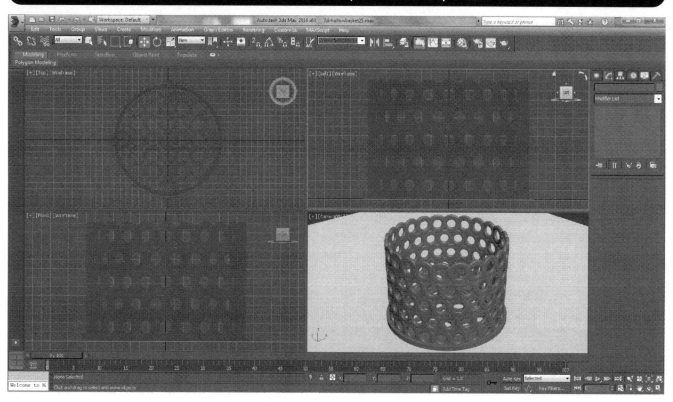

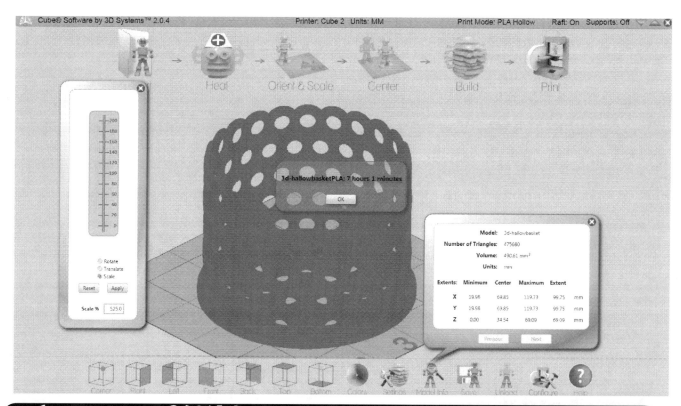

Product Renders

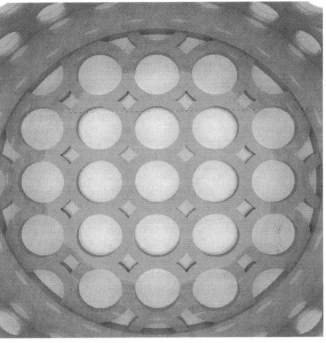

Physical Results

The entire model 3D printed perfectly using my 3D Systems 2nd Generation Cube... the build quality was amazing, I had some serious doubts about the build as I thought the "holes" would actually end-up drooping down and not be very strong. This was just as strong as my other models that were completely solid!

The total build took 8 hours and didn't use that much fillament due to the holes throughout the model.

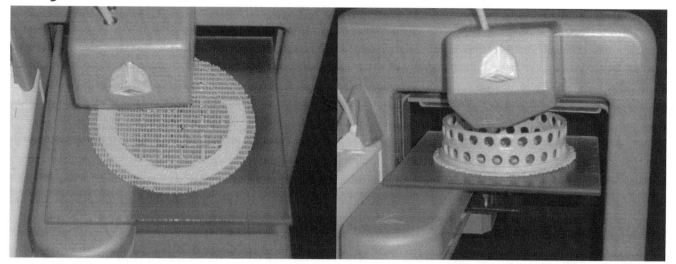

I think the possibility of extrusion 3D printers are limited but as this shows, you can actually build pretty solid models. I've since built many other models using a similar process to this weaved basket and the results have been the same.

Suffice it to say, I really love my Cube, even if 3D Systems have since come out with even more refined 3D extrusion 3D printers. I learned A LOT thanks to this machine!

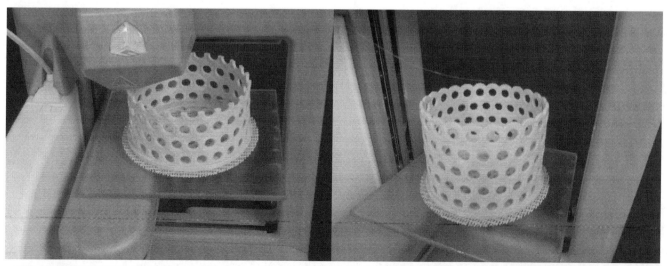

Designer's Corner

One of the pleasures of designing, selling and producing CNC projects around the world is that I get to know some pretty interesting people who, like myself, are incredibly passionate about what they do.

Having all these different hats in my background makes me as comfortable talking design with a guy out of Hong Kong as with a CEO of a large fortune 500 companies.

There are so many aspects to designing that I find myself getting ideas from completely unrelated industries. Looking at what Kade does with paper is incredibly inspiring, imagining how I can go about making those models using laser cut pieces or the whimsical sketches from Michelle that I would love to see in billboards. Creativity is everywhere!

CNCs are a tool, just like computers, that augment your creative and physical abilities but inspiration to actually design something yourself and build it yourself generally comes from within. I've been designing for so many years that I can pretty much build anything I set my mind to and, with all that experience, I still get a lot of excitement seeing an idea take shape in the real world.

Michelle Aryani, Product & Toy Designer

Michelle Aryani is a multidisciplinary designer. She was born in Jakarta, Indonesia. She took her Diploma in 3D Design in Nanyang Academy of Fine Arts, Singapore and continued her degree in Loughborough University, UK.

She is a bright and cheerful person who likes to explore materials and foods.

You can find her at http://cocomich.dunked.com.

You've been an intern and worked freelance in design. Do you prefer working on your own or being part of a larger company? How do you find your customers and projects?

As a graphic design intern in a marketing company, I feel like you are being forced to create a design in a 'cliche' and those commercial style, which I don't really like much.

Well, not everything goes in your way and that was what I learned there. The clients were asking me (through email) to move and scale the font hundreds of times which I find really wasting time to do the same thing over and over again. As for freelance job, I find my thing there.

It was fun and you are not being forced to do what you don't like. Maybe because I find that the company and I somehow clicked together and the people were so nice and willing to share. In the future, probably I would prefer working on my own.

Your sketches are incredible, you have some very talented hands and a great mind for design. How long does it take you, for instance, to render the axonometric drawing? Where did those ideas and concepts come from?

Thank you for the kind comments. I took around 4-5 hours to render whole A3 paper, full color. People, books, internet and my daily life are the main factors for my idea bank. I think daily life is the story behind most of today's design.

How to save space in these limited areas, how to use things efficiently, how to live healthy, etc, they are related to daily life problems.

Since I am from Indonesia, my background also took part in my design process. Especially if I render a traditional living room, I tend to use brownish and nature color for the overall theme.

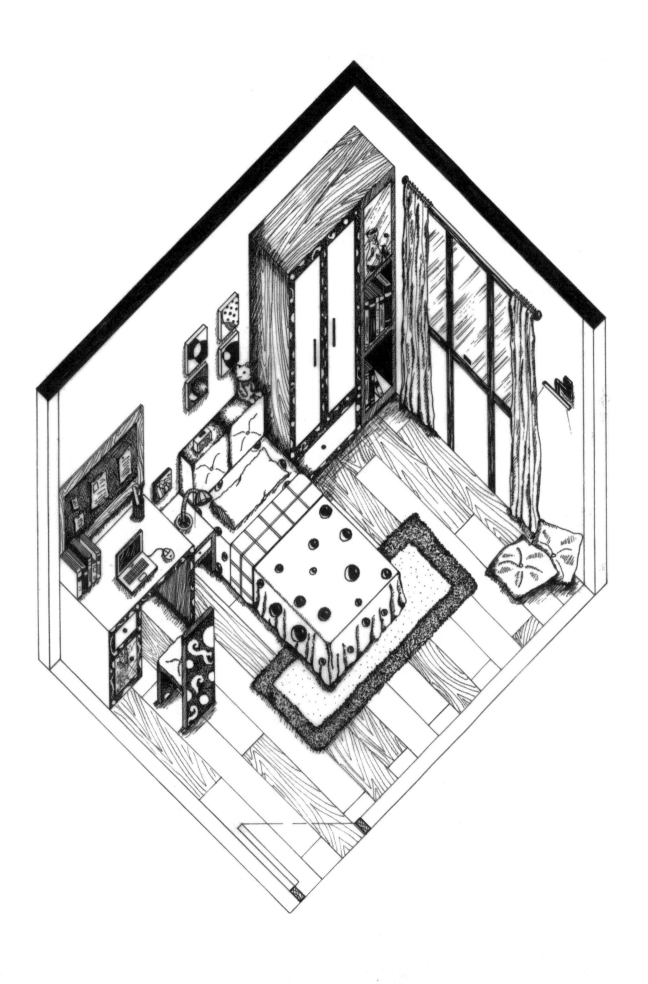

It's ironic that I've been looking at a unique and innovative way to CNC laser cut, using acrylic, a chess game - I love that game! I saw your chair chess and I must say - that's awesome! I've never seen anything like it and it looks great! How long did it take you to sketch, model, cut and build this chess set?

I love those chair chess too. It was inspired by my favorite Japanese designer, Kouichi Okamoto. Most of his designs were daily life related and red-white, so I symbolize daily life with a chair, a furniture or tool that we use almost everyday.

Once I got the idea, I tried to work with my paper and pencil and did some doodling. It was quite fast and I choose a few sketches then combine them together.

The laser cutting process is quite fast once you have all the template done in Adobe Illustrator, but the assembling part took quite some time. It took me around 3-4 days to assemble the little chair pieces.

Can you describe the design process behind your Lupe? I really like the esthetics of your paperweight wooden magnifying glass. Same with your cast resin light bulbs - I love this concept? Do they last as long as regular lightbulbs?

Lupe is actually a paperweight series I did for this unknown random man, captured by the talented hand of an American photographer, Scott Schuman. If you guys know this fashion blog called 'The Sartorialist', you will find many of great photos captured by him.

Lupe was born from the idea that comes from the analysis of this unknown man's fashion style and the way he looks. I imagined what kind of home he lives in, what kind of items he will have and I imagined a bunch of possibilities from that one particular photo.

Lupe series were made by CNC router machine. I did the parts with 3D modeling software, Rhinoceros and sent them to the machine.

The machine took almost 3 days to cut those 3 pieces of wood! Maybe because I used Nyatoh wood, which belong in hardwood type, so the process took a longer time.

As for the resin lightbulbs, it was actually a group project that I did in my school days. We were suppose to design a lighting and explore this material called resin. They do last as long as regular bulbs since we were using regular bulbs in this project.

What makes them different from the regular bulb is when the light turns on, the light will disperse through the resin and creates these beautiful effects.

How did you win the NAFA Merit Award in 2011 and what doors or opportunities has it opened for you as a multi-faceted designer?

I won the award due to my academic results and I have to say it really helped me a lot in my school tuition, because when you get the award your school fees will be cut by half.

The award haven't given me any opportunities yet, but it will be good if it can help me in my career. So collect a lot of awards, folks!

Now that you've been out of school and into the design world for a while, is it everything you imagined it would be or have your perspectives changed overtime? What do you spent most of your time doing now? Running after clients or are you focused solely on designing to attract them?

After graduating from a design school, the real working life can be very different from school. You need to be independent enough to reach for a client or work hard enough to polish up your portfolio so people acually notice you.

I spent most of my times designing my own product as I wanted to design freely and show my characteristics through my products and sharing it with other people that appreciates it.

What were your thoughts and goals behind the production of your Chassis Lampshade? Can you describe how you come about deciding what material to use for your projects and how much of that is directed by the client rather than your personal design preferences?

At first, the lampshade is a personal project that I want to design to create an ambient lighting, solely for social gathering spaces such as a cafe or a restaurant or a bar. Most of the ambient lighting out in the market usually is quite heavy, therefore I wanted to make this lamp more lightweight.

Before making the lamp, I actually did some research on ambient lighting and brass is often used because of its golden property, and when you turn on a light near the reflective brass, it is actually creates a wonderful effect.

I came accross this method of making jewelry called anticlastic and when I tried it, it resulted a spiral ribbon, almost look like the inside of a seashell when you perform an X-Ray on it.

Then I found this material called sequinette, which is a waste of the cut out sequins and it reflective enough to create the effect I wanted to achieve in this project.

When I put everything together, it works well and I am satisfied with it. The process of making it has always been the fun part, because I am learning so much new things everytime I design a product.

Pak Hei (Kade) Chan, Origami Designer

Kade Chan is currently studying Industrial and Product Design at Hong Kong Polytechnic University.

He is also a professional self-taught origami designer. He started folding paper when he joined the Hong Kong Origami Society in 2005 and, since then, has obtained numerous awards in various international origami competitions.

It's incredible how far he's pushed the art that doesn't allow any cutting and requires a square piece of paper to start.

You can find him at http://KadeChan.com.

What is it about design that made you want to go to the Hong Kong Polytechnic University in order to become a professional designer? How well are the courses preparing you for the jobs and challenges you face today?

Hong Kong Polytechnic University School of Design is very famous around the world. They allow students to choose their own design fields, such as Interior Design, Product Design, Visual Communication Design and Advertising Design.

For me I'm interested in doing 3D works so I chose Product Design discipline. I'm Year 2 now. During these two years I have learned so many skills on product design, sketching, computer rendering and I create my own brand.

And the professors love to share their own experiences, that inspired me a lot.

You've been on television and in magazines many times. Has this extra exposure helped you get paying projects or commissions for your awesome work? How did you get over your nerves? How have the numerous awards you've won also helped you gain exposure in the design field?

In Hong Kong, all the TVC and magazines interviews are non-paying. I didn't get a single dollar from them. But sometimes I will receive commission projects, that are not paying well, just enough for my lunch.

It's my pleasure to receive those awards, and the organizer also invited me to their conventions, giving me great opportunities to cooperate with famous designers around the world.

You've made some truly mind blowing Origami. How did you first get into it and what is the most difficult part about making projects using only folded paper? Do you use special paper?

Thank you so much. I started folding since 2005, when I joined The Hong Kong Origami Society. Remember that in 2005, I found a origami dragon tutorial from the Internet, I made that and posted to an origami forum.

Same day, The Hong Kong Origami Society saw that and send me an e-mail to ask if I would like to join them.

The most difficult part of origami is to design a proper proportion model. For example, when we designing a origami human body, we need to calculate the proportion of human and transfer the data on the paper.

We are not allowed to cut the paper, and the model has to be finished on a single piece of square paper, therefore we may need to try over 100 times.

We will use different paper for different models; sometimes we will add a layer of aluminum between two paper, to make a three layers origami paper. We call it tissued-foil.

It's because the paper is too soft and cannot stand firm. A layer of aluminum can steady the structure.

How long does it take you from initial idea to a finished, working origami model? How do you go about recording the steps you took making a model?

From the draft to the final model, usually I spend more than a month, and in this period, I have modified the model at least 10 times. And about the folding the final model, it takes around 10-20 hours, depending on the size of the model.

Once I confirm the final shape of my model, I will fold it again and video record the process. If I have time, I will also use Illustrator to draw the folding diagrams to share on the Internet.

Can you describe in a bit more detail exactly how you go about designing an Origami model? Do you start with sketches then step by step notes? I'd think it would be very difficult to remember each step in sequence, even if you do record it, to replicate and further refine a model as you only have ONE shot to make the model. If you skip a step, then the model won't work!

At the beginning, I will do some research about my target mode. For example, if I want to create a wolf, I need to search online about the proportion of the wolf, and then create the crease pattern, and try to finish it.

Sometimes I have to try several times, keep modifying the crease pattern until I am satisfied with the model.

Eagle 2013

Designed by : 陳柏熹 Chan Pak Hei, Kade 2013
www.kadechan.com (Hong Kong)

Crease Pattern

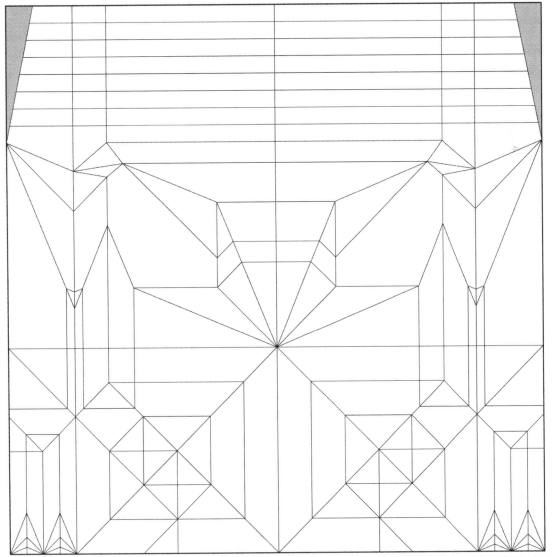

I tried origami when I was a child and it was incredibly difficult - it's quite a challenge. What are some tricks you tell people in order to become proficient in this art? What are some of the general rules about making a project using origami?

There are no tricks on origami, it's all about being patient. I always tell the beginners, how much time you put, how good your models will be.

Origami official refer to using single piece of square paper without any cuttings, to create the whole model.

Given unlimited time and resources, what kind of Origami project would you like to take-on and why? For me, it's a full scale laser cut plywood Moon car that astronauts drove on a few decades ago using my laser.

It would take me a few months to build full-time. I'm also thinking of a 4 meter long aircraft carrier, though I'd like to try that one using a CNC router.

In the future, I would like to use origami techniques in different industries, not just decorations. For example, in the space industry, I think we can use origami structures to minimize the size of solar array, make it easier to transport to the space by rocket.

Also, in the interior design industry, origami structures can be used in the furniture, so that we can minimize the size of them in order to have more space in the house.

Daphne Flynn, Director at Philips Design (Singapore)

Daphne took a journey similar to mine - my first trip to Asia was Malaysia so when I visited other countries around it. There is an incredible diversity there that you just don't see as much in Europe and North America. Even here in Australia I can easily think I'm back in Canada on colder days!

Daphne has been at Philips Design for 13 years and helps to keep their Asean & Pacific region pumping awesome ideas that are locally suitable for the populations and cultures they serve.

You can find out more about Philips Design at http://Philips.com.

When you were in RMIT University in Australia studying Industrial Design, was eventually becoming a director of a multinational conglomerate even in your wildest dreams? It seems like an incredible leap. What attracted you to design to begin with and what do you account for the tremendous amount of success you've experienced in the field?

You should look into design or becoming a tram driver these were options offered when I applied to study Sculpture at another institute in Melbourne at the time. I changed track to industrial design because it really captured my imagination; I could still 'create' in 3D with the added potential of helping people.

All seemed very pretty cool at 17, felt like I could make a difference. I also dreamt of seeing the world, so working for Philips has certainly ticked all the boxes. When my cohort of 10 graduated, 2 of us were offered an internship with the then Philips Corporate Industrial Design ...then 1 of us got a job...I was over the moon. After a couple of years there, I left for other experiences with design and development consultancies in the UK, Melbourne and Malaysia before starting back with Philips in Taiwan in 2000.

Can you give me an idea of what it's like working at Philips? What is a typical day like? What kind of duties and tasks do you need to keep track of and perform?

A typical day ....hmmm everyday can be quite different. My design management role is focused on how we can use 'design' to spark new business opportunity in the Asean & Pacific. Leveraging local insights to create locally relevant propositions in the area of health and well being. Using Philips global experience locally. Meeting business partners locally in Singapore or connecting virtually to plan, strategize... align.

The important thing is connecting quickly or facilitating workshops aiming at making things tangible quickly, test, learn and move forward. You don't always have all the answers but speed is of the essence for us as it is for any business these days. As location manager, I keep the coffee flowing and the team energized.

How does Philips attract the best and the brightest designers from around the world to come work for them? How important is recruitment for a company that's so successful and what are you looking for in a candidate?

At Philips, we really do put people at the heart of everything we do, and that starts with our employees. We constantly benchmark ourselves with the other best in class companies. Philips Design has built a reputation in design thought leadership over its over 80 years of existing as a function in Philips.

Most designers would be familiar with the journey of Philips Design, our leadership in people focused multi-disciplinary design process. Sharing our visions, process and methodology publically through exhibitions, events, books and papers.

Apart from this, of course, we engage and network with design communities, platforms and education. We look for creative, passionate, engaging and interesting self-starting individuals. In a team of 500+, there are many different roles in many locations; so diversity is key in our recruitment process.

What are some of the most notable projects you've worked on with your team and what were some of the challenges you had bringing them to market?

As you know, bringing something to market requires an end to end process with all factors aligned and considered. In Taiwan for Philips monitor business at the time - consistently challenged to breath new into a highly commoditized offer. The challenge to deliver a tangible value which can be monetized.

In Singapore we're thinking in terms of healthcare solutions and currently working on a new Tele Health solution which has specific tailor made touch points for Singaporean heart failure patients.

There are layers of challenge from the partners that need to be in place including clinical, technical, design, business, government...etc The 'design' challenge in this case, started with the patient and how to make the solution engaging and motivating so that they will keep using it over time. If this can work, then the benefits for patient and the healthcare system are possible.

You spent most of your career in Asia, from Malaysia to Taiwan. What are some of the challenges you had adapting to different languages, customs and cultures? How has this experience affected the way you see the esthetics of the projects you are involved in designing?

Asia has been a wonderful experience because of the diversity of cultures and the friendships I've met. Sure its been challenging. The most challenging for me was Taiwan.

On my first visit before I took the job, all I saw were similarities to Malaysia where I had been. But once I arrived, it was obvious very different. Having zero Mandarin, it was a bumpy landing but now I think fondly of the place and the people I met. For me, that first step of looking for something familiar to make it feel like home is really important.

My home and routine that travel with me, connections to national, professional or other groups and Philips colleagues. I guess, as a designer, these experiences have made me more aware of cultural differences at the same time similarities we all have a human beings.

Cultural differences that influence aesthetics from something as simplistic as colors to shapes which should be avoided that are reminiscent of tombstones. More interestingly, the cultural behaviors and insights that can be used to inform meaningful solutions.

Knowing what you do now about designing and running a multi-billion dollar corporation, what advice would you have given to yourself back when you were in University that would have saved you a lot of grief along the way to your directorship?

Just a reality check... I work in one small part of Philips but every little bit counts towards the whole. I'm sure my management will agree. Advice I would give is that you never stop learning from others. Collaborate because "no one knows as much as everyone knows!"

Brendon Vetuskey, Design Manager at Mattel

I've always wondered how the design process is handled in big toy design firms such as Mattel. They come-out with an endless array of awesome products across such a wide variety of licenses and Brendon, who is the design manager at Mattel, was kind enough to help shed light on it all.

I have to tell you, much of my childhood was spent playing around with Hot Wheels and Lego, the two went together so well! Being the design manager for these addictive little toys that all young boys collect, how do you go about deciding what gets manufactured and in how much quantity?

Actually, I don't. Vehicle selections are handled by our die cast design management and the assortments / quantities are handled by the die cast marketing team. I'm the design manager for Hot Wheels entertainment branded product.

I help oversee the design and development of licensed product like Monster Jam branded play sets and replica trucks, Marvel branded track sets and character based die cast cars, etc.

I have been fortunate enough to help the die cast team develop over twenty five different 1:64 scale Hot Wheels cars, as well as nine different 1:43 and 1:18 scale die cast vehicles for the adult collector lines. However, the vehicles and licenses are already chosen by those who oversee those lines, I volunteer my time to help with designing the product.

Which Hot Wheels are your favorites and how long does it take you to design one from initial sketch to finished manufactured piece? Any idea how many have been manufactured in total and how many unique Hot Wheels there are out there?

I have many favorite castings including: "Custom Firebird", "Rodger Dodger", "Large Charge", "Alive '55", "Greased Gremlin", as well as a couple I have designed including the "1967 Pontiac Firebird 400" and the "1955 Chevy Bel-Air Gasser".

There are many factors that affect the actual development time including if it is licensed/ approvals, which product line(s) it is for, and overall urgency of it, to name a few examples.

As for quantity, there are many more than I could count, and the amount of unique would depend if you are counting just the basic 1:64 die cast, or including the variants- (sizzlers, Farbs, Scorchers, Crack Ups, Cap Blastin Racers, Billionth Car collection, XV Racers, Atomix, Micro, G Machines, 1:87th, 100%, Elite, to name a few, etc.) I'm sure it's well into the thousands.

When you graduated with your BFA in Industrial and Product Design from the Cleveland Institute of Art, what did you think you'd be doing 10-20 years later? Was kids' toys always on your list of things you enjoyed working with and developing?

I started out in school thinking I'd major in transportation design, and felt I had an advantage as I'm very passionate and knowledgeable about muscle cars and hot rods (and cars in general), yet it was also a hindrance for me.

I would design cars that were essentially muscle cars and hot rods.

While realizing this wasn't working out, I had an early success on another project in school where I took a consumer product project and made a cool toy out of it. That summer, I had an internship at a local design consultancy known for making toys, and the summer after, I interned at Fisher-Price. I was hooked on toys ever since.

These days, I'm quite fortunate for being able to combine my passion for muscle cars, hot rods and toys all at one place.

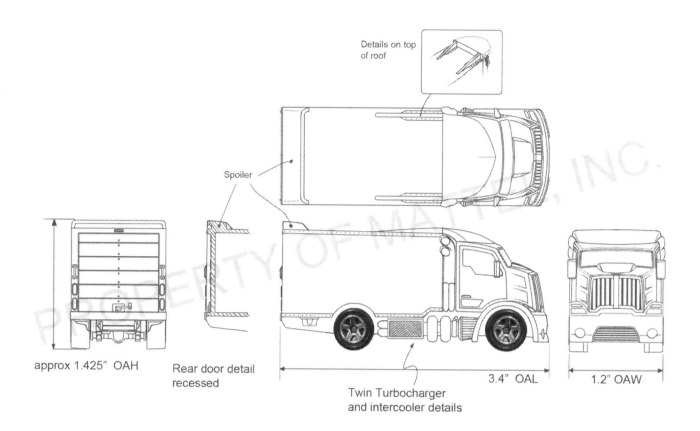

Details on top of roof

Spoiler

approx 1.425" OAH

Rear door detail recessed

Twin Turbocharger and intercooler details

3.4" OAL

1.2" OAW

I've designed over 250 CNC projects (laser, router, 3D printer) and it just never gets old... there is always a new challenge to overcome. How much have Hot Wheels evolved over the time you've been there? I know the packaging is much nicer now and the amount of detail is far more precise. What tools do you use to prototype and build them in the shop?

Hot Wheels cars have benefited from technology for both accuracy and reductions in development time. In the beginning, patterns were carved out of wood at about four times their scale, and they would pantograph them down for tooling. Working at different scales can affect the final design as changes in a larger scale are diminished when it's scaled down.

These days, they are sculpted at 1:1 scale on the computer and can be quickly 3D printed for a 1:1 review. We make changes in thousandths of an inch and finesse the details until it's just right. Digital files can also be electronically transferred to and from the factories saving on shipping time and costs.

You also manage other brands from Mattel and Max Steel to Marvel and Monster Jam. What are special design characteristics that you build into models that make them both attractive to kids and long lasting?

This is my primary responsibility, ha ha. I think it helps to understand the brand and consumer base that you are working on.

As one example, I have been a long time monster truck/ Monster Jam fan. I attended monster truck events as a kid and I still attend the Monster Jam events here in Los Angeles, as well as the Monster Jam World Finals held in Las Vegas each year.

I am active on a few Monster truck related forums and read what the collectors/ consumers have to say. We also work with our Consumer Insights department to help provide us research as a tool for additional feedback from kids and consumers alike.

How much creative freedom do you have when designing for a specific brand? There are so many directions you can take. How do you decide which is best and will be the most profitable for all involved?

I think the brands themselves help drive the direction. Using Monster Jam as an example again- to make a compelling play set it's good to know about the brand. Fans see monster trucks perform (jumping, racing, crashing, stunting, etc) mostly in an arena setting, so it makes sense to focus a play setting in an environment doing the types of things that monster trucks do.

Now the challenge becomes making each new set still compelling and different enough for the consumer to keep coming back.

We need to make sure we are making the set exciting enough for the older child, yet still simple enough for a younger child to play with and making sure the toy passes all safety requirements. We need to make sure the products are manufacturable. We also have approvals needed by both our management, and by the licensor(s).

The packaging needs to get the consumer's attention and tell the story quickly, especially if there isn't a commercial selling it in. We have costing to consider. We design the best product possible within the cost targets we are provided.

The coolest $100 set in world isn't very useful if the request is for a $20 set. Last, but not least, is the schedule. We have to develop the product on time. We need to balance all these factors in. It's more difficult than I think people may realize, but even with all that it is still a lot of fun and I couldn't imagine doing anything else.

Funding

The next step after designing a widget is funding, this can come initially from family and friends, then progress to angel investors and eventually venture capitalists... then IPO. Very recently, a new funding method has gained a lot of steam, crowdfunding. So I though it would be fun to interview people who have gone that route to learn how it all came about and what they'd do differently after the entire process is all said and done.

I've tried crowdfunding twice. It was a great learning experience and that's when I realized how easy it was to set-up and how hard it was to gain traction. Things have gotten dramatically harder since! If you think crowdfunding is a shortcut to becoming rich with a massive user base, think again. The competition is now fierce, the magazines and all the other media channels are now bombarded with "write about my crowdfunding campaign" and worse, it has become a dime a dozen category. I have friends who have succeeded wildly on this platform but I wouldn't put all my hopes up.

At the end of the day, any type of funding you try to get for your product or idea will come down to who you know and the spin you put on it. What's nice about friends and family is that they are investing in YOU but "strangers" are investing in potential, whether that's you or not makes no difference.

I truely believe that if you do go the funding route, you need to establish youself a track record (success or failure makes no real difference) and try to avoid going the VC or angel investor as much as possible until you TRULY need it.

I know many founders that took-on VC money and lost control of their company as a result or gave too much, losing a fortune when it was sold to outside investors.

Don't jump into the VC game too early, it isn't cheap money!

My Eiffel Tower design. Cut and painted by Mike Clarke from Trotec Laser Canada.

"FREE!" Marketing Strategies for Designers

One of the best ways to avoid the need for funding is to use the press to gain attention resulting in free advertising. You might not get money but you will have a new tool to leverage yourself. Money not spent is better than spending money then trying to get it back. For instance, I built both the Wooden Big Wheels and the Eiffel Tower purely for marketing purposes to try to get some attention for myself, my books and companies.

The Wooden Big Wheels makes really no sense at all on a purely ROI basis. It doesn't drive very well, it has too many pieces, too heavy and the list goes on. None of which matters if I could somehow get a picture of me "driving it". My ultimate goal was to produce a video of me driving it and launching that on YouTube.com but it will require some modifications to make that happen.

The result? I got a full page "ad" in Make Magazine (Volume 40, page 19) worth well north of 10K $US which cost me about 800 $AU to build. The magazine has an awesome demographic of both readers and advertisers and I was able to put myself front-and-center. My goal was to be in Make and getting a full page was far more than what I thought I'd get so I was very happy and so was ShopBot Tools Inc.. I couldn't get a better testimonial to the quality of their machinery in such a popular magazine with such huge exposure!

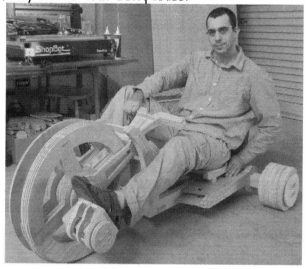

BIGGER WHEEL

CNCKING.COM

Too big for your old Big Wheel? Get back in the race by building an adult-sized trike from plywood.

Jon Cantin, a self-taught designer in Perth, Australia with a passion for CNC fabrication, scaled up the classic kid mobile's design to fit his frame and support his weight. "I want this to be strong, functional, and cool!" The finished project, about 5 feet long by 3 feet wide, uses no hardware — only "a herd of cattle hooves worth of glue" — to assemble its 237 parts cut from 10 sheets of plywood.

Cantin tinkered through design challenges using mental calculations and Autodesk software so he would only have to build the trike once. As his ShopBot Desktop CNC router limited the size of pieces he could cut, the design incorporates overlapping tiles so the front wheel could live up to its big title.

In a series of posts on his website, Cantin talks through the thought processes behind the design, the challenges of building it, and what could be improved next time. The site sells plans for this and other rad projects and freely offers advice and inspiration about CNC skills and entrepreneurship.

— Gregory Hayes

From the very start of my "CNC career", I knew that being a published author was a great way to gain traction in a world I really knew next to nothing about. If you compare my very first volume to the one you are reading now, it's like night and day... that's how much I've "grown" both personally and professionally. Not only are the designs better but so has the number of people I'm able to call on for help across a variety of fields.

With CNCROi.com for instance, being able to drop a book as part of my marketing to key clients I'm going for has been absolutely invaluable in being able to cloase deals. The CNC King is here to see you!

I had a major success with my Eiffel Tower design as well, you can see some pictures of it in my previous volume and it continues to this very day! Most recently being shown in the Japanese newspaper Tokyo Shimbun, which was laser cut and built by Kazuo Takahashi.

It has also been shown in Trotec Laser showrooms all over the place and has continued to be a pretty good seller on CNCKing.com as well! To me, this design was a home run that has far exceeded even my wildest dreams.

The advantage I have is that I can literally design anything. If I want to get some "free marketing" in XYZ country, I can efficiently design a CNC laser, router or 3D printed version of something neat within that demographic, cut or print it in my shop, take a photo and I'm pretty much done. That's POWER!

I do have some awesome ideas to built that I've shared with a few people. I know they will get some worldwide press, but my current CNCROi.com shop is too small to built these things and the cost will be a bit up there. The second problem is what to do with models after they are built!

The Wooden Big Wheels ended-up spending less than an hour on the side of the road before somebody picked it up as there was no way it was going to fit in the shipping crate headed back to Canada. The laser cut version is sitting in Trotec Canada's showroom, a gift to them to thank them for their support when I moved back.

The Eiffel Tower was cut by lots of people who used it to promote their business and to get attention at their booths, and my version is 3/4 scale that I bring to tradeshows and networking events to do the same.

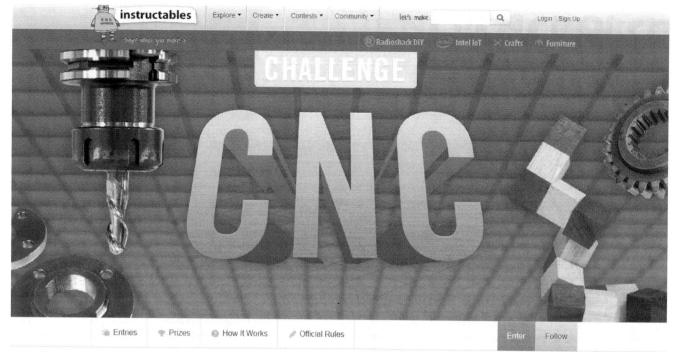

instructables

Explore ▾   Create ▾   Contests ▾   Community ▾   let's make

Login   Sign Up

Radioshack DIY   Intel IoT   Crafts   Furniture

⊕ Entries   🏆 Prizes   ⊙ How It Works   ✎ Official Rules   Enter   Follow

Another method of getting the word out is to partner with brand names that are in a similar "industry" as yourself. For instance, I recently partnered-up with Instructibles.com on a CNC Challenge. It was a perfect fit in so many ways. For instance, I use Autodesk software (their parent company) to design, test and animate all my designs on CNCKing.com. I would honestly not exist or be able to design WITHOUT 3DS Max!

Because of my design capability, I was able to sweeten the pie. When they approached me to help with the judging, I instantly told them that I'd design the award for the winner (which you'll see in Volume 6). This is a fantastic "client" for CNCROi.com that helps me promote my company locally and internationally. I got some great SEO juice by being featured in this contest and an increase in traffic across my related domains and book sales.

These kinds of opportunity are serendipitous. There was nothing planned, it just happened, but having a very active blog (almost 1 500 blog articles!) and constantly doing outreach means that the chances of huge opportunities coming to my door just grow over time.

For instance, the picture of my Wooden Big Wheels on the right (this is a very heavy model btw), I was sure it was going to be viral. I tried promoting it everywhere, the result? NOTHING! Now I know why I rarely see a strung-up wooden model in any promotions.

Now, if I made a stainless steel pig or crocodile maybe that would gain traction. Hmmm....

Philippe Guglielmetti, CEO of Zeepro

I've been talking back and forth with Philippe, CEO of Zeepro, for a while now. He's the founder of a host of companies including his most recently launched ZIM dual-head 3D printer which had a kickstarter campaign that achieved almost 350 backers, more than meeting it's initial funding goal of $ 300 000 US.

Their entire team came from across Europe and the U.S. to work out of a house in Sunnyvale, CA for the duration of their Kickstarter campaign.

It has not only solidified the team, but also allowed for spontaneous collaboration, making the product even better!

You can find Zeepro at http://zeepro.com

Can you give me a little background about yourself and how that lead you to see an opportunity in the 3D printing world?

I have been a serial entrepreneur since the age of 19. I co-founded and have been director of the board of several successful tech companies including iBase (pioneer of Direct Marketing on the Internet in Europe, acquired by Publicis) and Witbe (performance measures on the Internet).

In 1995, I co-founded (along with Zeepro's COO, Pierre Gerard) Integra, the leading pan-European company for managed web hosting and e-commerce web site operation. Integra was one of the first internet companies to be listed in Europe, and the sole company to be dual listed on the German and French stock markets.

At 35 years of age, I became the youngest CEO of the SBF120 Euronext index. Integra had operations in 10 countries in Europe. And the company, with more than 1,200 employees, was sold to a subsidiary of Verizon in 2001. Prior to co-founding Zeepro, I worked in the manufacturing industry as the CEO of Arcoa, a yacht builder.

I purchased a 3D printer for my son. Watching his enthusiasm for this new technology sparked my interest in building a team of professionals to design and manufacture the best personal 3D printer on the market.

What made you want to invest your time and treasure into starting your very own 3D printing hardware company when the market seems dominated by two massive companies already with vast resources such as Stratasys and 3D Systems? The payoffs even with success seem minor (you are building a commodity machine) and you cut your nose off from the start by allowing customers the option of getting their material from other sources (where the real money will be).

To answer the first part of your question, the companies you mention, Stratasys and 3D Systems, make 3D printers for manufacturing and prototyping; their offers are not intended for the home or small office. Even Makerbot, recently acquired by Stratasys, is more for design offices. With Zeepro, we wanted to create the best personal 3D printers for the home or small office. The key word here is Personal.

When we started designing Zim, we decided that we wanted an easy and safe way to load the filament. We also wanted a beautiful design hiding the "classic" filament spool. The only solution was to design our own specific cartridge. In addition to automatic loading, our smart cartridges also protect the filament, particularly the PVA, from moisture, and are convenient to store.

Now why offer a refillable cartridge to those who want to use their own filament? It is just because people who use 3D printer do it intensively at this early stage of the market. They use an important amount of filament and logically want to save cash!

Zeepro will also offer his own filament cartridges. Because they will be offered at market price, with a large range of colors, because they will be easy to load and to remove (so it will be easy to often change color), because people will be happy to store them easily, because our filament will be "pure" and perfectly adapted to our nozzles and to Zim drive gear.

We are confident that many users will choose to purchase our own cartridges, allowing us our share of what you call the "real money".

I'm astonished you've managed to beat the two major manufacturers in the areas of layer resolution and speed, yet are able to offer your 3D printer with more features at a cheaper cost per unit. How did you accomplish this especially with your dual-head... it's a steal by comparison!

We just wanted to make the best 3d personal printer in the world. Each feature has been very well thought out.

Our team has many years of experience in design, product development and manufacturing, and our experience combined with our research over the past year has resulted in Zim. And we will continue to work hard to improve continuously the performances of our products.

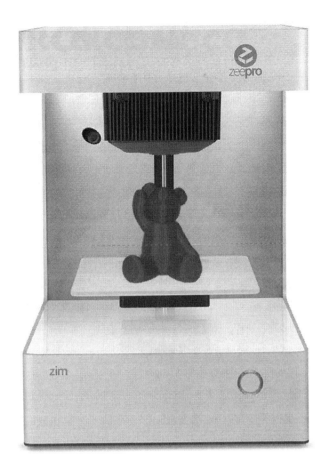

The Smart & Connected 3D Printer.

Much more than a device.

Why did you decide to go with extrusion over stereolithography (SLA) technology?

SLA technology produces very precise results that are excellent for labs and other sectors demanding low tolerances.

We believe that for home and office use, Filament extrusion provides quality results at an affordable price. I remind you that Zim can print from 50 microns layer.

There are A LOT of 3D printers coming onto the market these days, it seems like a new one is released every week - each promising incredible things only to vaporise a few weeks later. What aspects of your 3D printer make it unique enough to have staying power?

It's not about what makes our 3D printer unique, but more about how our company was set up from the start to adapt quickly to a changing market. Creating the product is only the very first step in building a successful company.

Financing, Manufacturing, Marketing, Distribution, Logistics, After-sales support are all in their own way essential to the success of Zeepro and we have built an incredible team of professionals, dedicated to this project and that have experience in all these areas.

One aspect that I really love about your Zim 3D extrusion printer is the camera... what a wonderful idea as the print times are atrocious for 3D extrusion printers. Being able to monitor a 3D printer wirelessly on your phone or desktop seems like such a smart idea... where did this idea come from?

Looking back, this was one of those "why has nobody else done this yet"? To us, an on-board camera seemed like such an obvious selling point! Our whole team has been using 3D printers for quite some time, and we are all aware of how long it takes to print.

Instead of sitting in front of your printer for hours to make sure everything is going ok, we stuck to our goal of making the best product and installed a camera.

In fact, this was such a collaborative team effort that just this morning we were trying to figure out who had been the first to suggest it, and we couldn't even narrow it down to one person!

Unlike the other 3D printers in the consumer marketplace, you are offering over 20 different print modes... can you expand on this a little more? Why so many and are they only simple tweeks or can they actually radically modify the print quality and speed of the output model? Can you give an example?

We have designed Zim like a high-end camera with several modes which allow the neophyte to print by clicking on a single button (AUTO mode), and the expert to make use of all of Zim technical capabilities (EXPERT mode).

If you choose the expert mode, you will be able to set several dozen printing parameters such as various printing speeds, layer thickness, filling of the hollow parts and many others.

In the standard mode, default parameters are already set-up to allow the user to balance between high speed and high quality.

You have decided to try your hand at Kickstarter to crowdsource Zim to both generate some funds to see this project through and to generate market interest in your machine. Are you happy with the results you received?

Yes, we are very happy with our Kickstarter campaign! Traditionally, a new technology in its early stages does not reach the general public. But because of the increasing popularity of crowdfunding and the media's crush on 3D printing, Zim is now reaching both early adopters and the general public simultaneously.

http://www.kickstarter.com/projects/1410146982/zim-the-first-dual-head-personal-3d-printer-fully

It's really great to have simultaneously a strong interest of both the technology community, such as kickstarter's, and well known resellers for consumers. We are really very proud of that!

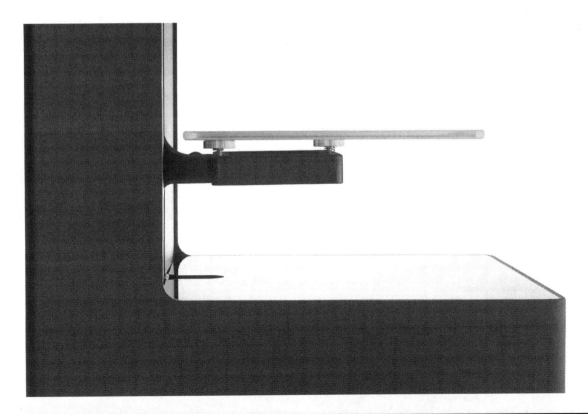

MiniMetalMaker's David Hartkop

There are a lot of 3D printers out there looking for funding but this one caught my eye... it uses metal clay instead of plastic! I contacted David to see if he was interested in talking a bit more about his awesome 3D printer and I'm so happy he agreed!

You can visit him online at http://minimetalmaker.com.

Can you give me some background about yourself and how you eventually found yourself into 3D printing in general?

I have a background in filmmaking and art. I took a series of jewelry classes in college at Loyola Marymount University in LA, and that's when I first encountered the university's 3d printer. It was 1998 and the machine was a huge stratasys the size of a washing machine with a 1 mm resolution, but it was still the coolest thing I had ever seen.

I had the opportunity to print some objects with this printer and to do a lost-wax casting with them to make metal forms from a 3d object file... awesome. Just awesome, despite all the work it takes to go through the lost wax process. You pretty much need a room full of tools & a couple days to do it.

My project on Indiegogo is really an outgrowth of that time, and my wanting to be able to make more objects directly with metal from digital objects. The new things on the scene now are low-cost robotics and a whole variety of these metal clays... neither of those were around in the 1990s.

I've seen A LOT of Kickstarter/indiegogo campaigns for PLA/ABS/resin but this the first for full 3D metal printing. What is it about metal that is more challenging than using plastics?

The challenge is that using metal clay in the context of 3d printing seems to be original! I actually haven't found anybody else doing it. Which was scary at the start, because most good ideas, it seems, already have a ton of people pursuing them.

In this case, it involved bringing together the tools of two very different cultures of people: Metal clay tends to be used by true hand-crafting artisans.

It is a tool for people who wish to make very special organic-shapes in metal. These people are artists & potters sculptors. The 3d printer and maker culture, on the other hand, is rooted in programmer-geekdom with engineering and DIY electronics at its core.

To take something that is traditionally only a 'hands-on' material and apply it to totally hands-off robotic manufacture is a kind of sacrilege.

The other part is the fact that most 3D printers trend toward bigger build volumes and lower cost print stock.

My 3D printer runs counter to both those features, in that I focused instead on a small (2.3 inch cube) build volume with really high resolution, and am using maybe the world's most expensive feed stock... gold! (or silver, bronze, iron, and a few other types of metals.)

So, was it a risk thinking people would want a 3D printer in this space with these qualities? Absolutely. It still is!

Fingers crossed.

*Since the time of this first interview, there have been 2 or 3 other startup companies starting to experiment with extruding metal clay. The common approach as been to use an air pressurized cylinder to push clay from a head attached to a modified off the shelf 3d printer. I haven't found any for sale yet, however.

You've achieved some amazing marketing coups like getting in businessweek etc., how did you achieve this? How did it come about?

You've got me. I think the fact that anything labeled "3D Printer" is getting news attention right now is certainly helping... but I'm just baffled and AMAZED!

It isn't often one has an idea that is 'on time' in the marketing zeitgeist sense... usually ideas come too late or too early for people to want them or 'get' them.

What are the advantages to 3D printing in metal over other materials? I saw some awesome examples on your site such as conducting electricity and being able to bend/file output models.

The main advantages are just that the finished product IS metal. It has superior wear properties to many plastics, can bend and hold shape, can be polished to a beautiful luster, etc. Objects made from metal clays are what is referred to as 'sintered' meaning made up of welded-together metal particles.

Sintered metals have many uses, but do tend to be a bit more brittle than traditionally cast or foundry-extruded metals. I see the mini metal maker being useful for certain specific engineering/technical applications, and extremely useful to artists and metal artisans.

Can you describe in more detail how you got your team together to design and market the Mini Metal Maker? Why did you all decide to go the crowdfunding route instead of using VCs or angel investors?

My team currently consists of myself, programmer Ben Aiken, and my two friends Tim & Chrissy Sparks. I have been in touch with Ben over the years and have consulted with him on various software related projects.

We saw this as a way we could really collaborate on something interesting. My experience is mostly along the lines of fabrication and 'mechatronic' engineering to create solar trackers and coffee roasting equipment for my other business.

Well, my team with the original crowdfunding campaign have sinced moved away or is no longer involved. Right now it is a husband and wife operation, just myself and my wife Lindsay. She handles the ordering and price shopping for stepper motors and parts and does the book keeping. I have handled the design, the R&D and the networking with other companies to arrange manufacture and supply of clay, etc.

I've made some good contacts through the process of doing the last crowdfunding campaign. That's a big part of the value of going the crowdfunding route: the marketing and advertising aspects of getting your project and product out there.

We actually are interested in the VC route, but the market-building aspects of a crowdfunding campaign are much more immediate and valuable at this point.

One of the main reasons we went the crowdfunding route vs. VC is that croudfunding not only helps you find project funding, it also puts you in better touch with your target market.

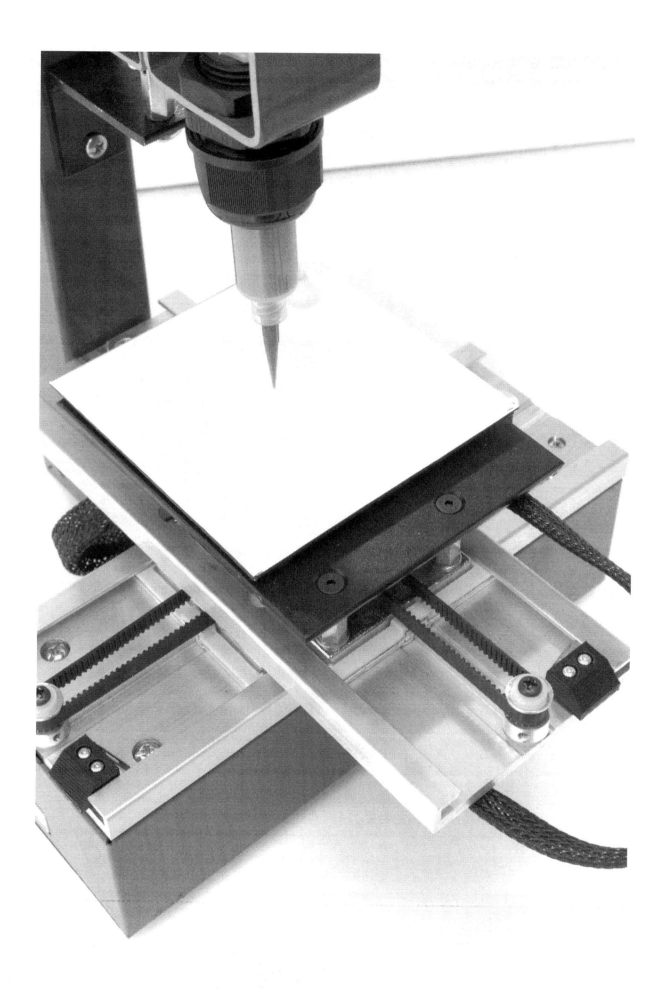

Are there any challenges present with storing raw metal clay filaments like there are for PLA/ABS which tends to dry-out or break when exposed to the environment?

So, first of all, metal clay is stored in a tube as a mixed sort of 'gel' about the consistency of thick toothpaste. The tubes keep it from drying over time, but there may be issues of long-term storage and the clay separating out more than desired.

Chemists and engineers have been developing metal clay for years, though, and most of these problems are well addressed. I didn't invent metal clay, I'm just putting it to use in a different way.

Your 10K goal is was small, why so little? 3D printing is such an expensive industry, this is such a shoestring budget!

I figured that, since I was able to develop the whole machine this far for under $1K, that I should be able to refine it into something salable for 10, at least something basic and kit-based. If we end up raising more funds than the initial goal, I will be able to create something better than my most basic plans. This includes a machine with a bigger build volume, two extrude heads, and I'll be able to do the research needed to produce a good 'support material' for use with metal clay when making overhanging shapes.

We actually raised just shy of $35K, which was 300+% of our goal! A very successful campaign! As it has turned out over the last year, the process of developing the concept into a production prototype was expensive but we were able to develop a great machine. In some ways, the current production Mini Metal Maker is far and away better than what our original plan called for. We plan to retail it for around $2100, so it's going to be more expensive than we originally planned, but also much better.

I see incredible opportunities in 3D metal printing from small industrial processes to jewelry as the alternatives in the market now are exponentially more expensive. How does your Mini Metal Maker compare to the big industrial guys?

Well -and this applies to 3d printing as a whole- I don' think it will ever compete dollar-for-dollar with large scale industrial production. What 3d printing lets you do is create small volumes of specific things, or individual specialty things that you couldn't get any other way.

An example is that a factory in India produces a metal button for 2 cents each ... if I lost one from my coat, however, I might have to order a bag of 500 of them and then wait 3 months to get them... I overpay on the item, the shipping, and on time.

A metal printer, however, would let me just print 1 exactly matching button. Even though it may cost 50 cents and not 2 cents, I actually SAVE money and time because of the accessibility of the manufacture.

Can you describe what the famous "Stanford Bunny" 3D printer test is and the results you can achieve with your 3D printer? What are we looking at in this model to know if you passed or failed?

The "Stanford Bunny" is one of more than a dozen common 3D test models that are commonly used to test various 3D computer graphics algorithms. The bunny is a 3D scan of a ceramic rabbit that was created for research at Stanford University in 1993-1994 and is an open-source 3D model - meaning it is available for anyone to use.

In the 3D printing industry, it is often used as a printing benchmark object. As a 3D object, it has a few different things going on, challenges to overcome from a technical standpoint. The first is that the 3D model itself has some small problems in terms of its surface geometry; there are parts of the surface that overlap in strange ways. Typically, you overcome this with a piece of repair software that patches holes and essentially un-wrinkles the geometry of a model's surface.

The next challenge, as with any 3D printed object, is to slice the object into a tool-path for a printer to use. The bunny has some beautiful contours in its outer surface and it also has some pretty severe overhangs, as seen under its chin and ears. With FDM type 3D printers (printers that create by extruding a line of material), overhanging parts must be supported by some additional support structures.

The support structures must be printed along with the rest of the model and then removed afterword. In the case of 3D printing with metal clay, it was a bit challenging to find the best settings for constructing the often very thin support structures out of clay.

We used the program Slic3r, which allows for lots of manual control and tinkering with the settings. In the end, we found that an angle threshold of 40 degrees worked well, and we had to carefully balance the extrusion multiplier for the given clay blend.

The final challenge had to do with the clean-up of the printed model. The support material had to be removed carefully after the clay was dry. I used a bladed clay tool and some tweezers. For some applications, the ridged contour-map appearance of the surface curvature is fine, but I wanted the bunny to appear smooth so it could really shine.

This was achieved by lightly sanding the model to remove stray bumps and clumps of clay left during printing. Then, the model was wetted with water and a paintbrush. Finally, a couple coats of clay slip were applied with the brush to fill in the grooves that remained after sanding.

The test is not a pass/fail as such, but provides some good indicators of print quality. Over all, the Mini Metal Maker provides good dimensional accuracy and layer adhesion.

The surface contour details are decent, on a par with most plastic printing 3D printers. Where the Mini Metal Maker differs the most is in the cleanup stage.

Highly countored objects (IE not flat) will need some degree of cleanup, but this cleanup is as easy as smoothing with a wet finger, or can be done precisely by sanding and painting with slip.

It is essentially an opportunity to make final changes before the object is 'set into metal' during the firing process. Once it is fired, there are other things you can do, such as polishing, grinding, etc. But most surface changes are much easier to make before firing.

You are about to embark onto another crowdfunding campaign, can you give me a glimpse into HOW MUCH WORK is involved with launching and achieving success in these campaigns now vs your first crowdfunding campaign over a year ago? How much have things changed since then and why indiegogo and not kickstarter? Can you share any tips that helped you last time around or lessons you learned?

We are embarking on a new 45 day campaign on Indiegogo, launching on March 1. The kind of work involved in a crowdfunding campaign is quite different from the work we did developing the product over the last 18 months. The biggest challenges have been simply getting the product to the point that it is ready to 'show off' for the campaign. The rest has been developing the social media channels.

We are in the midst of the pre-campaign right now, which involves setting up the website, and building some buzz in facebook, twitter, Pinterest, instagram and through any other groups that might pass us on to their audiences.

We are going to be featured in the IGUS newsletter - Igus is the company that makes the plastic bearings in our project! I'm also doing some free workshops at the Library District here in Pueblo to get the word out. On that note, thanks for writing this article!

Why indiegogo and not kickstarter? Well, I ran three unsuccessful kickstarter campaigns and one successful campaign on indiegogo... so I figured I would go with what worked!

I like Indiegogo's version of flexible funding, wherein you get to keep whatever you earn even if you don't make your goal.

I also like that the scope of your project is not so much subject to approval/denial as with Kickstarter. (One project I set up for Kickstarter was simply a no-go because my project at the time was essentially a non-profit humanitarian venture and Kickstarter is for-profit and project based.)

We're just putting together our campaign video this week and next, and pulling together pictures and examples of things we've printed with the MMM. Tips: don't promise super expensive gifts or difficult-to-make gifts! We didn't lose money from the last campaign, but we sure didn't make any either!

Not after making a bunch of 3D printed custom objects, 25 fully assembled machines, and buying KILNS for some people! Yikes, lesson learned. We're really going to just stay focused on our product. And the prizes will be the printer or some smaller but easier items like t-shirts etc.

You came out with a MMM DYI, how does it compare to its big brother, what was the thought process behind developing and releasing a DYI version of your metal 3D printer? What are some of the technical challenges you had with it?

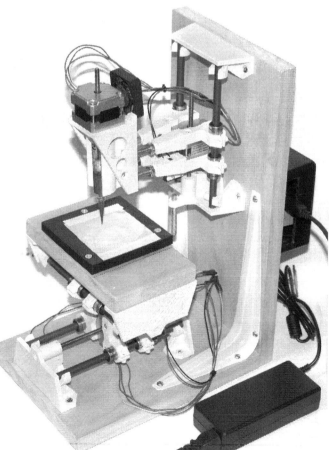

This is a good question! Our original plan for the Mini Metal Maker was that it would be a do-it-yourself product. Essentially just a download and some instructions for making your own. In fact, the first 9 months after the campaign were devoted entirely to pulling together a DIY version.

It includes 3D print files for making the bearing holders etc. I'm actually really proud of the MMM-DIY; I used it to print a bunch of test objects and objects for prizes.

It's a great machine and it is super simple to set up once you have the parts printed and some wood & parts from a hardware store.

It actually has a higher working resolution than the soon-to-be-commerical Mini Metal Maker. Where it falls short, however, is clay-pressing power and mass-produciblility.

The extruder for the MMM-DIY works well for small syringes of metal clay that a person mixes up him/herself.

I wanted to be able to use larger cartridges of clay in any would-be machine we make to sell. Larger diameter cartridges requires more power, which meant reinventing the extruder section.

The MMM-DIY can press with a force around 40 pounds, which is great for small syringes of clay. It works out to be around 60psi within the syringe which will work if you mix the clay correctly. The Mini Metal Maker, on the other hand, has an all-steel extruer frame which can handle higher forces, and a larger stepper motor with orbital gear reduction and a screw drive that pushes a stainless steel piston.

Working with Metal Adventures, who is developing our special formulation of clay, we have measured an extruder pressure of over 300psi.

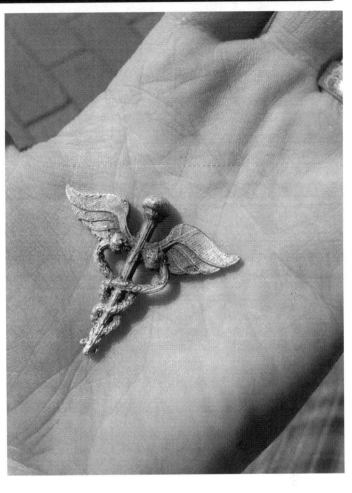

This means we can use nice large clay loads of 50-150g and we can also extrude through much smaller nozzles (300 down to 150 micron holes).

The Mini Metal Maker is also made from more standardized commercially available components and is fabricated from sheet metal in relatively few pieces. I went through four entirely different designs, reducing the total number of parts each time, before we settled on this design.

The metal parts are mostly just sections of commercially available steel tubing, and there are only three small parts that we have to have printed or injection molded. Also, relying on light metal fabrication plays into the strengths of the metal fabrication capacity we have here in Southern Colorado. Pueblo knows how to make things out of steel.

This makes it more suitable for mass production right where I live. I think both versions of the MMM are great. The MMM-DIY plans will be on our campaign page for $25 per download, and the full MMM will be a prize for $2100 and above.

Protection and Profits

Putting everything else aside, the sole focus of a company is to make money, the more, the better. Part of that is finding ways to monetize existing IP and expanding it into other areas by diversification across multiple verticals.

CNCKing.com, for instance, makes money from book sales, digital plans, Youtube views and the list goes on... CNCROi.com from designing projects for companies and producing them using the laser and other CNC equipment I have access to. Neither site has any advertising by the way, on purpose.

The two very much work in tandem to generate even more revenue even if the demographics of their customer bases couldn't be more different. I easily leverage my skills in one to augment my skills in the other.

I think that if you are a designer, it's only a matter of time before somebody rips you off or steals your design. It has happened to me and just about every other designer I know... and it sucks!

The problem with fighting some of these battles is that they are too expensive and, to be quite honest, the effort is best put elsewhere. IP protection is a nice idea but it can quickly sink you if you aren't careful.

My way to protect my IP is pretty straight forward: I jump onto copyright conventions. Part of the reason why I publish books of all my designs "to date" is so that the ideas and the designs themselves are protected by copyright.

This also serves a dual purpose, there is physical proof that yes, I'm the designer (something that's hard to prove otherwise) while at the same time, increasing my profile so when there is doubt, I can use it to my advantage to "win".

Before ISPs ban websites by taking them offline or authorities getting involved, they want PROOF. A published book that you can point to with page number has helped me tremendously!

I believe this method can work for just about any invention and idea you may have, even if you don't sell any copies, the fact that there is a record of it somewhere like Amazon.com puts you miles ahead in my non-professional-opinion than mailing yourself a design using the postage date.

Another way to protect your design is to keep making and improving your skills. The designs you see in my very first volume are almost childs play compared to what's in this book... if you copied my earlier designs, you are now behind the 8 ball in approach, efficiency and esthetics. I've evolved and moved on, the copier has not.

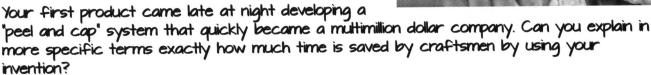

Paul Akers, Inventor & Founder, FastCap

Paul is the founder of FastCap that started when he invented a very easy to use and incredibly effective "peel and cap" system which has since grown into a multimillion dollar business that's now helping other inventors distribute their products around the world.

His company has also recently moved into a brand new custom 50 000 square foot building optimized around his lean philosophy with two Big Ass fans!

With over 2700 distributors around the world and booming sales across a variety of verticals, Paul has achieved incredible business success and is now a published author to boot!

You can visit his company at http://FastCap.com.

Your first product came late at night developing a 'peel and cap' system that quickly became a multimillion dollar company. Can you explain in more specific terms exactly how much time is saved by craftsmen by using your invention?

It saves 900%! It's really outrageous! It would normally take 35-45 minutes to cap a typical job because the screw caps traditionally, the mechanical head, fell out and the screw head had to be perfectly flush.

Ours could simply be peeled and stuck right on the top and what happens when the screw cabinets come together, or you screw them to the wall, the bugle head screw generally goes in a little too deep because you want to cinch things up. So now the screw is below the surface and then the mechanical head doesn't work very well.

Ours happens to work perfectly in that application, so the amount of time is the difference between 45 minutes and 5 minutes. It's dramatic!

I think that's one of the reasons why it was so appealing a solution.

Additionally, it came in so many different colors and variations like real wood, unfinished wood, textured, smooth, speckled and we were able to match the interior of all these different projects, where traditionally, they had only a few colors to choose from and they all looked terrible.

How did you handle the incredible financial growth curve you initially experienced? When you start making crazy amounts of "easy" money, how did you keep yourself in check?

Those are two excellent questions! Number one, my wife and I were fortunate enough, even though I'm a C and D student, I wasn't the brightest guy in the world. I did follow the mentorship of my father and invested in real estate.

We started in the ghetto and near and around Los Angeles where we bought our first home and we made a goal to buy a rental property, to accrue a portfolio of one for every year we were married.

So while my wife and I had friends going to Hawaii and buying nice cloths and cars, we buckled down and saved our money and invested in real estate.

We bought very bad homes in bad Neighborhoods and even had our life threatened many time while we were just trying to make ends meet, but we were able to do that so we started too small and as the properties matured, we grew into higher quality properties and then into commercial property.

We started at the very bottom with nothing and, because we had the real estate background, we had the ability, to some extent, to self-finance FastCap. But then, when it grew beyond those financial capabilities, we had to borrow money from the bank. Even with our portfolio, the banks didn't want to lend us money, so finally, when they saw us as a credible company, they were able to lend us money.

So we had a period of time there for 2-3 years where we used bank financing but the answer was that I always knew the prudency of not spending or living beyond my means and before long, FastCap was able to self-finance itself.

We had very little bank interaction in terms of them helping us grow because we just didn't spend money we didn't have. We grew at the rate that we had capital to grow. We could be a 100 million dollar company right now if we borrowed money but we choose not to because we wanted to be very financially stable.

How do I keep myself in check? It's the simplest equation possible, I'm grateful. I've never been able to figure out why it is, that I was not born in Bangladesh or some other third world country begging on the side of the street.

I feel like gosh, how was I fortunate enough to be born to amazing parents and in the United States full of boundless opportunity. I was born in a free market system in a democratic country! It's just a staggering truth to me.

So I'd be in my driveway everyday and think "I'm the luckiest guy alive!" So I remained grateful!

The other thing I do is that I'm always on the shop floor, I don't have an office. We are building a brand new 50 000 square foot building and the first thing people ask when they come in is "where's your office?" and I tell them that I don't have one.

The most important work in our company is done on the shop floor and that's where I am. My office is on the shop floor in a small rolling cart.

I'm always in touch with my people, I'm accessible to everybody and that keeps me grounded. I'm just a regular guy and there's nothing special about me other than applying enormous discipline and focus to my life.

I follow-through with everything and the result of that is enormous success!

Really, that's the key for anyone. If I evaluate people around me and in life in general, the people who aren't successful but want to be just lack discipline, a vision and are unwilling to council with smarter and older people.

You have a lot of other awesome innovations on your site, from BestFence to Kaizen Foam... which ones are your favorites?

Well, I have a lot of favorite products but the bottom line, the product I'm the most proud of, is BestFence. I took an enormous amount of time and almost a quarter of a million dollars developing that. We worked with our internal design team and about 70 contractors externally to make everything just perfect. Even to this day, we are constantly improving on the initial design even though it's already an incredible product.

It was a huge undertaking and a much grander project than anything else developed by FastCap and I'm most proud of it due to the investment it took to develop it from start, to be able to pull-off something that significant.

In terms of the product I like the most, because it has the greatest appeal to everyone and the most useful, Kaizen Foam. It's incredible, we developed that for our own internal lean processes, to make our shadow boards more effective and easy to do. People saw them on the tour and said we should sell that stuff. We said "OK!" but actually, we sell it but don't make much money off of it.

We sell it roughly the same amount it costs to manufacture and it's a very popular product that everybody uses, from Bentley and Rolls Royce to Virgin Air to Delta Airlines, everybody buys Kaizen Foam because it works!

We have customers all around the world that love the product. It has the widest appeal and helps the most people. People get the most joy out of getting organized and becoming efficient.

I really like the videos you make on your website promoting the innovative products you offer, are they as much fun to make as they are to watch? It really personalizes it tremendously and adds a lot of trust, was this on purpose or did FastCap just happen to evolve in that direction?

You know what, I'm extremely proud of our videos, the reason why is that we don't have a production crew. I do most of the videos all myself, and the cool thing about it is that I'm not trying to be perfect on any of the videos I make and none of them are perfect. They are just ME!

We try to present ourselves as being regular people who are down to earth because that's really who we are. So most people would be all caught-up with the graphics, the audio isn't perfect, the stage isn't perfect, all the props weren't perfect - we couldn't care less about any of that. What we care about is delivering value to our customers.

What the customers want to know is how does the product work, in a real-world, non-canned environment. So we give them exactly that. We can produce 3-4 videos a day which is really unprecedented - we have over 700 videos online and produce way more than that.

That is really a cool thing and really the message behind lean, just get good about communication by simply shooting a before / after video on all your lean improvements. It's basically what we do with all our product videos and everything else in our company. We just make everything very simple.

The vast majority of our videos we shot that are online were done with my iPhone. We want it simple and we want it to flow. A customer wants to know something, like how do you use FastEdge, we pull-out our iPhone and in 5 minutes we shoot the video and upload it to YouTube.

The customer then look at us and say they never heard of a company that can do this. We move that quickly because we understand the power of flow.

I know for my site, CNCKing.com, there has been a definite synergy between product quantity / diversity and overall order value. Have you discovered the same?

The great synergy between product quality and diversity with overall order value is very simple. Products that are innovative and enhance a process or improve how something is done to add more value and eliminate the wastage of time and motion... that's the greatest synergy between all our products.

We also celebrate the creativity of other people's products because 80-90% of our products come from cabinet makers and general contractors. So our theme is "other people's innovations."

What was it like launching your own radio show "The American Innovators" and how has it helped your company's profile?

What was it like launching my own radio show? Fear and intrepidation, I don't know... it was a big step. I have no background in broadcast or anything like that but I had a message that you can run a more successful business if you learn how to innovate and learn how to continuously learn while creating that culture within your organization. I thought that sure, I'll screw up, it won't be perfect, but I knew I could do it.

I called a radio station and pitched my idea. They said no. I called them again and they said no... and after enough calls they finally considered my idea. They then called me back and told me they liked the idea.

It didn't just happen, it was a lot of work and persistence over the course of 9 months to a year on my part.

I will never forget sitting in-front of that microphone the very first time when they said "on the air" and I had to literally fill the airways for an hour and it was a daunting task to be able to do that. But I did it!

I rehearsed and practiced with lots of discipline and went over my subject matter, which I knew very well, then I realized that it wasn't really that hard although it does take a fair amount of work.

It was a big deal! It really was a big deal but you know what, anybody can do it if they have one ingredient, PASSION! What the world is lacking is passionate leaders and people with passion.

Most people are so subdued in expressing themselves and there is nothing fascinating about being subdued.

Now that you have a variety of distributors (1700 of them!), how much of your business is online vs offline?

The vast majority of our business is with our distributors, which now number 2700 around the world, and represents 95% of all our business but the online business is undoubtedly growing and it's there to provide access to people who normally couldn't access our product lines.

Our products are generally sold through commercial and industrial distributors, not retailers. As a result, the retail market generally has trouble accessing our product lines so the website fills that void.

What advice would you give Paul to both your fellow inventors with great ideas but no money and "jobs" that prevent them to following-through to a finished product?

Be humble, don't think you are a genius or deserve a million dollars. These are the two biggest problems I run into with inventors - they think they are God's gift to the world - which you are not as anybody can innovate - and you just need to be humble about that.

You also need to be very persistant, you can't give-up and be a continuous learner. In the process of doing that, you'll discover the innovation you want to bring to the market but if you get stuck on just one thing, and THIS IS THE ONE, you are crazy.

I came-up with so many great ideas prior to coming-up with the FastCap and they were not marketable.

All great ideas, improved time savings, all helped me, but the issue you need to know whether you have a great product or not is so simple. It's something called a "strong felt need."

What that means is simply this: when you show the product to someone, and they say "where can I get that? How much is that, I'd like to buy it!"

You know you have a great product. If they respond, "that's a cool idea", that's not necessarily a good product. Everybody will say that as it's just part of being polite.

What you want people to say is "I WANT THAT! How much is that? Where can I get it?" Those kind of questions are a clear indicator that you have developed something that is very cool.

What is your advice specifically regarding patenting a device or product idea?

Patents are the biggest joke in the word and a massive amount of wasted money. I have tons of patents and by and large, they aren't worth the paper they are printed on. Unless you have millions of dollars to defend them.

I have had lawsuits with major corporations and they try to run right on top of me but because I have enough money to fight them in court, only after I've spent a hundred thousand to a quarter of a million dollars in legal fees, they finally say "ok, I guess this guy is serious and isn't going to go away, we'll settle."

Unless you have the ability to do that, the patent is worthless and you have to calculate that. I say, unless you want to waste your time with developing patents which costs 20-30 thousand dollars, develop your product and get it onto the market instead.

Product positioning is far more important than a patent and at some point, when you can afford to throw away 20-30 thousand at an item, because you think it will be really big, and have the money to defend it, yeah, go ahead and get a patent.

With all the tremendous success you've had, do you still spend some time in the shop making things?

Not necessarily woodworking product. I built my home, all the furniture in my home, my guitars, everything, but I don't have much time to do that, I do dream about being able to do that again.

I'm constantly building new things, like our new 50 000 square feet facilities, innovating from one end to the other, so I'm in a very creative mode.

A lot of other people do a lot of work but I still even today, literally, I'm working on our new facilities putting up speaker wires so we have a phenomenal sound system. So I'm a very hands on person but I don't get to make a lot of woodworking projects.

What is in your book and what made you want to become a published author?

Here are the reasons why I wrote the book. First of all, I have a lot of people touring our facility all the time and they saw all the work we have done. They were curious along with a few comments like "you should write a book." I thought about it and I said "yeah, I should write a book!"

So that was one reason. Another was that I read a book a week and I realized that people that were capable of having the maximum influence in life were people who could articulate their ideas well. Additionally, these people were generally authors as well. So I realized if my goal in life was to be as big an influence on society and people as possible, being the biggest thing in the universe, that it was necessary for me to have a book to make me both credible and for me to take the time and discipline to formulate my ideas.

So I realized that writing a book would be very advantageous for my personal development as well as helping other people to develop a lean culture. That was the impetus behind writing my own book.

Tim Bourke, Founder & Inventor at Just Right Products

Tim is the president and head of product development for Just Right Products, a company that prides itself in "Made in the USA" innovations and product lines.

He has four registered patents and two more on the way and is best known as the inventor of the Super Rope Cinch.

You can find him online at http://JustRightProductsllc.com.

Can you give me a little background about yourself and how you got into "inventing as a career" with Just Right Products?

I've always been my own boss. Dropping out of high school halfway through 10th grade, I went to work knowing I had to teach myself everything I wanted to learn. Inventing was no different.

I started Just Right Products because I knew I would have several ideas and wanted to control what happened with them.

Where did the idea for Super Rope Cinch come from? What makes it revolutionary?

In 2010, I wondered why are we still tying and untying knots in rope? We have been to the moon and back but still have to do this? I really started thinking about this and knew the answer. It was because we never had a choice before.

Three days later, I had the first prototype in my hand and now we do have a choice and it's called, "Super Rope Cinch"! Never tie or untie a knot again. We were shocked how many people don't want to tie or untie knots anymore. It's a TON...

You've been picked-up by Walmart. How easy or hard of a process was getting your own invention sold at their stores?

Playing with the big boys, Walmart, Home Depot, Do It Best, Orgill, Walmart Canada, etc. took three years and a million dollars doing everything ourselves.

Time and money are the two biggest things you have to have and plan on needing more of each of them.

Delving a bit into manufacturing, I'm assuming it's plastic molded. What were some of the headaches involved with getting the process sorted enough to begin mass production?

The tool/mold we run at this time is a 16 cavity tool that produces 317,000 Super Rope Cinches every 30 days. The tool cost was $130,000 dollars and was built after all the testing was done on a very small tool. knowing we had a ton of testing and changes that would be made, changing a small tool/mold is way more cost affective than changing a large one.

As soon as it's justified, we are on track to triple manufacturing and produce 1 million parts a month.

This year you've sent over 10 000 units to the UK. What are some other countries that you are distributing your invention in and which markets are you planning on entering in the near future?

With 317 million people in the US and 800 million people in the UK and Europe, we knew we had to setup shop over there. On 10/1/2013 Just Right Products UK & Europe Ltd. was born. Just Right Products Global is next and should happen next year. This will really help us introduce the Super Rope Cinch to the world.

What advice do you have regarding the acquisition of a patent? Is it worth it or should people just get a provisional and put all their time and money into developing the market?

I'm on patent number 6 with 2 pending. As a Full/Time inventor, I know it is a must to do EVERYTHING you can to protect your inventions and your rights to them. Money changes people and if your invention is capable of making money, people will try to knock it off. At Just Right Products, we file for utility patents, trademarks, etc. on everything we invent.

If you had a time machine, what advice would you give your younger self before jumping into inventing and distributing your own inventions?

If I could go back in time and change things, I don't think I would change to much. It takes time, money, and the right people to really make things happen in life. It takes a village.

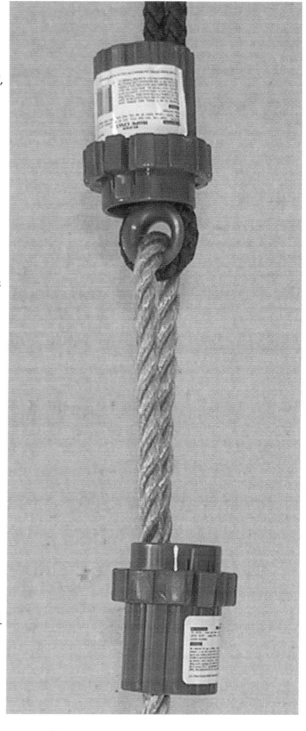

Make sure that village of people you surround yourself with has the same goal in mind that you do. If you surround yourself with millionaires, chances are you will be one.

Surround yourself with crackheads, well you can see where this is going. Taking your idea from your mind all the way to retail is not easy.

If it were, everyone would be doing it. Know right upfront, the more you want to do and have control of, the more hard work, time, money, etc. you will have to bring to the table.

Ask yourself this. Do I want to do this? Not can I do this? Because if you want to do this, you will. You can do anything you set your mind to do. I'm no different than anyone else.

Believe in what you are doing, put it in your heart, work hard, give back by helping others, maybe thank someone from above, and watch what happens.

You can do anything and everything. It is all in your mind. What do you want to do today??? My answer is EVERYTHING and has been for a very long time.

I get asked all the time, how do I do it? It's really easy I explain. No matter what you do in life to get more out of it, do one more thing today that you did not do yesterday. This applies to everything, not just inventing.

To better yourself do one more email, make one more phone call, teach yourself something new, that you did not do or know yesterday. You will move forward in a way you won't believe.

When I said I wanted to retail the Super Rope Cinch for $3.99 and make it in the USA, everyone told me I was crazy. Knowing China didn't need to change but we did, I had to prove it could be done.

What I had to do was setup manufacturing just outside Dallas with our packager and warehouse 10 miles down the road. I'm so proud to say everything is 100% made in the USA.

My point is this: let's get busy people and make things happen because we can.

This is the USA and if you are not a millionaire, it's because you don't want to be one. Remember, you can do whatever you set your mind to do, I promise.

Anthony Santangelo, Inventor, Entrepreneur & Attorney

Anthony has lots of hats, from a Marketing MBA to inventor, attorney to entrepreneur and it seems... anything else inbetween! There is a lot of awesome insight, especially on the legal side (in plain English) that I think anybody in business should carefully review and study for their own sake. If you are a designer, inventor or entrepreneur, I think you should seriously consider getting a hold of Anthony for a legal opinion - there aren't that many people with such a wide grasp of business intersecting with ideas.

You can follow Anthony at his law office website at http://njtriallawyer.tripod.com/ and on Twitter at https://twitter.com/santangelolaw.

You have a rather diversified educational background, jumping from your MBA in Marketing to becoming an attorney focused on the fields of business, real estate, admiralty and taxes. What made you want to become a lawyer after studying marketing for so many years?

Well Jon, I've always been a compulsive Inventor but I'm also an adult with ADD. I'm very restless intellectually. I need to learn something new every single day. I sort of perpetually am the square peg trying to fit in the round hole.

I like to base important decisions on thorough research and careful reasoning. I knew that I had picked the right career one day when I was working as an intern for a popular judge.

During the trial, he pointed at a witness and looked at me and said. "Anthony we need to know if that witness is qualified to be an expert here."

The response to that question was a 46 page typed bench memo which encompassed the law of expert witness. It was also a careful review of the particulars of this witnesses education and abilities. Frankly, he did not qualify as an expert.

This is the type of careful research, review, analysis and writing that I always wanted to do. I always detested the typical American business persons shoot from the hip attitude about important business decisions.

I would have stayed in business except that I was not good at doing what you need to get ahead. I always found that American business is exactly like the play "How to succeed in business without really trying." If you come from the same alma mater as your boss and you drink the same scotch as your boss and you play a good round of golf with your boss, you will advance rapidly through the corporate ranks, otherwise your career might not be so satisfying.

I always attacked every job I ever had as if the business was mine. I call this being an intrapreneur. Unfortunately, being an intrapreneur in business does not necessarily get you ahead. Regardless of how many new sales or profits you gain for the corporation, you might not get promoted.

I am generally not a big fan of the way business is typically conducted in American big businesses. One of the things that I like the least are long ceaseless boring meetings. Most of the meetings I've been to are the painful, socially awkward type that you would usually see on a sitcom like "The Office".

At one such meeting they began to discuss a topic that I was an expert in. The topic was generic injectable pharmaceuticals. My Director asked if we should cancel a particular line of products because it was not very profitable. Without an agenda or any background information at all, my boss wanted to know if we should shut down one of our factories!

This product line represented about $40 million in sales from a 20,000 square-foot facility running for several shifts and impacted the jobs of hundreds of employees in a town that I had a personal affinity with. To keep all those people employed and keep that piece of real estate occupied, I would continue to run that business even if it was only at breakeven.

Of course that business, even at breakeven, would use a tremendous amount of ancillary services such as packaging shipping materials and supplies which would benefit other companies. I personally would be in favor of keeping this piece of our country's productivity running even if it didn't throw off a profit.

I was thinking that if this product line was canceled, all those people would lose their jobs, the facility would be closed, that space in that industrial park would be empty and it would have an negative impact on the town that I liked. While I was thinking through the particulars of that decision, some other wonk spoke up and said "Let's dump it, it's a dog." And that's basically how the decision was made.

Afterwards my manager came up to me and said, "Anthony, that was in the area of your expertise, why didn't you contribute something during that meeting?" I told her that I was thinking through the ramifications of the plant closing before I could give an accurate answer and she told me that next time I should think faster.

What I find fascinating is that you've had your name attached to over 270 inventions in one form or another, with that wealth of experience, what are some commonalities you've seen with inventors who end-up being successful with their inventions? Are there some common pitfalls that you've seen as well that could have been avoided?

The number one most interesting thing about successful inventors is that they all demonstrate sometimes an irrational belief in their own ability to succeed.

If you think about it for a minute, you'll realize that this is exactly the thing that every Inventor must-have. In my experience, every single person I speak to about a new invention says or demonstrates the opinion that it's the stupidest thing they ever heard. Just like in the movie "Big", everybody you tell your idea to will just look at you with a blank face and say "I don't get it."

To get people to even understand what a new idea is, you need to give them a good description, show them a picture or accurate prototype and then relate to them the market conditions that will satisfy that products commercialization.

This is something that you can't achieve with an elevator pitch. That's usually not enough to convince a layperson that working on this new thing is not really the mental equivalent of going off the reservation.

Inventors make a lot of mistakes. In fact, they probably make more mistakes than they do get things right. The most common mistake that every Inventor makes is inaction. In the patent law, there are times when a lack of diligence for just two weeks has lost the person their battle for some patent right.

If you believe that your idea has some benefit, you should work on it diligently until it's fleshed out and on the market or where you decide that you no longer want to move forward with-it because of financial considerations.

The other big problem in the marketplace is these Inventor marketing companies. It's estimated that inventors will spend between $200-$300 million with these companies and that up to 75% of that money is wasted.

One of the first things I always tell inventors is that, "If it's to be, it's up to thee." You're going to have to be the person that has to flesh out your idea and convince other people to raise money, do research and development, bring it to market, whatever.

If you delegate that to somebody else, that money is probably going to be wasted. For example, why would you pay an invention promotion company, let's say $200 or $300 an hour, to do research that you could do at your local library, on a database, with a little help from your research librarian.

Inventors need to do two things to bring their product to market, they certainly need to work diligently and they also need to be willing to learn some new things in order to satisfy the requirements of investors and licensees who may be interested in commercializing the product with them.

How did you feel when the American Patent Office recently changed their rules from first to invent to first to file? Do you think patents are a worthy investment or is that money best used to get a provisional and marketing?

I think that the system we had worked just fine. I was not in favor of changing patent regulations in such a wholesale manner because the effects cannot be known. It's just like Obamacare, you're faced with 1 000's of pages of legislation and nobody really knows what the final outcome is going to be.

Nowadays though, when I speak to inventors, I tell them that they have to see the patent system as if they were one of the great gold prospectors in the gold rush of 48. Just imagine two prospectors side-by-side digging in the ground in the mountains and they both pick up a little pebble that looks like it might be gold.

What's going to happen next is they are going to have to make a run to the land office to stake a claim and the one that gets there first will get the claim and the other one gets nothing.

People now say that we have to change the patent laws because there are too many cases. This is like saying we should make auto theft a non-crime because we have too many car thieves on trial.

If there are disputes between affluent patent holders, that is just fine. If we don't have enough courts and judges that's a different point. Charge the players a fee to use the system if you want.

I like to get technical when giving business advice. In the financial world they will always form a decision by determining the net present value of the anticipated stream of future cash incomes.

All this really means that whatever effort you make, you should maximize your monetary benefit. Perhaps it would be more profitable to work at McDonalds than promote the next kitchen widget.

Inventors have to realize that first and foremost they are in the business of monetizing their new thing. All of their decisions should be based on maximizing their personal income from the efforts that they make. In bringing your product to the market you will swiftly learn what the requirements are for you to succeed. You have to completely satisfy your customer in order to be successful in this world.

Unless you're going to self-finance your idea from beginning to end as an inventor, your first primary customer is either going to be your investors and business partners or the companies that might license your invention.

You have to get to the market before you encounter the public customer. For example, you may have invented a new product and it's the type of product or industry where all your potential investors and licensees tell you that they won't consider you without a prototype and an issued patent.

Your decision is going to be whether or not spend the money on the patent and the prototypes to move forward or to just stop at this point.

On the other hand, if your idea is perfect for late-night television, the as seen on TV people will consider idea submissions even if there's no intellectual property filed because they know the life of that product is going to be short.

Some great ideas may not even be patentable. Your decision-making has to be driven by business necessity. I don't think that a general response can cover this question.

This is another reason why the old first to invent system was good. If you invented something, you could work on it for a while in secret to determine whether or not you should put any more effort or money into it before filing any paperwork.

If someone else invented the same thing later than you, it didn't matter if you could still substantiate an earlier invention date. Now for all intents and purposes, a patent filing is an immediate necessity.

The massive hole that still exists in the patent system, is that the inventor has to defend and protect their own patent - which can easily cost hundreds of thousands of dollars - and if you don't have the resources, you are basically voiding it as you've allowed somebody to infringe on your patent and you did nothing about it. What are some solutions to this issue? I've had a friend go knee deep with their inventions with companies willing to spend large resources just to see if it will be defended.

Yes this is one of the glaring problems of our system. I'm hoping that these situations can be adequately solved by patent law firms taking cases of merit on contingency.

There are no perfect solutions however. Unfortunately, in a capitalist republic such as we have, some amount of cruelty and discomfort is built into the system. For example, using eminent domain, your town can condemn your house to build a highway or jug handle or new school and there's little you can do about it. If something like this happens to you, it's probably best not to perseverate on it.

The answer seems to be something along the lines of get richer faster. I think the problem is overblown though.

Right now, in personal-injury cases, nobody goes forward and finances their own case against somebody that injured them. Most plaintiffs use a personal injury attorney who will take a share of the recovery if there is any.

This seems to me to be the most likely avenue to resolve these patent infringement claims.

The inventor of the NMR machine, Raymond Damadian basically had this happen to him by General Electric. GE continued to develop it's own NMR machines and violated his patents.

The original inventor expended all of his resources trying to defend his patents. Finally I think it was an intrepid grandchild of his who took up the cause and found a Beltway patent firm who would take the case on a contingency.

The story famously goes that Jack Welsh himself smugly approached Dr. Damadian and handed him an $80 million check to settle the litigation for which he wanted complete rights to the inventors entire patent portfolio.

The Inventor tore up the check in his face which completely stunned everybody especially the attorneys. They went on to win the case which returned them a judgment of just under $130 million and they did not have to give up the rights of their patents to anybody. Other infringing firms such as Siemens quickly settled.

If there's merit in a case, it will probably be able to find a firm that's willing to gamble some of his effort against a big payday.

If you leave your ego at the door, what is the easiest way to avoid getting into increasingly messy legal fights with business partners? For instance, you may win a legal battle but unless the other party has some resources, still get no money out of a judgement and during the course of events, the business may faulter due to all the distractions.

The best way to follow and to avoid problems with your partner is to consider what might go wrong and incorporate the resolution of that problem in an agreement between the partners. Before you get into partnership, consider what will happen if one of the partners wants to be bought out. What happens if one of the partners no longer wants to participate actively in the business. What happens if one of the partners and you have such a falling out that you can no longer speak to each other civilly.

One approach is to pick a surrogate and a mediator for the agreement.

For example, if we get into a disagreement, my side will be argued by my accountant and our mediator will be a retired judge and we will pick an office which is roughly between our two homes. You can agree that the mediator's judgment is final.

The partners should previously have entered into long discussions about what they expect from each other in the deal moving forward.

The problem with lawsuits is that they engage the principals so they incur a huge lost opportunity costs. Instead of operating a business profitably, all of that owner's attention is turned to some legal proceeding.

Consider what's the worst that could happen and then make a contingency plan for it. Also a little research in this area will turn up at least the 10 most likely problems to be encountered in any partnership.

Entrepreneurship has many more valleys than peaks - many end-up just creating a job for themselves... hardly the high-life you see advertised in the news. When should an entrepreneur focus on getting Venture Capital and how do they avoid giving too much equity in return for funds? When things go south, are there some common legal problems with funded companies or is the industry mature enough where everybody just amicably walks away from the table?

In my thinking, you immediately need to secure capital sources if your idea has a large cost of development, such as a high tech or Internet idea.

Those inventors who come up with high-tech ideas need the most development before they have an actual product.

For example, just delivering an electronic product would require a website with e-commerce capability, a shopping cart, credit card etc. Developing the electronic outlet alone can cost quite a lot of money.

Otherwise you should delay or postpone equity investments as long as possible. For example, you will do better if you start a business with money that's borrowed from friends and relatives instead of an angel investor.

When the company is established, you can get better terms from lending sources. You may not even need to give equity away to get loans if the business fundamentals are good. For example, winning a big contract from the government will result in many lenders stepping up with loans.

There are of course many sources of loans, grants and loan guarantees. A quick search will turn up economic development companies with grants and loan programs you should explore before giving away much equity in your company.

Most garage type inventors may find that they need more money than they thought. They forget that the thing invented is going to have to be developed and designed to be appropriate, safe and appealing for the marketplace.

Additionally, if you are not good at something (no one is good at everything), you'll need to use experts. Some of the most common experts are designers and draftspersons, writers, people that negotiate licensing and, of course, people who are experienced with dealing with venture capital companies.

In general, getting money from Angel and venture-capital people should be avoided as much as possible. The most typical scenarios leave the innovator with only a small percentage of his company at the IPO stage and he has usually been eliminated from the company even before that stage.

When you're winding down a business venture that has been unsuccessful, this will be the time where you receive the benefit of the effort that you put into negotiating your working agreements and other instruments such as asset securitization.

All those agreements you wrote and all of the assets that are securitized should have been created with the mindset of what would happen if the business fails.

For example, if you gave your landlord too good a lease, now is going to be the time but he tries to get you to pay for your entire lease term and forfeit your security. If you guaranteed any loans personally, now is the time when those people will attack your bank accounts and try to garnish your wages.

Whoever received a loan securitized by equipment is going to show up and get their security. If you gave someone a loan which wrapped over all of your business equipment and materials, they can come take all of that as security. Obvious only now is that you should have only given guarantees with the minimum amount of collateral that it would take to make the loan.

If you were thoughtful enough to sell equipment or loan money and retain a lien on something, now is the time to go out and either collect the payment or recover your security. You can sell notes or liens at a discount to people who buy them and, of course, you can sell your accounts receivable to factoring companies.

You'll find that many people that wind up a business forget to recover their security deposits and to collect their accounts receivable at the end of the business.

People also pray on unfailing businesses by neglecting to return outstanding items and failing to pay invoices when due. I have heard of people taking loans out on failing or merging banks hopeful that their loans would be lost in the process.

There's usually not even a little bit of money left to wrap up loose ends like this. Of course, income tax returns still need to be filed. Sales tax returns still need to be filed and any other required reports need to be filed even if the company is defunct.

It would be nice if there was some money that has been prepaid perhaps to the accountant to cover some of the wind up expenses.

Since most people assume a business venture will be successful, many people will end up going into personal bankruptcy and foreclosure on their personal homes in the event of a catastrophic business failures.

Another point is that most people are completely unprepared for business failure. It's hard to let people go, it's hard to tell your landlord that you have to be leaving and you have to negotiate the end of the lease. It's hard to get your security back. It's hard to get your utilities turned off. It's hard to sell equipment.

Everything is hard. I dealt with one business owner whose business failed after a tremendous amount of investment by her and her family. Of course, she personally guaranteed all of the loans and all of the company's debt.

Firstly, she would've been much better off if she had designed her business with more consideration of what would happen if it failed. Secondly, when the business did fail, she was completely emotionally unable to help herself on any level. One way that I was able to help her was that I helped her negotiate the return of everything she purchased for the business to the suppliers that she had purchased them from.

Since she, of course, assumed her business would be successful she had purchased a huge amount of new business equipment, tables, packaging materials, stationery and other items which, in most instances, could be returned in satisfaction of the claims, in satisfaction of the debts that were owed on those things. It's an easy sell, "Do you want your equipment back or do you want nothing?"

One particular item was molded confection made out of chocolate. She even managed to return the molded chocolate items to the company she ordered them from who then were able to remarket them. The preprinted packaging materials she had created were also returned. The packaging company apparently could also remarket those for some uses.

You've worked hands-on with requirement contracts with pharmaceutical buyers, how do you go about getting the absolute best price while making sure everybody is happy with the deal?

To be effective at completing RFQ's, you need to be an expert in the market that you're dealing with. As an administrator intrapreneur, I pioneered the creation and maintenance of a competitive intelligence database which encompassed almost 1100 line items.

As contracts were let out, we would carefully review the pricing and terms in contracts that were let go and add that information to our database.

Any time a company released a pricelist, we would enter that information in our database. Any time we heard a rumor or we were asked to make a price concession, we would enter that information in our database .

We also carefully scanned industry information for news about our competitors. For example, if our competitor was either sold out on a product or had a factory for certain product closed for compliance reasons, we would know that the overall supply for that item was that much smaller and we could possibly raise prices accordingly.

When we prepared our RFQ's, we would then have the market intelligence necessary to win Business profitably. Of course, happiness is not really part of the equation since the people we sold to would be perfectly happy if we sold everything at a huge loss and they got the lowest possible price.

Winning requirements contracts is, of course, a great way to make a ton of money if you're an entrepreneur.

Anything else you'd like to add?

I'm very idealistic and very optimistic. I believe that innovation especially innovation which keeps in mind social issues and environmental issues can go on to make this world a much better place.

Of course, innovation entrepreneurship and inventorship can all be learned and I certainly would like to help teach people how to do all these things

William Seidel, President & CEO, America Invents

He's a court approved expert witness and a speaker at national conferences sponsored by AT&T, HP, the USPTO and LES. He held senior corporate positions and worked with awesome entrepreneurs, leading innovators, bestselling authors and business visionaries.

Through his companies, clients and customers, he has executed thousands of license agreements, developed hundred-million dollar products and fostered the success of billions of dollars in product sales.

Wanting to share his deep understanding of the industry, he has a proven track record having taught Marketing, Innovation & Entrepreneurship at UC Berkeley and Product Design at San Francisco State University.

When you were growing-up, did you imagine you'd be spending your day creating opportunities for inventors and retail partnerships around the world for your clients? What were your original aspirations and educational background?

When I started at the University of Pittsburgh I wasn't sure what I was going to do. I always liked product design but schools with industrial design departments were rare in the 60's. I went to Arizona State for post-graduate study in their outstanding solar architecture program and got a masters at San Francisco State with a focus on product design and product development.

I really started out wanting to design better products. As I got into the real-world business of products, I found that product design was a small subset of manufacturing which was an even smaller subset of marketing. To know what R&D and design needs to develop they need knowledge from the market. In fact most companies have very limited design and development because the products they develop are small evolutionary improvements to their existing successful product lines or improvements to their competitors products.

So the revolutionary products that made a real design and function statement were of little or no interest and too much company risk. I quickly learned that the corporate position was usually, "nothing ventured, nothing lost."

So I did an about-face and moved into the marketing of products to find out why this happens and how to work with it. I was fortunate to work with some of the leading product, marketing and licensing companies as well as some of the top entrepreneurs, innovators and bestselling authors.

I paid my dues earning senior corporate positions and maintaining my own business on the side (since 1978) as well as teaching Product Design at SF State and Innovation & Entrepreneurship at UC Berkeley.

How did you first get into the invention business and what aspects of it do you enjoy the most? Do you hold any patents yourself personally?

America Invents is not in the invention business, despite our name. We are in the product business and we develop, license and market new products. That's very different. We develop 3 to 10 product concepts and prototypes a year, license 10 to 40 product concepts a year and market 3 to 5 product lines each year.

We are a small boutique company and we cherry-pick 5 to 30 projects per year. Some of our principals are named on a few patents but we do not own any. However our founder has over 100 patents.

Many people think a product and an invention are the same and they are not. When people say the word product, in their mind it could mean an idea or a patent or a prototype, none of which are products.

Products are produced, packaged and available for sale. They generate revenue and the business they generate is managed. An invention is an original idea that may or may not be patented and it may or may not be a product and it may or may not make money.

THE INVENTION	THE PRODUCT
Inventions cost money	Products make money
License an invention	Sell a product
Inventions are patented	Products are packaged
Inventions are defended in court	Products sell in stores
Inventions are prototyped	Products are manufactured
Develop an invention	Distribute a product
"Productize" an invention	Market a product
Inventions have potential	Products have cash value

The best part is the deal, that's where everything comes together.

You have some incredibly impressive clients and success stories. How long does it generally take from idea/prototype to selling tons of units? Do you have some examples of how fast or slow the process can take?

For an individual, the average time from idea to introduction on the store shelves is seven years. For a sizable company it runs about two years, like the Swifter. To launch a line extension where there is little research and no development and existing distribution, corporate product introduction can be as fast as six months (given the available shelf space).

Product introduction, launch and rollout are very different. The individual often introduces the products but cannot rollout because of budget, capacity or distribution. This usually leads to disaster and knock-offs. If there is a demand you can't fill, you will be knocked-off, patented or not.

Selling "tons" of units is quite another question and that usually has to do with financial and distribution capability and rollout effectiveness. It is generally the rollout that takes the most time and is the greatest expense. When you begin to discuss "tons" of units then the sales cycle, shelf space and operations management become critical factors. When the demand increases it is great.

When the demand increase sustains it is exceptionally great! America Invents and myself were involved with many products like: the first baby monitor which had a big five year run until competitive products took the market and the Fast Track Tie Rack is still selling in select markets after 30 years.

Rules Of Thumb (I call them ROT because they rot your thinking) don't work in this business. Every product, industry and market is different. So how fast or slow, how much or few and how big or small depends on many factors that are different for every product. And different in every market. The average life of a successful toy product is 3 years, an appliance 7 years and a fashion item 3 months. The planning and implementation of Air Flow Fabric for heated and cooled seats in Ford's Lincoln line took 14 years and the inventors patents expired in the process.

What are some common problems that inventors stumble into and how do you manage expectations when everybody thinks their idea is worth millions when it may not be?

In my thirty-five years of developing, licensing and marketing products and teaching this at leading universities I have found that myths and falsehoods abound in most every area. When people become confused about the development, licensing and marketing of a product it can usually be traced back to myths that led them in the wrong direction.

These myths lead to inventor and entrepreneur downfall, false hopes and costly mistakes and ultimately to the graveyard of failed products and wounded inventors.

The tasks and problems are enormous when you develop, manufacture, distribute and market a new product. Bad information is everywhere and immediately available for the naive and inexperienced. Mark Twain said it best:

"If you don't read the newspaper you are uninformed."

"If you do read the newspaper, you are misinformed."

Mark Twain was right then and he is right now. Bad information comes from everywhere, usually in the form of opinions from people with no experience and no success. This is not information to act on.

It is easy and common to seek product and business advice from your attorney or rich uncle Bob but they are not qualified unless they had success with a similar product in a similar situation. And even then the time, contacts and climate are completely different. Because they graduated from law school or made $30 million in the concrete business does not make them an authority on the marketing, licensing or distribution of your product.

When seeking outside advice you must ask the question, "what products have you successfully developed, licensed and marketed and where are they currently available." This flushes out the theory, opinion and bullshit. If they don't have successful products, then don't work with them and don't follow their advice.

Here's an enormous myth right up your alley. "Product development is about developing new products." This is false. Product development is about obsoleting the competition. The objective of product development is to provide a "complete product" while the mission is to make the competition obsolete.

Consider the Super Soaker squirt gun, it made other squirt guns obsolete at 60 times the price. And all the leading toy companies turned down the SuperSoaker.

Another myth: "This idea is gonna' make me rich." The truth is that ideas never made anybody rich! (Just another myth.) Ideas have no value, no presence and no revenue. Ideas can't do anything, they just sit there. You must do everything. What you do may make you rich, if you know what to do. The idea is a seed that takes a lot of care, maintenance and you have to water it with money to grow into a viable concept and a complete product.

Bottom line, it's the action you take, the labor, budget and knowledge you employ to advance that idea to make it a product, then exchange the products for money. It's not the idea. It's knowing what to do with the idea to put it into a form that successfully generates revenue. And then, if it works, you get rich.

The myth that all you need is one simple idea and it will set you up for life is a rare occurrence. Oh there are many stories and TV shows about an idea that succeeded but that is the exception, not the rule. Here is some more ROT, the following numbers are what every independent developer needs to know:

One in 100 patents make any money
One in 200 patents make enough money to pay for the patent
One in 300 patents make a profit
One in 641 products remained after three years (Tested by a leading home shopping network.)
One in 1,000 product concepts from independent inventors succeed (Udell, Gerald. Innovation (in) Review. United States Patent and Trademark Office, Vol. 1, No. 7 May, 2001.)

11% of the products introduced by small existing businesses remain on the shelf over one year; 78% of the products introduced by leading corporations remain on the shelf over one year; nine in ten corporate products introduced are line extensions of successful brands

Free Advice Ain't Worth the Price. It is easy to find hundreds of 'feel-good' stories and books that tell you how to do it on a shoestring. That's a nice story but that's all it is. It is not appropriate for your product in the hardware business, the toy industry or anywhere else. It is not appropriate even if your product is in the same product category because it is a different time, a different place, a different product, and every company, channel of distribution and category (product category) are different. And you are different: your goals and objectives are different, your product and company needs are different and your purpose is different.

To the second part of your question, "managing expectations when everybody thinks their idea is worth millions." If we are talking value, then that's simple. How much money did it make last year? (This is the first question on Shark Tank.) Value is not an opinion. The valuation of the product/business is the revenue it generated as a product not an idea. If it sold $300,000 last year then it's worth millions - by financial ROT numbers, 3 to 5 times annual revenues is often used to determine the value.

If there are zero annual revenues, then it has a zero value. An idea has potential but the value is a number. The potential of an idea is very debatable because it has no value that can be documented.

Big product successes is pretty clear. The small success is really the issue because it is hard to define, mostly unknown and out of the mainstream of what everyone tends to see.

The $5 million product from a private company can be a great success for the individual but it is unreported and under the radar of Wall Street investors. Often these small successes are the ones that can experience the greatest growth.

There are many factors to consider when defining a product success because everything is different for every product in every industry and for every business. A hundred-thousand units per year for a novelty product is good where a hundred-thousand units per month for a candy product is bad. The real truth lies in the life of the product and the picture of costs and profits.

Myth: "I just know it will be a success." When I hear this I ask, "what kind of success?" And no one has an answer, unless they have the spreadsheets to show me. I define five different types of product success. These are products that stay on the shelves and continue to sell-through the store and make money. We take success to mean a product that has repeat sales and predictable and profitable results for a limited or a long time.

1. SuperStars are disruptive and revolutionary changing many industries like the smart phone and the personal computer. It defines how everything else works and it impacts the distribution and revenues of other businesses and industries.

2. A Classic product changes an industry like the first baby monitor, which changed the pattern of parents behavior while minding the baby. Often these are simple ideas that alter our lifestyle.

3. A Hit product has sales over $50 million and it is selling in leading chains. You may recognize a "Hit" product because you saw the ads or know someone who bought it. It could attain big sales for a short time as in the toy business.

4. A Product Success will sell $20 million(+/-) over eight years.(+/-) The Product Success has a strong product life, establishes repeat sales and maintains a defensible shelf position.

5. An Item will make $200,000 to $5 million(+/-) over a short product life (one to five years). Many of these items are successful because they have a profitable structure for a small business or are one of many products in a product line. Items can be very profitable to the individual that wants to do it all themselves. We have a lot of clients that choose this path and we support it when the numbers work. (Meaning when the profit margins are large enough.)

The inventor may have an opinion of the potential of a product concept or high hopes that the product will succeed but until it is made and available for sale and the actual sell-through measured, there are no sales and no reorders to determine growth, potential or value.

If your product has a place in the market, then it will fit one of the above categories. I suggest that everyone considers what type of product success fits their product concept. When you begin to work the number of stores, the sales per month and the profit margin, you can begin to see where it will fit.

What is the value of following-through with an idea from paper to physical prototype before approaching America Invents? Who does this benefit the most: the manufacturer, retailer, designer, inventor or yourself in selling the concept?

Companies don't buy ideas and they are not interested in patents. What companies really want are profits, the bigger the profit potential the greater the chances you can lock up a sweet deal.

The further developed the product concept, the faster to market and less risk and that benefits everyone. The further the development, the less time it will take and fewer mistakes will occur.

If you already have sales and demand, then you will attain a much better deal much faster because it becomes a distribution agreement or a minimum risk deal. The retailers has nothing to do with it, they are simply resellers, no licenses, no prototypes and no ideas. Retailers must have complete products and they prefer proven products.

America Invents starts at any stage in the process of development, ideas, designs, patents and even failed products. The Fast Track Tie Rack was an idea with no protection, no design and no definition.

In fact, America Invents' founder is named on the patent as a co-inventor. The Fisher-Price Luv U Zoo, Crib N' Go Projector was a concept with pending patents when we licensed it.

The Triazzle puzzles were proven and successful in the specialty toy business but never made the jump to the mass retailers. America Invents licensed this proven product line (17 products) to the fourth largest toy company who secured distribution into Kmart, Wal-mart, Toys R Us, Target, etc.

The Crazer Laser failed multiple times when it came to us. We repositioned the product and successfully licensed it to launch into the pet industry, currently available at PetCo, PetSmart and pet stores everywhere.

Every company and every industry works differently. Some require patents and prototypes, while some require the product to be proven with sales of 100,000 units. While other companies will license a product concept.

If you don't know the company, their terms and their relationships, then you are at an enormous disadvantage and there is a chance you will be ripped-off.

If the objective is to develop it and show it to everyone in the business (which is foolish), then you must have everything in order including issued patents and limited sales success.

My background is self-taught designing projects for CNC machines (laser, router, plasma, 3d printers...) and knowing this, if I had an order for a thousand much less a million widgets, there is no way I'd even attempt this myself. I've also taken on the royalty system for my designs over manufacturing myself. What is the value in your opinion of licensing vs. manufacturing?

This is a question I get all the time and it is really very simple. If you have small margins (3 times to 5 times product cost for a low priced item), then it is best to license it because you can go broke. Building the business and competition can react fast and take the business after you prove the product.

If you have large margins (6 times to 15 times product cost for a low priced item), then you need to seriously consider raising the need funds to do it yourself. There is plenty of money in the margin to build the sales and distribution and make a few mistakes in the process.

A good example is the Splash Guard which we attempted to license unsuccessfully because it was too small of a product to get the attention of the five giant players in the business.

So we regrouped and reevaluated the potential with new costs and saw the potential for a nine-times margin, which made it worth the risk and effort. The first sale we made put the company in the black. Big margins solve a lot of problems. Selling 9 million with a 9 times margin pays for the mistakes and makes it worth it.

What is the real point and purpose of what I am licensing, isn't the company going to do it all over again anyway? What does a typical deal look like between the inventor, yourself, the retailer and manufacturer percentage wise on each sale? How do you keep everybody honest?

I hear this a lot and it is another Myth. One thing that is true is that companies want profits not product concepts they have to do over. If they have to do it "all over again" then paying you will always be a question. The more the company must do, or do over, the less their interest and the worse your negotiating position.

The further the development the greater the chances for success. It will be reviewed numerous times inside the company and your product/prototype/concept must be strong enough to stand on its own and sell itself. If you have a proven product, then the profits are documented and it is of enormous interest to all potential licensees because it reduces their risk and you can have a bidding war.

There is no "typical deal." Every industry, product category and channel of distribution is different. Retailers are resellers and do not license. Their mark-up is generally 100%, less for the discounters and more for the speciality retailers.

Regarding "how to keep everybody honest" there is no problem with honesty if you are working with people and companies with integrity. Any licensee must perform to retain the rights (unless you have a bad deal). As I said, if you don't know the companies you are working with, then you are vulnerable to all kinds of problems.

Licensing can be very tricky because it is not simply a deal with a company. It must be the "right" deal with the "right" company. Finding the "right" company and knowing the "right" deal is very hard. The royalty percentage is irrelevant! Every inventor, even some of the professionals, get hung-up on this percentage and that is really meaningless. It is not about a percentage, it is about revenue.

The royalty percentage is irrelevant because a high royalty rate from a small company is far worse than a low royalty from a giant. I'll take a 3% royalty from 3M or P&G before I would accept a 15% royalty from a third rate company. This is the difference between a million dollar idea and a total loss.

The profit margin is the most important factor. The royalty as a percent of the profits is a different number and a different situation. While a 5% royalty (5% of the wholesale revenue) appears to be a small number, it usually ranges from 20% to 50% of the licensees profit on that product. The net profit margin ranges for consumer products from 10% to 30%.

In some private label products (and others) the margins can be much higher.

Most people come to America Invents hoping for a 2% to a 5% royalty. Our average is just under 9% of the wholesale price for consumer products and 12% for commercial and industrial products. The highest royalty I have directly experienced for a consumer product was 33%. We got a high royalty because the product cost was $0.32, the package was $0.24 and the retail price was $19.95 direct to radio and TV.

In 2010 I consulted to an oil equipment manufacturer that had excellent protection for a great idea, an improved seamless pipe innovation for the oil industry. The licensee manufactures and sells pipe products directly to the end user with minimal sales and marketing costs and sizable mark-ups. They needed the technology and because they have an enormous profit margin they could afford a 24% royalty. This amounted to 32% of the company profit margin for this product.

Finding the right company that will honestly review your concept and seriously consider it for a license is a complex task riddled with booby-traps and bad advice. Marketing your product concept or idea to a license agreement requires that you target qualified prospective companies. And you must have a plan of attack.

This means you must first get it to the right companies and then to the deciders inside those companies. When you don't have the contacts this is very hard.

The royalty percentage is what the licensee can afford to give up from the profit margin and maintain a satisfactory profit. The importance of the idea is only part of it. The reasons you get a high royalty are:

you have a very high margin,
you have a very unique or protected market (not product) and/or
your product is already proven. (Preferably all of the above.)

If I had a great idea, the first thing I'd do after a 3D model is to head over to the patent office. What is your opinion of spending money to market a product vs. patent lawyers? Which is most important, first to market or patented design knowing you need massive amounts of time and money to defend them?

Unfortunately this is not an either/or situation. You need protection and marketing. And patents are only part of your protection strategy. You also need much more marketing money than the cost for the patent and defending it.

The marketing and distribution costs can be 5 to 10 times the cost of the patent and manufacturing.

My opinion is one thing and what the patent office recommends is quite another. The patent office recommends that you first get a "commercial assessment." This is where the problems begin. Unlike a real estate appraisal, which has a lot of comparables, intellectual property has no comparables.

To patent or not is always a sticky question because if your product fails, a patent is of little value. However, if your product is a success, then a patent is critical to owning it and keeping it. Patents also play a key role in any agreement and the revenue you receive.

Myth: Advice from a famous patent attorney, first you patent it then license it to a manufacture.

Fact: this advice is 30 years old, out of date and wrong. Patent attorneys will tell you to patent it because that is their business. However, the US Patent Office recommends a commercialization study prior to patenting which patent attorneys do not offer.

I know for a fact this patent attorney never licensed anything - he wrote many license agreements but he never found the deal and didn't know how to make it happen.

Writing a license agreement is not the pro-activity that actually makes it happen.

Again, if you ask the question, "what products have you successfully developed, licensed and marketed and where are they available?" it will tell you who to listen to.

The second myth of this statement is that most manufacturers are contract manufacturers that have no distribution or marketing capability. You walk into a plastic manufacturer who is squeezing plastic for 15 different companies and he likes your idea but says, "I have to show it to my people," which means they show it to their customers who are the ones who have the distribution and marketing capability you need.

Now you have a real problem because you showed it to the wrong people that cannot fund your effort because "they know a guy that knows a guy." And you lost control. Even with a patent and an NDA, you can still be knocked off.

A patent doesn't stop someone from stealing it - it simply allows you to sue. Many honorable companies that are prime candidates will not sign your NDA and require you to sign their release.

Your best protection for an idea or concept is to work with honorable companies that have integrity. Your best protection for defending your products position in the marketplace is to partner with a heavyweight that can defend it.

If you don't know the company you are presenting to, you are at a disadvantage. Even attorneys falsely believe an NDA will protect you. It does provide limited recourse but if you are dealing with a bad company no agreement will protect you. The reason everyone uses NDA's is because they don't know who they are dealing with and that is a bigger problem.

You do not want to be in a position where you must enforce an NDA. So many developers and inventors go so wrong by presenting the wrong products to the wrong companies and to the wrong people. This is one of the reason so many companies refuse to review products from outside inventors. It is also one of the reasons why so many inventors get ripped-off.

About 30% of the projects we license have no patents or protection. We often negotiate into the license that the licensee will pay for the patents in our clients name. This is an enormous advantage because in addition to saving money it usually results in better protection.

There is a lot of talk of the first-to-market which works if you have existing distribution in place and if you can defend the shelf space and if you can move fast with a big marketing budget. If it succeeds, you need a lot more money to fill the pipeline and continue the product flow. First-to-market has an enormous associated cost to succeed.

The example of the pioneer, Diet Rite and RC cola and how they innovated with the first diet drink, the first caffeine free drink and the first low calorie drink and lost it all. The industry leaders who could adapt fast, increased promotion and took the shelf-space and took the business that Diet Rite pioneered and created.

First-to-market may work for a small entity when you address a niche market that has little or no competition and the product category is too small for competitors to consider. For example, a premium, high priced granola has very little competition because the big companies offer low price, high volume products. It is possible to "cream" the top of this product category successfully. Often small, niche items can capture and defend shelf space.

The inventor of Laser Pegs (a light up construction set) went into competition with the giant Lego. It is too high priced, too unique and too small of a market niche for Lego to compete. However, if Laser Pegs begins to take market share from Lego, they will have trouble protecting their position. This is a great strategy to capture a market niche and defend it. And it can be very lucrative.

You taught innovation and entrepreneurship for over 20 years. What is it about teaching that you don't get out of your business that keeps you coming back? I know for me, sharing knowledge is just as much fun as making money.

I stopped teaching in 2001 but still speak at conferences and events. I started teaching Product Design at San Francisco State where I also taught How to Patent, Market and Develop Your Idea.

This class grew into a seminar titled Entrepreneurship & Innovation that I offered through 26 universities in the California University Systems. Fortunately, U.C. Berkeley wanted to offer the seminar as a full credit business elective where I taught it for 15 years.

Though I stopped teaching, I have a series of books planned for the fall of 2014 titled ProductologyTM. The first book in the series is The iMyth: Why Your Idea Doesn't Work and What to do About it. This deals with many of the same issues we are discussing here. And yes, it is a takeoff on Michael Gerber's, E-Myth: Why Most Small Businesses Don't Work and What To Do About It.

The second book is the Everything Must Be Right: The Productology PathTM and it is the path to product launch with 146 tasks defined in detail. It is kind-of like the simple 1, 2, 3 steps of the process except it is 1, 2, 146 steps in the process.

The third part is the software to plan each of the 146 tasks, assign the responsibilities and quantify the costs and time. This provides a cost and revenue plan and a timeline for any project or product. It is similar to a Critical Path Method but specific to early stage product development and preformatted for the first time entrepreneur.

If you want more information you can check out the Engineering Science Lecture at the Department of Engineering Science, School of Science and Technology, Sonoma State University.

America Invents has had some amazing successes with almost 2 billion in retail sales but I'm sure you've had your fair share of duds. What did these products have in common and what systems have you established so you limit your risks on any given deal?

The trick is accepting the "right" projects. We look for products and concepts that can be economically made and distributed with an acceptable cost, sold at a profitable price, addressing a growth category and having instant understanding to the customer. If it fits this criteria, then we think it can be successful.

We believe the market is of most importance because if the market isn't there it doesn't matter how good the product is. The high-design products often fail and the idiot-simple products often succeed and the low-price crap will always succeed. Don't get me wrong, a good product and a good design is enough to get it on the shelves but successes are made from repeat sales.

A "me-too product" already has a proven market and the lower price will get it the sales velocity needed to stay on the shelves.

It is a much bigger risk for a company to fund, market and prove an innovative product. If there is a viable market, then even a marginal success can make big money. When we evaluate a product we really evaluate the market for the product not necessarily the product. And we closely analyze the marketing that is needed (the expensive part) to make a product succeed.

We have certainly had our share of successful products with first-hand development, licensing, marketing and sales of some of the biggest. But we have also had many small successes with Items and Product Successes that financially work for everyone. Little successes are also success.

Often, very simple things like the Stunt Streamer which does simple stunts for a little girls dancing ribbon/streamer. This has been selling very well for 12 years and we just finalized an enormous order with Walmart. It just keeps on selling.

We don't scoff at "Gidgety-Gadgety" products like the Pet Rock, Talking Toilet Paper and the Chia Pet. We certainly laugh at them when they are funny but we take the marketing of such products very seriously. It quickly becomes a question of market acceptance, size, cost to address it, profitability and the life of the product.

The Pet Rock launched in 1975 made big money selling two million units fast (in six months) but it had a very short life. Talking Toilet Paper was introduced in 1998, we developed the product but declined to market it. It still has steady and consistent sales today. Though its sales didn't set the world on fire, it is predictable and profitable and has a long and healthy product life.

The Chia Pet began in 1982 and sells about 500,000 to a million(+) units per year for 31 years. For a novelty/gift item this is large volume and a very long life.

All of these are examples of brilliant marketing not a quality product. The point being they are all successful and proven at different rates and times. If the marketing was not "right" in every way for these products they would never make it.

Entrepreneurs and innovators figure things out for themselves. That's why they are entrepreneurs and that's how they innovate.

There are no rules, no standards and no right way to do it, however everything must be right. The approach and path is unique for every new product and every situation.

The more knowledge, contacts and experience you have the greater your odds for success.

When you look deeper into any success stories, you see that experienced professionals often influenced successful product deals in a small way or a large way as investors, partners or mentors. And if you understand how to use marketing to prove the product and build value, funding your project will be a much easier effort.

If your marketing is together:

> The value will increase,
> The money will appear and
> Your plan will exceed expectation.

I hope this answers your questions and satisfies your readers. If not send the complaints to me.

Afterword

I've been fascinated with manufacturing in general for years, when I ran my industrial animation business almost 20 years ago. The part I enjoyed more than anything else were the shop tours. Seeing how things are made by generally overbuilt machines constantly moving is just inspiring to me.

A few years later when I got my ShopBot Desktop, my first CNC machine, I was hooked on the potential of this technology. To me, this CNC respresented my first glimpse into the freedom and endless potential. I then got a 3D Systems 2nd Generation Cube and wow, my eyes were opened even more as I taught myself how to design 3D meshes that actually worked and reproduced consistently in the real world.

I then got my Trotec Speedy 400 flexx CNC laser and wow, I realized that with these three machines, I could design and build virtually anything. I was now a one-man IKEA!

One thing I've found out about shop owners is that they just can't seem to stop themselves from acquiring more CNC machines and I've become the same way. Some of my customers have machines up to the rafters and still, they talk about acquiring more stuff, even if it just sits there. They are passionate about the possibilities one more piece of equipment can bring to their shop and the clients they can service as a result.

I saw a 2.7 kw Mitsubishi EX series laser and talked to the sales rep for half an hour. I was mesmorized. I want that machine as it would be another huge leap in the capabilities for my shop and open it to a whole new level of customization for my clients and my own design aspirations. I would be able to cut solid steel and a host of other things, then laser engrave it or carve into it using a bit and so forth.

The synergy of having more than one machine, and knowing how to use it properly, isn't a 1 + 1 = 2 equation but 1 + 1 = 3 because you can start to find efficiencies in the projects that were simply not possible anymore. Throw in the fact that you can do more inhouse verses being at the whim of a supplier and it's tough to say no.

The more capabilities I acquire, the more I want to learn and the more I realize I'm capable of doing. I can only imagine what future volumes of this book will look like, the projects I'll be able to handle and the people I'll meet along the way. I couldn't have predicted getting a CNC laser when I completed my last volume!

See you in the next volume!

Image Credits & Info

Unless otherwise mentioned below, all images and photography found within this book were taken or rendered by Jonathan Cantin and he holds all rights to them.

Thanks to all those who provided pictures and content to make this dream of a massive educational design book possible.

Special thanks go out to Ted Hall and the ShopBot Tools team for believing in me all those years ago with their ShopBot Desktop, I cut my teeth on that machine and still works great all these years later! Looking forward to upgrading to a full sheet ShopBot machine soon enough!

Simon and Reece Moore for sharing their laser knowledge and continuing to be a massive resource for me as I build-up my business and opportunities.

Cathy Lewis of 3D Systems who opened my eyes to the true possibilities of 3D printing.

Other Books by Jonathan Cantin

CNCKing.com Volume 4: Rise of the CNC
456 pages, ISBN 978-1896369518

Are you interested in saving years off your life and tens of thousands of dollars trying to learn how to design for your CNC machine? My name is Jon and what I have written on the right is a culmination of five years of intensive trial and error which allowed me to design over 250 CNC table router, 3D printer and laser cutting projects!

Let me start-off by saying that ANYBODY can design amazing projects for CNC machines! I do not have an engineering degree (B. Sc. In Biology degree), I'm not an artist (I can't draw) nor did I have direct access to any of the machines I was designing for! Oh yeah, I also hate anything that requires measurements, so I made designs that didn't even require any math skills!

Despite a complete lack of knowledge about proper design and machinery to cut them, I made some basic assumptions and used my passion to overcome all these massive liabilities. Now, I want to help you do the same and let me be the first to say, I know for a fact that you have far more skills RIGHT NOW than I did when I first got started. At the very least, you know what a CNC machine is... I didn't even know they existed!

I've had my designs featured at trade shows and fairs around the world. I've been written about in magazines, newspapers and even manufacturer's own newsletters! I built CNCKing.com to become the go-to source for CNC operators and enthusiasts globally as a great source of inspiration and digital project files.

Elementary, high schools and even universities have used the resources I've built to teach their students how to make things with their CNC machine... I even got noticed by the real driver of the Mars Rover! I'm now the guy that tells engineering and architectural graduates that their designs will not work for the machines they are designing them for. I know my stuff and want you to learn from all my mistakes and then some!

I approached other designers who are well known in their field, whether that was 3D printing, laser or routing... and got them to share some insights on their design processes. I also got some amazing interviews with industry movers and shakers to give you a bigger picture about the CNC industry as a hole and where it's going in the future.

I want to give you the knowledge and the tools required to succeed in the CNC design world - that is the entire purpose of this book.

CNCKING.COM
RISE OF THE CNC

Learn how to design for CNC Table Routers, Laser Cutters and 3D Printers without using G-Code

Gain insight from key innovators within the CNC industry

Know what to look for in quality CNC machinery

Jonathan Cantin
Foreword by Benjamin J. Heckendorn

WoodMarvels.com
Create Unique Memories

Volume 1: Top Sellers
by Jonathan Cantin

WoodMarvels.com
Volume 2: 50 Laser Cutting Plans

Jonathan Cantin

WoodMarvels.com Volume 1: Top Sellers
102 pages, ISBN 978-1-896369-44-0

The book that started it all with woodworking projects that use round wooden dowels; our blueprints are completely measurement free. This book includes the following models: Abacus, Bird Feeder B, Bird House, Bread Box, Brontosaurus, Dolphin Future Car B, Parasaurolophus, Pen and Pencil Holder B, Portrait A: Sunshine, Portrait C: Waves of Hope, Ring Stacking Game, Showcase, Stegosaurus, Table Protector, Table Protector C, Tower of Hanoi, Wood Stacking Game, Abstract Bank, Chessboard, Crab, Cutting Board, Pterodactyl, Medieval Castle Walls, Platform Crane, Straddle Carrier.

WoodMarvels.com Volume 2: 50 Laser Cutting Plans
200 pages, ISBN 978-1-896369-46-4

This book includes woodworking projects from our site; our blueprints are completely measurement free. This book includes the following models:

> Level 1: Centrosaurus, Dolphin, Elephant, Future Car A, Future Car B, Hammer and Stake, Pen and Pencil Holder D, Pet Bowl Holder, Rhinoceros, Submarine, Time Teaching Clock A and B, Whale.
> Level 2: 1956 Porsche Speedster, Abstract Bank B, Bed Tray and Table, Crab, Crumb Tray, Desktop Organizer C and D, Elastic Marble Game, Halloween Serving Coffin, Halloween Sword Shelf, Mayan Temple Bank, Pen and Pencil Holder C, Pterodactyl, Pyramid Calendar, Serving Table, Small Table, Super Snail, Tracing Light Table, Trip Games.
> Level 3: Amazing Train, Cantilever Side Table, Halloween Guillotine Tray.
>Level 4: Bus, Desktop Bowling Game, Ferris Wheel, Shuffle Board Game, Medieval Castle Walls B, Mobile Crane B, Rusk Fortress, Straddle Carrier B, Zulu Main Battle Tank. Dowel-Based: Full Armor Gear Series Bull, Tank and Transporter.

WoodMarvels.com Volume 3: Evolution of Design
200 pages, ISBN 978-1-896369-49-5

This book features woodworking projects at five different skill levels with 3D rendered step-by-step assembly instructions. What makes our philosophy unique is that all our blueprints are completely measurement free, which means you can build them to whatever scale you wish using only the thickness of the wood as your guide.

This book includes the following models: 1911 Ford Model T Torpedo Runabout, Light Table, Medieval Tower Bank, Shopping Cart, Submarine B, TV Bank, CH47 Chinook Helicopter, Easter Island Secret Storage Head Bookend, Home Gym, Mangonel, Medieval Castle Bank, P38 Lightning, Physics Trophy, Platform Crane B, Spring Basket, Stereo Bank, Army Transport Truck, Baliste, Ferris Wheel B, Flying Car, Mangonel B, Mars Explorer, Sydney Harbour Bridge, Semi-trailer Truck, Mars Rover, Medieval Castle and Sydney ANZAC Monument among others.

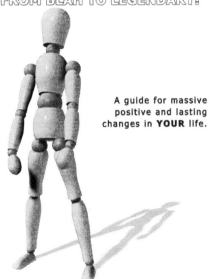

A guide for massive positive and lasting changes in **YOUR** life.

Transforming Your Life From Blah To Legendary!
140 pages, ISBN 978-1-896369-45-7

The largest obstacle getting in the way of the life you wish to lead is yourself. Generating enough momentum to create lasting changes that improve your lifestyle takes time, along with a fundamental change in habits and attitudes. You cannot lead a life of personal success and achievement without first understanding yourself and developing your inner strengths.

If you are serious about leading a lifestyle that will be fulfilling and possibly talked about by future generations, then the lessons in this book are a wonderful first step in the right direction. You will only ever have one life--you might as well make it worth living!

HowToChinese.com: A Practical Mandarin Chinese Course
412 pages, ISBN 978-1-896369-50-1

Learning a new language is fun -- and having a book guiding you every step of the way, written from a student's point of view, is a great start!

Experience Lucky's passion for teaching Mandarin Chinese to students around the world through her comprehensive and professionally produced online video series to help you build fluency in record time!

This is a fantastic book for both beginners and advanced students with a step-by-step learning process with each chapter building onto the next and multiple in-chapter exercises to reinforce new learnings along with real-life conversation dialogs and pinyin and simplified Chinese characters throughout.

2847 A.D.: Solar Horizons
213 pages, ISBN 978-1-896369-47-1

The year is 2847 and the human race has barely held on due to the aftermath of devastating explosions that almost saw the end of the entire species. The world is now a very different place; extraterrestrial colonies dot the Solar System as well as planet Earth, and trading has become a necessity to be able to regain some semblance of normalcy. The main cast of characters includes a Professor who, along with Excur, the most advanced computer man had ever built, helps to save the Earth from certain annihilation after an unexploded neutron sphere is discovered deep in Zulu territory. They are joined by three mining Alabarsi, an offshoot of the human species, who help in the endeavor. What is Project Baptistina? What is the relationship between Glass Lake and the events that may lead to the extinction of all humans on Earth?

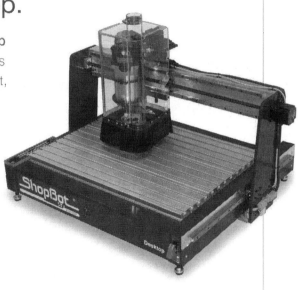

3DSYSTEMS

THE WAY YOU DESIGN WHAT YOU CREATE HOW YOU MANUFACTURE

We invented it. Now it's your turn.

Our 3D digital design and fabrication solutions are transforming the way consumers and professionals design, create and make, and offer endless possibilities with a range of materials, including direct metal, precision plastics, durable nylons, multi-material, full color, and even ceramics and sugar. With advanced applications in aerospace, healthcare, automotive, entertainment and food, 3D printing is defining new ways for the paralyzed to walk, cars to drive, planes to fly, children to play, and nations to work.

Explore what you can do with 3D printing.

MANUFACTURING*THE*FUTURE

www.3dsystems.com
moreinfo@3dsystems.com
Tel: 803.326.3900

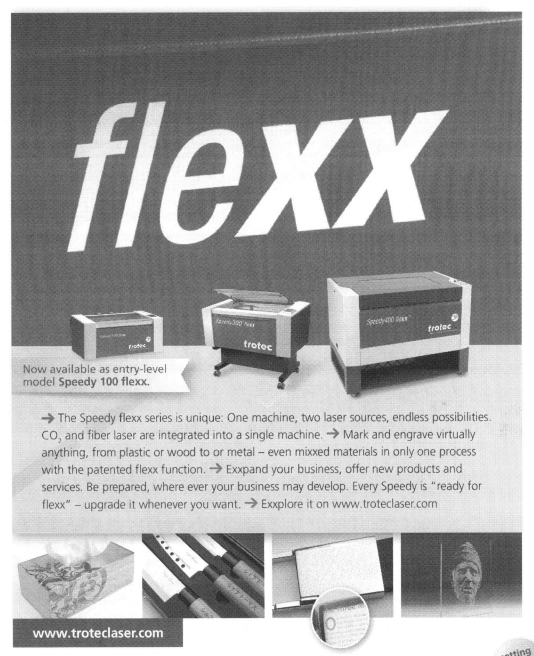

Made in the USA
Charleston, SC
09 August 2015